The Future of Arid Lands – Revisited

Charles F. Hutchinson • Stefanie M. Herrmann

The Future of Arid Lands – Revisited

Revisited

A Review of 50 Years of Drylands Research

Springer

United Nations
Educational, Scientific and
Cultural Organization

UNESCO Publishing

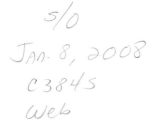

Charles F. Hutchinson   Stefanie M. Herrmann

Published jointly by the United Nations Educational, Scientific and Cultural Organization (UNESCO), 7, place de Fontenoy, 75007 Paris, France and Springer SBM, Van Godewijckstraat 30, PO Box 17, 3300 AA Dordrecht, The Netherlands.
The designations employed and the presentation of material throughout this publication do not imply the expression of any opinion whatsoever on the part of UNESCO concerning the legal status of any country, territory, city or area or of its authorities, or the delimitation of its frontiers or boundaries.
The authors are responsible for the choice and the presentation of the facts contained in this book and for the opinions expressed therein, which are not necessarily those of UNESCO and do not commit the Organization.

ISBN 978-92-3-104053-5

Printed on acid-free paper.

9 8 7 6 5 4 3 2 1

Foreword

UNESCO commemorated its sixtieth anniversary in 2005. It was a year for reflection – a time to look back on the progress made and the achievements accomplished over the last 60 years. To celebrate the importance and relevance of science at UNESCO a publication entitled *Sixty Years of Science at UNESCO: 1945–2005* was launched in 2006, which offers an insight into the organization's commitment towards and endeavors in science from the past through to the present day.

Within the United Nations System, UNESCO has one of the longest traditions in addressing dryland problems from a scientific point of view. As it happened, arid zones were precisely at the centre of UNESCO's earliest efforts at international scientific collaboration in the study of natural resources. The first international research program dealing with these zones was launched back in 1951 under the direction of an International Advisory Committee. It was continued until 1964, after being raised to the status of a Major Project of the Organization in 1957. This Major Project was a pioneer program in many respects. One of its merits, and not the least, was that it blazed a trail in its interdisciplinary approach to the study of natural resources and its holistic view of the problems of arid and semiarid zones. It was followed by a series of UNESCO intergovernmental programs having significant components relating to drylands, such as the UNESCO Program on Man and the Biosphere (MAB) created in 1971, and the UNESCO International Hydrological Program (IHP) launched in 1975 as a follow-up endeavor to the 1965–1974 International Hydrological Decade. Both programs have continued their dryland studies to the present day.

It was, therefore, not surprising that UNESCO and the Rockefeller Foundation sponsored the "International Arid Lands Meetings" that took place in New Mexico (USA) in 1955 and which were organized by the American Association for the Advancement of Science (AAAS). Edited by Gilbert F. White, the collected papers emanating from these landmark events were entitled *The Future of Arid Lands* and were published in 1956. Back in the mid-1950s, many "uncertainties" existed with regard to dryland research and land degradation, due to the inadequate availability of reliable data and the overall complexity of temporal and spatial variability of dryland climates. Some of these uncertainties still prevail today. However, since 1955 national and international efforts have helped to fill some of the knowledge gaps in the fields of dryland research and environmental conservation. Most importantly, the human factor in sustainably managing dryland ecosystems is now widely recognized.

Today, an increasingly serious problem is looming on the horizon – global climate change. The effects of the gradual rise in atmospheric temperature has begun to have devastating effects on weather patterns causing such erratic and catastrophic events as severe flooding, increasingly intense storms and, of course, drought. The impact of global climate change on drylands is therefore obvious and more than ever we must unite our research efforts and muster political will to mitigate these effects as early as possible as the future of drylands depend on it.

The year 2006 was declared "International Year of Deserts and Desertification" by the United Nations General Assembly. This proved to be a timely occasion to revisit Gilbert F. White's book *The Future of Arid Lands* and assess the development of scientific research relative to the projections made 50 years ago, which were based on the knowledge at that time. Only by looking into the past can we determine the scientific advances made in the drylands – this increasing knowledge base can be employed to address the current challenges faced in the drylands and thus prepare for future changes.

Professor Charles F. Hutchinson and Dr. Stefanie Herrmann at the University of Arizona were assigned this mammoth task. The UNESCO-commissioned book *The Future of Arid Lands – Revisited* comes some 50 years after the publication of *The Future of Arid Lands*. I am sure it will prove to be as much a landmark publication on scientific research on drylands as its illustrious predecessor.

This new book can help to determine the scientific path for future operations to promote sustainable development in countries affected by desertification. UNESCO considers the book an important contribution to the UN Decade of Education for Sustainable Development (2005–2014) for which UNESCO has been designated lead agency. As the world's drylands are among the most poverty-stricken regions of our planet, and in line with the UN-wide joint effort to reach the Millennium Development Goals, we need to mobilize all our collective efforts to ensure sustainable development in the world's marginal areas that are the deserts.

I wish to thank Professor Charles F. Hutchinson and Dr. Stefanie Herrmann at the Office of Arid Land Studies for their excellent research in *revisiting the drylands* by comparing the state-of-the-art knowledge on the world's drylands in the 1950s and today.

Assistant Director-General for Natural Sciences   Professor Walter Erdelen
UNESCO

Preface

The Future of Arid Lands, edited by Dr. Gilbert White, was published in 1956. The book, and the process that created it, spawned many streams of activity – some intended, some not. The volume that follows is the outcome of two of those streams of activity. The papers contained in *The Future of Arid Lands* were presented at a meeting that was convened in Albuquerque, New Mexico (USA), organized by the American Association for the Advancement of Science. The first paper, "History and Problems of Arid Lands Development," was contributed by Dr. Homer Shantz, retired president of the University of Arizona. The meeting itself, Dr. Shantz' participation in it, and the interest in arid lands research that it signaled, created a stir at the University of Arizona. The faculty's response was to create an ad hoc interdisciplinary "Committee on Arid Lands Studies" to coordinate research across campus. This effort was successful, attracting a grant from the Rockefeller Foundation in 1958. This was followed by a grant from the US Army Research Office in 1964 to produce a summary of what was known about deserts. The Office of Arid Lands Studies (OALS) was created to carry out this large task. OALS is the interdisciplinary research unit in the College of Agriculture and Life Sciences that Charles Hutchinson directs today.

Since 1968, OALS has been the administrative home to a graduate interdisciplinary doctoral degree program in Arid Lands Resource Sciences (ALRS). Stefanie Herrmann is a product of this program, from which she graduated while completing this volume.

In 2004, the 50th anniversary of the publication of *The Future of Arid Lands was* approaching. Hutchinson suggested to UNESCO that a volume considering *The Future of Arid Lands* and the progress made since then might be an appropriate commemoration. The premise was that we are now living and working in "the future of arid lands" that was predicted by the earlier work. UNESCO saw a much larger opportunity that would celebrate *The Future of Arid Lands*, acknowledge the UNESCO Major Project on Arid Lands launched some 50 years before, and contribute to the designation of 2006 as the International Year of Deserts and Desertification by the UN General Assembly. The centerpiece was a UNESCO-organized conference on the "Future of Drylands" in Tunis (Tunisia) in June 19–21, sponsored by various UN agencies and international organizations. Thus the divergent streams of activity that were spawned in 1956 by the Albuquerque conference and book on *The Future of Arid Lands* have now come together again in a very special and productive way.

The two authors assume collective responsibility for the scientific content of the book, even though each took charge of some chapters specifically. Hermann wrote chapters 4, 6, 7, and 7, and Hutchinson wrote most of the rest.

Many others contributed to the completion of this volume. We specifically thank OALS editor, Katherine Waser, who has been of valuable help. She edited drafts, dealt with the bibliography and was instrumental in gaining copyright permissions. Wiebke Förch (OALS) assisted with the collection and assimilation of a great deal of background material. Nina Weisslechnerova, a visiting graphic arts student at the University of Arizona from Slovakia, produced the initial drafts of selected graphs and maps. Michelle Hertzfeld, a recent OALS Space Grant intern and graduate of the university of Arizona Eastern Asian Studies program, did final revisions on Ms. Weisslechnerova's work and produced further graphs in their entirety. Furthermore, we are indebted to Chiyo Yamashita-Gill for helping us to stay organized and on-task and to the Controlled Environment Agriculture Center at the University of Arizona for offering a quiet spot to write on weekends.

Finally, we thank our reviewers, Robert Varady (University Arizona), Andrew Comrie (University of Arizona), Uriel Safriel (Hebrew University of Jerusalem), Richard Watson (University of New Mexico [retired]), Michele Betsill (Colorado State University), Richard Thomas (ICARDA), and Andrew Warren (University College London) for their very helpful and constructive reviews. Of course, we accept responsibility for any oversights, inconsistencies, misstatements in what is presented here.

Tucson, Arizona 2007   Charles Hutchinson
                                                                              Stefanie Herrmann

Contents

Chapter 1
Introduction: The Future Is Now

1.1 The Future of Arid Lands

In 1956, the American Association for the Advancement of Science published *The Future of Arid Lands*, edited by Gilbert F. White. It is a collection of the papers presented by a panel of experts convened at a meeting in Albuquerque, New Mexico (USA), to address the problems that confronted arid lands.[1]

The Future of Arid Lands comprises 34 papers organized into four broad categories. Although unstated in the title, the assumption on which the book was based was that arid lands represented a resource. Thus, the papers and the thrust of the book were not necessarily about understanding the nature of drylands, but about defining the limits of the knowledge that might enable more productive use of them, and to chart out a course to address those limits. The categories of papers provide a general flavor of the book and the thinking at the time:

- *Variability and predictability of water supply.* Productive use was restricted to agriculture, broadly defined. Plants and animals required water, so the ability to reliably predict the occurrence of water in time and space was a critical concern. It was known that variability is a fundamental characteristic of dry climates; the objective was to better understand that variability.
- *Better use of present resources.* This meant crops and livestock. This category might be made broader today (to include energy, minerals, natural environment, environmental goods and services, and lifestyle amenities).
- *Prospects for additional water resources.* The development of drylands was and is constrained by the availability of water. Technology offered tantalizing opportunities for "new" water resources. Some of these technologies have since become familiar (e.g., desalination), but have failed to become as inexpensive and widely used as was then hoped. Other notions that were explored, such as

---

[1] In 1955, the "International Arid Lands Meetings" were organized by the American Association for the Advancement of Science (AAAS), sponsored by the United Nations Educational, Scientific, and Cultural Organization (UNESCO) and supported by the Rockefeller Foundation. Following the meeting in Albuquerque there was a workshop held in Socorro, New Mexico, that was charged with developing a research agenda.

C. F. Hutchinson and S. M. Herrmann, *The Future of Arid Lands – Revisited.*
© Springer 2008

cloud seeding, have lost some interest as research topics and are not widely applied, though they persist in some places.

- *Better adaptation of plants and animals to arid conditions*. Ever since the first productive use of drylands, most, if not all, effort had been devoted to engineer the dryland environment – largely through irrigation – to allow the production of crops originally developed in other, more humid regions. In 1955, there was at least the glimmering of a notion that a more efficient approach to making drylands productive would be to select or ultimately to engineer plants and animals better adapted to the dryland environment.

Throughout *The Future of Arid Lands*, the authors bemoaned a general lack of data on which to build a fundamental understanding of how drylands behave and how best to manage them. To underscore this fundamental obstacle, the target of the meetings then was to be "centered upon those areas of investigation where prediction of the future currently must be based upon insufficient understanding and data" (White, 1956, p. v).

The Future of Arid Lands, and the process that created it, are still important in two respects. First, they heralded the opening of a period of sustained interest in the drylands, beginning with the UNESCO Major Project on Arid Lands in 1957. This concern with drylands has become a recurring theme for United Nations agencies and programs, largely because many of the countries of the drylands are comparatively poor and underdeveloped. Until recently, the opportunities for agricultural development in drylands were judged to be meager beyond those areas that might be irrigated, putting these countries at a particular disadvantage in attracting international assistance. The continued prominence of drylands problems on the UN agenda has, overall, helped to highlight the plight of dry countries by periodically addressing specific issues that would otherwise go unnoticed in a world where attention increasingly focuses on opportunities for investment. The degree to which drylands have realized any benefit from the increased attention, however, might be debated.

Beyond marking the beginning of international awareness of the special problems confronting drylands, *The Future of Arid Lands* has value in itself. Although broad statements about trends were made in the preface to the book, the chapters themselves were not so much about the future as they were about the state of knowledge in the mid-1950s in each of the topical areas presented. As a result, they made statements about needs for the future in terms of research, or areas that seemed particularly promising within each author's area of expertise. These were scientists describing their own research interests and what they felt was needed. As a result, *The Future of Arid Lands* affords us an opportunity to look back in time and assess how we have progressed. This allows us to consider changes in science and technology over the last 50 years, the context in which issues were then framed and, perhaps most important, which issues of the day were considered most critical. From this, we can learn something not only about the progress of science and the issues on which it should be brought to bear, but also about the origin of some of our current problems, how potential new problems might be foreseen and, equally important, how crucial it is to take steps to ensure that policy is built on the best science.

Among the lessons that might be learned from comparing what is found in *The Future of Arid Lands* with what we know today is a better appreciation of the "law of unintended consequences". This can be summarized as the realization that the actions of the people – and especially of the government – always have effects that are unanticipated or unintended (Merton, 1936). Many of these, unfortunately, are negative. By no means are we immune to that law today, but it is the failure to recognize or anticipate these possibilities in *The Future of Arid Lands* that draws our attention and offers lessons. On the other hand, much of the focus then was on transforming arid lands from what they were into something different, so it may be unfair to judge the success of these transformations with our current sensibilities.

The concept of "rainmaking" in drylands has tantalized drylands occupants since time immemorial, being the stuff of persistent myths and superstitions. *The Future of Arid Lands* demonstrated that, for the first time, our growing understanding of the physics of the precipitation process was providing a new and real promise to make it rain as much, where, and when it was most desirable, through techniques such as "cloud seeding". While later this proved to be possible in very restricted situations over small areas, it was of such limited and often unpredictable value that it has not emerged as a generally applied tool even after more than 50 years of intense research.

We know today that humans' inadvertent influence on climate – as in climate change – is of an entirely different order. Increases in temperatures threaten the modest water resources of arid lands in several ways. Clearly, increases in evaporation rates as a function of higher temperatures not only threaten reserves stored in reservoirs and soils, but also increase water demand by plants. A more ominous threat for many regions, however, may be decreases in the amount of water stored in snow pack in the mountains surrounding many of the world's drylands, as a result of increased minimum temperatures.

The Future of Arid Lands demonstrated a firm belief in the use of exotic animal and particularly plant species that might "do better" than native species to make land more productive, often for livestock. The challenge then was to find the "right" species for a particular situation and to introduce it into that new environment. Today, a major struggle for those concerned with conservation of landscapes and biodiversity is to develop ways of dealing with these introduced species because many of them spread quickly, outcompete local species, and transform the landscape.

The Future of Arid Lands is, above all, a testimony to the then unshakable belief that much more of the drylands could be brought into productive use through the application of technology. Often, the envisioned increases in productivity were to be achieved by irrigation, with water derived from existing surface sources, augmentation of those sources (e.g., through cloud seeding), or "new" water from untapped sources (e.g., through desalination of seawater). What actually happened was that existing sources were increasingly used, often with very serious, long-term consequences. The diversion of surface waters was obviously the simplest and least expensive of the strategies that were proposed, and diversion was pursued on very large scales in the areas where surface waters were available. But there is little "free" water in the drylands, as the development – and destruction – of the Aral Sea has testified. In this case, the upstream use of water by the Soviet Union for irrigated agriculture first destroyed downstream fisheries as water levels in the Aral Sea declined, and eventually created an environmental disaster as the seabed, along with its toxic blanket of agricultural chemicals, was exposed. The states that formerly comprised the Soviet Union struggle with this legacy. While recent concerted interventions offer the prospect of some limited recovery, the Aral Sea drama continues to provide an object lesson in the hazards of water management in the drylands (Box 3.1).

1.2   The Future of Arid Lands – Revisited

If a list of topical areas critical to drylands were to be assembled today, it would differ considerably from the list that was assembled in the 1950s. The differences are driven by our improved knowledge of drylands, the processes that govern their behavior, and the economic, political, and social issues that shape their use.

First, while the major challenge in the 1950s was lack of data, today it is the opposite. Fifty years ago, there were very few data to allow the understanding of processes, particularly at regional or global scales. For example, the first weather satellite was still in the future and, as a result, there were no means for making synoptic weather observations. Today, we have a fleet of satellites that observe not only land, sea, and clouds, but also surface temperatures and winds, all of which has allowed us to develop more reliable models. These data and models allow us to make reasonably timely predictions about the specific nature of the weather tomorrow, or broader forecasts about the general nature of the rainy season 3 months hence. But today we are sometimes overwhelmed with the sheer volume of data and how best to manage it. Furthermore, we must find ways to separate the good from the bad and the relevant from the irrelevant data, and make this distinction clear to those who must rely on them.

Second, the discussion that took place in 1955 dealt largely, but not exclusively, with drylands in the industrialized world. To be fair, almost all the participants came from these regions and drew on their own experiences. Today, the drylands of the developing world, which comprises 72% of the total global dryland area (MA, 2006) would assume at least equal importance.

Third, the social sciences were given a short shrift in 1956; today, the emphasis in development has shifted from a rigid concentration on the physical and biological sciences to a broader effort to understand and manage the social dimensions of change. We are now increasingly concerned with the policies that govern the management of dryland resources, how these policies are formulated, how they are implemented, and what mechanisms they provide to overcome or resolve conflicts between concerned parties. This profound shift in emphasis from "hard" to "soft" issues is particularly noticeable in the field of water resources (Varady and Iles-Shih, in press).

The Future of Arid Lands – Revisited affords us the opportunity to revisit the earlier volume, knowing that we are living and working in the future, which was that book's theme. Beyond allowing us to appreciate the changes in science and technology, looking back in time gives us a better understanding of the political and socioeconomic contexts that framed those changes. Finally, it allows us to understand what were then considered the critical issues of the day and to place the actions then taken to deal with these issues in a historical context.

1.2.1 Scope

The scope of *The Future of Arid Lands* was prescribed by Meigs' "map of the arid lands" (printed on the endsheets of the original book) comprising hyperarid, arid, and semiarid regions (Shantz, 1956). Here, we use the more widely adopted category of "drylands" to delineate the geographic scope of this volume. According to UNEP (Middleton et al., 1997), drylands include hyperarid, arid, semiarid, and dry-subhumid areas (other than polar and subpolar regions). The semiarid areas are the largest dryland category in spatial extent and, together with the dry-subhumid areas, are the most densely populated. Therefore, these areas are the focus here.

1.2.2 Audience

The audience we seek to reach is composed of policymakers and upper-level managers. We also hope that the volume will be of value to the informed and interested layperson and to students who are interested in identifying some of the major issues that confront the use and management of drylands. The references and examples provided herein will also lead readers to other, more specifically focused materials of value.

1.2.3 Objective

Our primary objective is to provide a general understanding of the major issues that underpin the productive and sustained management of drylands and how these issues have evolved over the last 50 years. This is not so much about conveying the content of the science itself as about understanding how science has affected policy in the past. The intention is to show the importance of science and suggest how it might inform policy in the future. A major deterrent to more effective decision-making is the length of time that passes between the general adoption of theory within the scientific community, and the appearance – or at least appreciation – of that same theory in management policy.

We hope that this consideration of what has happened over the last 50 years will help policymakers appreciate what has been achieved and, with this in mind, to move more quickly towards applying current scientific understanding to current policy issues. This is particularly important given that the time we still have to successfully address the environmental and development issues that confront us may be limited, and we may be unable to make up any time wasted on outmoded policies (Rischard, 2002).

Chapter 2
Contexts

A perfunctory comparison of what appeared 50 years ago in *The Future of Arid Lands* with our viewpoint today would not be instructive. It would cloud the lessons that we might learn from that early attempt at synthesis. Instead, this chapter places *The Future of Arid Lands* in the broad context of the scientific knowledge and attitudes of its time, considering in particular how these might have shaped its perspectives.

2.1 The Situation in the 1950s

2.1.1 Ambience: The Post-World War II Years

Gilbert F. White, the editor of *The Future of Arid Lands*, returned to the topic of drylands many times during his long career. In his 1960 work, *Science and the Future of Arid Lands*, also for UNESCO, White captured the concerns about drylands that existed in the mid-1950s, in terms of both the problems they presented and, more important, the potential they offered. At that time, perhaps even more than today, there was a growing concern about how to feed the world's burgeoning population. White's work is representative of a great deal of thought at the time. Four points are of particular importance, providing a consistent direction to both the times and White's 1960 book.

First was the belief that problems already existed in the drylands that were a threat to their future use and were largely the product of mismanagement. In *The Future of Arid Lands*, the tendency was to concentrate on proximate causes such as inappropriate or poorly informed practices used by local land managers. While often valid, this viewpoint promoted the search for packages of technical solutions that were typically designed independently of the economic, social, and institutional environments in which they would be implemented. As White (1956) pointed out in his preface, when such small-scale technical interventions proved ineffective, the recognition grew that mismanagement could result from a host of causes, many of which fell outside the power of local land managers to change.

7

C. F. Hutchinson and S. M. Herrmann, *The Future of Arid Lands – Revisited.*
© Springer 2008

Secondary causes might be national or international rather than local, including such things as land and resource tenure laws that governed access to resources and, as a result, influenced the management and investment choices made by land managers. This realization was crucial, because it opened the door to formulating effective policy that led to better decisions by land managers. For example, a land manager who did not own the land or have recognized rights to use it had little incentive to invest in it. The lack of access to credit, for whatever reason, would diminish a manager's ability to invest in improvements or technology. The degree of access to external markets could affect a land manager's decision to concentrate on providing for the immediate needs of the household as opposed to exploiting opportunities offered by local, regional, or international markets. All these things could be ameliorated only by policy.

In other words, rather than attempting only to "correct" local mismanagement, or introduce technical solutions to increase productivity, policy should be directed towards treating the drivers of the destructive management decisions (e.g., by revising land tenure laws). Understanding human behavior and the incentives and disincentives to which people react continues to be a primary objective of social science, and one that is critical to effective and equitable policy.

A second belief that seemed to underlie interest in drylands during the 1950s was that developing the drylands was imperative for the survival of humans on this planet. Drylands were viewed as underutilized space. Part of their potential value was passive, simply providing room that could be occupied by people and the infrastructure needed to support them. However, the drylands' larger potential value was their offer of space that could be brought into productive use, largely through agriculture. This belief was fueled by a Malthusian view of a future in which we would simply run out of room to house and feed people and was reflected in many of the chapters in *The Future of Arid Lands*. As noted later by White (1980, p. 183), "beginning in the late 1940s fundamental questions were raised about future capacity of the globe to support its rapidly growing population." If we survey the world's land masses – then and now – there are only two large blank areas (Fig. 2.1). Antarctica was vast, but the physical and climatic challenges to live there and bring it into some kind of productive use were too extreme. In contrast, much of the drylands area was in the midlatitudes and offered a favorable climate for agriculture: all that was needed was to "just add water". From a Malthusian perspective, there was nowhere else left to go.

It may be that this perspective forced an unwitting bias in *The Future of Arid Lands* and led its authors to consider only a very narrow set of land-use options. Virtually without exception, the scope of discussion then was limited to the use of drylands for agricultural production through crops or livestock. This did not go unnoticed at the time. One contemporary book reviewer noted that "it is tacitly assumed by all contributors that the optimum use of arid land, and ideal end-result of all scientific and technical effort is to bring it under cultivation" (Logan, 1957, p. 281).

Third, intertwined with the Malthusianism of the 1950s was the belief – or reasoned hope – that although dryland development presented significant challenges, these could be met and overcome by science. As Dickson (1956, p. 48) noted, "Today we know that Malthus was just ahead of his time and we have to ask

Fig. 2.1 Night lights of the world. Areas with few night lights represent opportunities for development from a global perspective.

ourselves whether adequate food requirements of the people can be provided from present sources with all the technological experience available to us."

In tune with his times, White in 1960 at any rate saw the world's drylands as a source of potential resources that could be tapped to meet the needs and aspirations of the world's rapidly growing population. While the problems involved were of pressing concern, White (1960, p. 5) was optimistic because "Most fortunately, man's need to exploit the arid and semiarid areas occurs at a time when the great advance of scientific research gives him grounds for hoping that he will be able to solve the problems arising there."

Finally, making productive use of the drylands was viewed as an international undertaking. Dryland development was in everyone's interest because the future of humankind could hinge on our collective ability to exploit these lands. More practically, given the global nature and scope of the challenges (and opportunities) involved, coordinated international effort would be required to address them (White, 1960, p. 6):

> The universality of the results of arid zone research and the advisability of pooling them on behalf of all countries make this work an ideal field for international action, especially by Unesco [sic] which is required under its Constitution to promote scientific research in order to improve man's living conditions.

Some saw it not only as an inherently international undertaking, but also as one compelled by moral obligation (Dickson, 1956, p. 63):

> [T]eamwork should be between individuals, between universities and research institutions, and between peoples – in other words, between UN organizations.

Particularly does it seem appropriate that we who belong to those sections of mankind that enjoy the highest standards of living should see a plain duty to help in every way possible to benefit the less well-off sections of mankind?

In many ways, the zeitgeist of 1950s was unprecedented. After World War II, economies were generally on the rise, belief in science and technology was strong and, for much of the world, it was a time of growing confidence and belief in the future. However, an undercurrent of fear also accompanied the development of nuclear arms at the end of World War II; this was fanned by the ensuing arms race between the USA and the Soviet Union and the competition it spawned between them on almost all fronts. The race to build more powerful weapons and the means to deliver them across vast distances also led to competition in science and technology that was gaining momentum at the time that *The Future of Arid Lands* was published. This competition brought nuclear power, ushered in the Space Age and a new ability to observe the Earth, helped spur research into weather modification, and even led to the initiation of climate modeling (Chapter 4).

The climate of drylands from a global perspective presented a puzzle to the scientists, land managers, and policymakers of those years. The southwestern USA was in the grip of a major drought as the symposium on *The Future of Arid Lands* was being held, although little if any concern was registered at the meetings. This indifference to drought might have been due, in large part, to US government programs that built major water delivery works in much of the western USA, like those along the Colorado River. There were also other federal insurance programs that had been enacted in the wake of the disastrous droughts of the 1930s to protect farmers and ranchers from financial loss (Hurt, 1994). Thus, even in the areas then suffering from drought, policies had been put in place to guard against misfortune, and this appeared to dampen concern.

Furthermore, in sub-Saharan Africa, the 1950s and the 1960s were an unbroken wet period in the Sahel – a veritable calm before the storm that began with the droughts of the 1970s. While certainly a boon in many ways, this wet period helped to make the impacts of subsequent droughts much more severe than they might otherwise have been, in a pattern that is familiar to the drylands (Box 2.1).

Both of these situations contributed to a general sense of optimism about the future of drylands globally. Those areas that were perhaps most economically and socially vulnerable were in the wet phase of the boom-and-bust cycle. Conversely, many areas that were then experiencing drought were among the least vulnerable, being comparatively well-off and having previously put in place programs and institutions to blunt drought impacts on local populations.

2.1.2   Science: Belief in Technology

Then, as now, there was a general optimism about the contributions that science might make to society. World War II had been won by science and technology. In *The Future of Arid Lands*, Kellogg (1956, p. 26) noted that "History ... tells us that man can live on [arid] lands, but to live well and to prosper he must make full use of science and technology for the combined use of all the resources."

Equally important, a "scientific" brand of organizational management that had sprung up to support the war effort was taking hold in almost every sector of economic endeavor. There was a sense that the world had entered an "advanced" era. Even in agriculture, formal research had been organized for more than 50 years, both commercially and in the land grant university system (in the USA), and the promise of the "Green Revolution" was just dawning in Mexico.

But the science that underpinned the management of natural environment was less robust, particularly in the drylands. Leopold concluded (1956, p. 115), "... our understanding of the semi-arid environment is poor." This was largely due to lack of data, and also of adequate models. This hindered the ability to make reliable predictions, and, of course, provided the impetus for organizing the *Future of Arid Lands* meetings. True, enough local data could be gathered to satisfy local needs (such as assessing rangeland condition). There was also a coordinated system for gathering climatic data from around the world, but these were neither spatially comprehensive nor were they necessarily available quickly. There were no systems designed or operated for routinely gathering data with global coverage. It was not until 1960 that the first weather satellite – TIROS – was launched. However, in large part, the lack of data about most of the drylands reflected the comparatively small role that managed dryland ecosystems played in most national economies. Without comprehensive data, it is difficult to arrive at a robust understanding of a system or develop anything other than very simple models for predicting conditions in the future. These problems were one of the major themes of *The Future of Arid Lands*.

One glaring omission in *The Future of Arid Lands* – at least to the reader today – is the absence of social science. To be fair, editor Gilbert White's preface (written after the Socorro workshop) did note the importance of social factors in influencing management decisions, but this was not mentioned again (with one exception discussed below). Perhaps defensively, Kellogg (1956) suggested that this was not necessarily an oversight, but was because the social sciences lagged behind the natural sciences in their ability to provide information that would be useful for management decisions. It must be said that the reluctance to consider social sciences as relevant to land management was more a characteristic of this volume than of the period in general. It was this topic to which White returned several times in subsequent papers (White, 1960, 1980).

The single exception to the dearth of social science in the 1956 volume was the inclusion of a paper on "The Economics of Water Sources". This was an admitted afterthought offered by Louis Koenig, a "natural scientist" and not an economist. He limited himself to comparing the alternatives for water development that had been considered by the workshop – artificial precipitation, demineralization, and water reuse – from a strictly economic perspective. He largely dismissed the first alternative as unproven, discounted the second because of transportation costs, and felt the third was constrained both by the limited quantity of water it made available and the technical difficulties of producing a suitable product. His comments on the use of water in arid lands were provocative and, in the end, quite sobering regarding the future. He noted that, in contrast to humid regions, land's value in dry regions was not related to qualities that made it suitable for agriculture or industrial use, but depended on the price of water that was available at that point. For that reason, he concluded that irrigation was not appropriate in drylands. Instead, since "the railroad trains run in both directions", he believed that "the arid lands should look toward industrial rather than agricultural expansion" (Koenig, 1956, p. 328).

In other words, crops should be grown in those regions where it is most efficient to do so, not necessarily in drylands. In these conclusions, Koenig was far less enthusiastic about the development potential of drylands than any of his fellow authors, and his arguments undermined the general spirit of the workshop. By encouraging people to determine what comparative advantages drylands held and to exploit them, his comments foreshadowed current arguments regarding globalization.

From our perspective 50 years later, another glaring omission in the 1956 volume was any consideration of the environmental consequences that might accompany the kinds of interventions that were being discussed. For example, neither the collateral physical and biological effects of induced precipitation were discussed, nor were the potential legal ramifications of inducing rainfall over one area at the expense of another (Chapter 4). The brines that are inevitable by-products of water desalination represent a considerable disposal problem, but these too went unaddressed. Similarly, the difficulties of weighing the potential benefits of developing major water control structures against the huge investments, inevitable societal disruptions, and environmental impacts involved, were essentially ignored (Chapter 3).

In 1969, another UNESCO conference was convened in Tucson, Arizona (USA), to consider what the prospects might be for the drylands (Dregne, 1970). In the comparatively short period of 13 years (1956–1969), the downside of promoting development without considering the environmental consequences that might accompany it had been recognized. In commenting on the need to attend to the environment, Dregne (1970, p. 9) noted that "Its practical significance...was overlooked by governments as long as the arid regions were remote, unknown, and thought to be unimportant to a nation's economy. Easy access to the farthest reaches of the world has changed all this."

This had been apparent to White in 1956 and was a theme he addressed consistently (White, 1980). He noted that the general tendency in 1956 was to consider only single interventions rather than the type of integrated mixes he was advocating, and that there was little interest in social and economic impacts. In this, he sounded very modern.

The overall tone, both of the book and of its decade, was very much forward-looking. Yet some contemporary reviewers took pains to point out that there was a great deal to be learned from the past. One contemporary reviewer made a case for more consideration of traditional systems (Sears, 1957, p. 90):

> Today, when we are trying desperately to deal with population pressure by any means possible except a frontal attack, the ancient glories of the desert take on new interest. There is ample reason to respect the soundness of ancient engineering works as a guide to modern rehabilitation.

The strategy of learning from the past was already, and continues to be, a strong theme in land management, water development, and "new" crops (Chapters 3, 5, and 7).

2.1.3   Policy: Focus on Growth

In the 1950s and 1960s, policy tended to be strongly influenced by optimistic views
of the wonders that science and technology might achieve. The notion of unanticipated negative outcomes was still some distance in the future. The promise of the
Green Revolution was dawning, but some of its unfortunate consequences were still
to be revealed, as in Carson's *Silent Spring* (1962).

This is not to suggest that White and his colleagues were shortsighted or turned
a blind eye towards the "tough" issues. As they themselves pointed out, there simply was a great deal that was unknown at that time. Thus, many of the questions on
which we now concentrate – such as sustainability – were not even broached. While
this was the Atomic Age, it was not yet the Space Age. The Information Age was
in its infancy (Fig. 2.2); computers were comparatively rare and would not begin to
come into broad use in the sciences for another decade (Hoagland, 2003). These
constraints on knowledge made it difficult for anyone to imagine an all-inclusive
"Earth system" or conceive of how humans could interfere with it.

Fig. 2.2 The world's first disk drive. The RAMAC 305, developed by IBM in 1956, had a storage
capacity of 5 MB. (From IBM Corporate Archives)

2.2   The Situation Today

The absolute need to make productive use of the world's drylands appears to have abated somewhat with the passage of time. Increases in agricultural production have come about largely through irrigation, fertilizers, and improved crops, rather than through the wholesale conversion of new land to agricultural production (Trewavas, 2002). However, as we will find, most of these improvements did not reach the drylands in the first wave of the Green Revolution (Chapter 5), so in terms of development their plight has been addressed only partially, particularly in the developing world.

2.2.1   Ambience: Towards a Globalized World

The Future of Arid Lands was based on the belief that progress is good. Since then, the realization has grown that progress does not come without problems; thus, it is now viewed with some degree of apprehension (Sardar, 2000). Concern grew when it became apparent that negative changes in the environment, particularly air and water, that accompanied progress could be damaging to human health (White, 1980).

It might be argued that this realization came about, in part, as we gained a truly global view of the planet and came to understand that the Earth does have limits in what we might expect it to produce to support us (Fig. 2.3). Beginning around 1970, the realization grew that beyond economics, both the environment and social issues must be addressed in planning for growth (McNeill, 2000). In response, sustained efforts were undertaken to develop more robust methods for estimating the true costs and benefits of development projects, something that was not envisioned in *The Future of Arid Lands*. Similarly, studies of the environmental impact of development projects are now a routine, instituted in attempts to minimize the likelihood of significant "unintended consequences". In parallel, mechanisms for public review and comment on development projects have evolved so that the views of various "stakeholders" can be heard and their concerns addressed.

Along with the realization that progress had a price came the realization that not all benefited equally from the progress that was achieved. Fifty years ago, the assumption may have been that "a rising tide floats all boats", and that advances in science and technology would benefit all equally. Overall, this has proven to be true: measures of well-being in general have risen over the last 50 years. However, it has also become apparent that the tide may indeed rise, but not all boats are equally seaworthy. So, concern has increased not only about progress, but about differences in the rates of progress in development that are being achieved, particularly between the rich and poor, and the developed and developing worlds (Rischard, 2002).

The contrasts may be even starker when we examine poor countries in the drylands. Most drylands are politically and economically marginal. They have also

Fig. 2.3 Earth rise. This photograph, taken during the Apollo 8 mission in December 1968, became an icon of the environmental movement of the 1970s. (From Apollo Image Gallery, http://www.apolloarchive.com/apollo_gallery.html)

failed to draw the attention of investors, outside of the irrigated areas. The new sources of water that were proposed in 1956, such as desalination, have become less expensive, but are still too costly to satisfy all but municipal needs and are unlikely ever to be economic for agriculture (Chapter 3). It is true that very high-quality desalinized water can replace lower-quality water for domestic use and allow that lower-quality water to be put to other uses. Those sectors in which drylands might offer comparative advantages – solar energy, for example – have not yet evolved to the point where they can compete with other energy technologies and be deployed on a large scale. Exploitation of nonrenewable mineral resources (e.g., copper, uranium) is of course possible, but the prices of these products are subject to the whims of international markets. Other opportunities that exploit low population densities and the absence of competing uses, such as waste disposal, military training, or weapons testing, raise many problems. Beyond the irrigated areas or locales that have beaches or unusual and attractive scenery combined with stable governments, the opportunities for drylands development have been few.

2.2.1.1 Globalization: Industrialized Countries

Globalization of the world's economy is a contentious topic. Loosely defined, it refers to the integration of global markets so that goods, services, and investments flow freely, unhindered by national boundaries. It has been argued that this is a process of "democratization" of technology, finance, and information (Friedman, 2005). Contention revolves around the types of outcomes that result from globalization. On one hand it is seen as a force for economic integration; on the other, it is seen as providing few if any benefits to large parts of the world's population, particularly in developing countries (Jenkins, 2004).

Those who promote market integration point to evidence that globalization leads to faster economic growth as measured by Gross National Product (GNP) (Collier and Dollar, 2001). This is attributed to the tendency of globalization to enable participating countries to exploit their comparative advantages, whether these be their low labor costs (i.e., much of the developing world, such as India and China) or market windows (i.e., "out of season" markets offered by the contrasting seasons between northern and southern hemispheres) (Dollar and Kraay, 2001).

Opponents counter that, while globalization may lead to faster economic growth overall, it can also cause great harm to some places and people through inequities in the distribution of the benefits of growth. The poor are often ill-positioned to participate in the benefits of globalization because of their geographic distance from the centers of growth. Less education, poorer health, or poorly established traditions of social organization, and an inability to mobilize may also proscribe participation (Bhagwati and Srinivasan, 2002). These conditions, in turn, are highly context-dependent. For example, while East and Southeast Asia experienced dramatic growth over the past generation, other parts of the world have been left behind, particularly in Africa (Streeten, 1998). Where abilities to participate in economic growth differ, the poorest tend to suffer most, both economically and politically; this may lead to further political strains.

Conditions that lead to marginalization within the global context are amplified in the drylands. In addition, because most are in developing countries, drylands may also be burdened with nonrepresentative political institutions, ineffective governments, poor internal infrastructure, low levels of education and health care, underdeveloped communication systems, anemic industrial and commercial bases, and generally weak economies based largely on subsistence agriculture. To add to this list of obstacles, drylands are subject to extreme climate variability, which often amplifies the vulnerability of their dominant agricultural production systems. Given these conditions, it is not surprising that many dryland farmers and other resource managers, communities, regions, and countries struggle to find a comparative advantage in the world's marketplace. Perversely, globalization itself presents a threat to farmers who find their local markets filled with imported crops priced lower than those they can themselves produce.

2.2.1.2 Globalization: Industrialized Countries

In the developed world the case for globalization is different but still revolves around the arguments Koenig made in 1956. He suggested that irrigation was not an appropriate use of water in drylands, and that attention should be concentrated instead on industry, at that time restricted in definition to include only "manufacturing". The passage of time, the development of new technologies and the growth of economies has broadened the scope of endeavors that the term "industry" now encompasses, many of which offer the drylands a comparative advantage. For example, the advent of comparatively inexpensive air travel, coupled with the attractions of warm climate, clear skies, broad vistas, and striking landscapes, has created a tourism "industry" that is critical for drylands in many developed and developing countries (e.g., Death Valley in the USA, Uluru in Australia, the Aïr Massif in Niger) (Chapter 7).

The dawning of the Information Age has also broadened the definition of what Koenig might have called manufacturing. In his time, industry focused on manufacturing "hard" goods like ball bearings or refrigerators. Locations for manufacturing such products were and are chosen for access to raw materials, energy, and transportation. Today, it is argued, high-technology industry develops products based on research (e.g., electronics, computers, software) and is driven by the creative talents of people. Such industries need to locate in areas that creative people might favor for their amenities like cultural diversity, urban lifestyles, climate, and access to recreational opportunities (Florida, 2002).

Despite Koenig's pessimistic outlook, agriculture still plays an important role in drylands, and this is largely a result of globalization. More efficient irrigation technology and improved transportation linkages now allow many of the drylands to exploit their comparative advantage by supplying other regions with winter vegetables. For example, the southwestern USA and northwestern Mexico supply many of the winter vegetables consumed in North America, just as southern Europe, northern Africa, and the Levant provide winter produce to northern Europe. The past decade has seen this trend intensify through the development of highly efficient and consistent greenhouse vegetable production (Cook and Calvin, 2005).

In this new world that Koenig could not have imagined, water has indeed become scarcer and thus more valuable, particularly in the drylands. And, as suggested by Koenig, alternatives to traditional agriculture have emerged that use water more efficiently and more profitably.

2.2.2 Science: Complexity and Uncertainty

In science, the comparison between now and then is dramatic. A primary reason for organizing the 1955 meetings on the *Future of Arid Lands* was to address the problems caused by lack of data, particularly data that would allow predictions to be made about the temporal and spatial availability of water. Today, it is argued that we are overwhelmed by data, from both ground-based networks and satellite systems. The challenge has thus become to organize data and ensure that they are easily and universally accessible – a situation now being addressed through such initiatives as the international Global Earth Observing System (Battrick, 2005).

Over time, research has become more focused on the basic processes that govern phenomena and systems rather than on their individual characteristics. A better understanding of physical and biological processes leads to the development of ways in which they might either be modified to improve their performance (as in the case of agriculture), or modeled in order to enable prediction of their future behavior (as in the case of weather). Improved agricultural technology ranges from new plant varieties that are higher yielding and/or more drought- and disease-resist-ant, to new chemicals that increase yields and ward off predation by pests, to new mechanical technologies for harvest, transport, and storage of crops. All of these have combined to increase crop yields by a factor of 3 since 1950 and allowed us to "foil Malthus again, and again" (Trewavas, 2002). Similarly, with a far better understanding of global atmospheric and oceanic circulation and the effects of periodic changes such as El Niño, it is now possible to predict months in advance what general conditions will be in some parts of the world, thus providing farmers and decision-makers with the time to adjust to them (Chapter 4).

Now, although there is still great confidence in science and technology, this confidence is colored by a better appreciation of the complexity of the systems with which we are dealing, the interdependence of their components, and the asso-ciated uncertainty that comes with that complexity. Perhaps more important is the hard-won understanding that almost every change we might make has a multitude of consequences that ripple through other domains – physical, biological, social, and economic – just as suggested by White (1956). This is also reflected in the ways in which future managers and scholars are now trained, with an increasing emphasis on advanced degrees in interdisciplinary studies at such internationally renowned institutions as the United Nations University (M.S. program in Integrated Land Management), Columbia University (Doctoral program in Sustainable Development), and the University of Arizona (USA) (Doctoral program in Arid Lands Resource Sciences).

Last, but far from least, much of our improved understanding has been institu-tionalized – sometimes imperfectly – in the ways in which virtually all projects now undertaken include cost–benefit analysis, environmental impact statements, and mechanisms for stakeholder involvement.

2.2.3   Policy: Focus on Sustainability

As science has improved, and the data with which to apply it have become more widely available, we are increasingly challenged with making the transition from research to policy and actual practice. This is a fundamental challenge, but it is perhaps especially crucial in dealing with drylands – particularly in developing countries – that are marginal and isolated. This is especially true beyond the irrigated areas, where opportunities for significant returns on investment are considerably lower than within them. These challenges still remain.

The whole concept of the interconnectedness of the Earth system, and the human systems that rely on it, has come to frame most attitudes about development today. In 1956, the intent of *The Future of Arid Lands* was to do things "better", with an eye to improving production efficiency (i.e., better use of present resources, better adaptations of plants and animals). Now, our goal is to promote and achieve development that is more "sustainable".

The notion of sustainability has been defined from a variety of perspectives. The Brundtland Commission (WCED, 1987, p. 8) defined sustainable development as development that allows people "...to meet the needs of the present without compromising the ability of future generations to meet their own needs". With time, this simple definition has been enlarged to include more explicit environmental or ecological considerations, but it is still grounded in the economic considerations that dominated thinking 50 years ago. Certainly the concepts of sustainability apply in all environments, but perhaps even more so in the drylands where ecosystems are tuned to interannual variability but where economic development seldom is. For example, drought is an inevitable feature of life in drylands (Box 2.1). However, during times of drought stress, economic interests (e.g., irrigated cotton) usually are given priority when decisions are made about water allocations. Thus, water continues to be diverted to crops to satisfy economic demands at the expense of local ecosystems (such as downstream riparian vegetation) (Walker et al., 1997).

There are also issues of equity – who deserves and who gets what. Some of these questions relate to equity among currently existing individuals and groups. Increasingly, though, questions are raised about equity between those of us now alive and those who will live in the future. Should we use all the water now? Why not? It is perhaps this consideration – intergenerational equity – that has prompted the most debate, particularly given our poor ability to predict future technologies and economies and, hence, the demands future generations might make on the Earth system or the opportunities from which they may benefit (Padilla, 2002).

In 1956, White suggested that the challenge of making "better" use of drylands was constrained not just by technology or science, but also by policies that governed access to land and resources, and prioritized the use of resources among competing sectors or interests. By 1980, White had noted that the earlier concentration on production and efficiency had shifted to include the maintenance of environmental quality. Today, it is argued that a far more critical challenge will be confronted over the next 50 years. During this time, it is projected that the human population will reach its maximum level, about 50% greater than today. As a result, we will need to meet the concurrently increasing demands on the global environment in a way that is sustainable and does not diminish the chances for later generations to exist on the Earth (Tilman et al., 2002).

In 1956, there was optimism about what might be achieved in the drylands through science and technology, if pursued in the spirit of international cooperation.

Box 2.1 Drought follows the plow – boom and bust in drylands

Rather than deviating only slightly from some average condition on a year-to-year basis, the rainfall regime of drylands is highly variable. A few good rainfall years are typically followed by a larger number that are below average. Throughout history, good rainfall years have repeatedly raised expectations about the future productivity of drylands. For example, a period of above-average rainfall in the late nineteenth century led the US government to promote migration and agricultural development of the Great Plains, a region previously considered unsuitable for cultivation due to low rainfall. Early settlers hoped there was some association between their agricultural activities and what they saw as a favorable climate. Apparent cause-and-effect relationship gave rise to the notion that "rain follows the plow" – a myth that was questioned only after thousands of settlers were forced to leave their homes by severe droughts in the late 1890s.

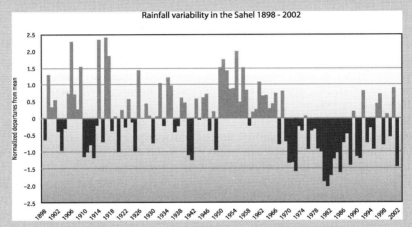

Fig. 2.4 A century of rainfall variability in the Sahel expressed as normalized departures from long-term mean (Nicholson, 2002)

Similarly, a series of unusually wet years in the west-African Sahel in the 1950s and early 1960s (Nicholson, 1989; Fig. 2.4) encouraged farmers to extend the frontiers of rainfed agriculture northward into a zone that was previously pastoral. Production of cash crops (particularly peanuts and cotton) boomed for a time but ended with the unprecedentedly severe Sahelian droughts which struck the region in the 1970s and caused the newly established production systems to "go bust" (Timberlake, 1985). The tendency to ignore the natural alternation of wet with dry periods in semiarid climates led one researcher to turn the nineteenth-century saying on its head and offer the observation that, in fact, "drought follows the plow" (Glantz, 1994).

Now, there is less general optimism. There is also less commitment to international cooperation, and more reliance on market forces to effect change in drylands – and everywhere else – through globalization. The degree to which this will affect the drylands is unclear.

Chapter 3
The Search for Water

Water – or rather its absence – defines drylands. Paradoxically, the dryland climate in the low latitudes has much to recommend it as a place to live and grow crops: clear skies, warm temperatures, long growing seasons.

As Koenig (1956, p. 326) pointed out, "… the value of a given piece of land [in drylands] is not inherent in the land, but is the value of the available water at that point." If your intent is to develop drylands, this is clearly a challenge. However, the message is straightforward: find more water.

With water at such a premium, the pursuit of new water sources has been intense and unrelenting. The pursuit has been joined not only by scientists and technologists, but also by dreamers, eccentrics, and con artists. Thus, separating feasible from not-so-feasible methods for increasing water supplies has been another challenge for those intent on greater development. For example, much of Australia is dryland and the search for water there has been a national obsession. The National Archives of Australia (NAA) has recently developed an exhibit and web site, "Just Add Water" (http://www.naa.gov.au/exhibitions/just_add_water/jaw.html) that describes this search over the past century. The desperate poignancy of these efforts is captured in one of their educational pamphlets, *Water Dreaming* (NAA, no date.), which examines four potential solutions to water development and the years when they were tried: water divining (1920), prayer (1944), cloud seeding (1957), and finally nuclear explosions (1963).

Practically speaking, there are relatively few options for developing water resources: find new resources, reduce demand (conservation), reuse all resources that might otherwise be lost, or distribute resources among competing demands through some form of optimization.

3.1 The Situation in the 1950s

Among the questions posed at the 1955 meetings in New Mexico were the following:

- What are the prospects for usable groundwater occurrence in arid areas?
- What is the practicability of locating and estimating volume and rate of natural recharge of underground water supplies? (White, 1956, p. 65)

22

C. F. Hutchinson and S. M. Herrmann, *The Future of Arid Lands – Revisited.*
© Springer 2008

- What constitutes wise allocation of available water supplies among the various needs in arid land drainage areas? (White, 1956, p. 177)
- How practicable is it to demineralize saline water?
- How practicable is it to reuse waste water? (White, 1956, p. 254)

Conservation, a strategy to manage the supply side of the water balance equation, received little attention in the 1950s. Perhaps reflecting a general optimism, most of the attention in *The Future of Arid Lands* was given to two broad supply-side themes. One was improving the ability to predict rainfall and hence streamflow. The second was finding and exploiting new or additional water resources. In both cases, there was a great belief in technology. The range of options in North America had been summarized by Woodbury (1955, p. 200), who concluded that "Much of the land will be doomed perpetually to nonuse or only partial use unless additional water supplies can be provided. Additional sources of water might lie in the Columbia river basin, the ocean, or perhaps the Mississippi river basin."

If nothing else, they were thinking big, and more such schemes have continued to emerge.

3.1.1 Surface Water Development

Since agriculture evolved, surface waters have irrigated the drylands. One argument put forward in the 1950s, and still made, was that the social organization needed to construct and maintain large-scale irrigation systems was the fundamental building block that led to the development of civilization (Wittfogel, 1957). Perhaps this realization contributed in part to the flurry of surface water development that began at that time. But part could also be attributed to the Cold War competition between the USA and the Soviet Union, and their attempts to curry influence in much of the developing world by building dams (McNeill, 2000).

Although some large dams, such as Hoover Dam on the Colorado River, had been built as early as the 1930s, the 1950s were the dawning of the era of large dam-building (Figs. 3.1 and 3.2). In the 1940s, only 913 large dams were commissioned globally; during the 1950s the number commissioned rose to 2,735. While the 1970s were the most active decade, with a total of 5,418 dams commissioned, every decade since then has also seen numerous dams commissioned (WCOD, 2000). Along with this concentration on constructing large dams for the storage and distribution of surface water came two major themes in *The Future of Arid Lands*. One was to manage watersheds more "efficiently", so that they might yield more water to be delivered to users downstream (Dorroh, 1956, p. 160):

[I]s there not every reason to believe that the part of the…water which is not now reaching points of downstream use and which is not now being put to beneficial use on natural watersheds, represents the real potential for increased production of needed commodities in our particular arid area?

If the answer…is yes, it appears that we should direct our attention, action, and our research toward ways and means of changing the use of water on our natural watersheds from non-beneficial to beneficial use.

Fig. 3.1 Construction of Hoover Dam (1931–1935) on the Colorado River. For many years the largest dam in the world, Hoover Dam was constructed to meet irrigation needs and provide flood control and electric power for the southwestern USA. (From US Bureau of Reclamation)

Fig. 3.2 Lake Mead, formed by Hoover Dam on the Arizona–Nevada border, in 2002. The exposed lakeshore signals/indicates a drop in water level resulting from a prolonged drought. (Courtesy of Ken Dewey, High Plains Regional Climate Center)

In the 1950s, it was believed that watersheds and even the weather itself (Chapter 4) might be manipulated to increase the amount of surface flow and thus enhance supply. With increased flow, however, would come a greater need for storage. In this regard, sedimentation of dams was very much a concern. Bailey argued (1956, p. 175), on one hand, that "greatest threats to the usefulness of streamflow as a source of water for arid lands are sedimentation in downstream water storage structures...." On the other hand, he complained about (ibid) "inadequate understanding of the source of sediment and of soil formation and erosion processes". Thus, the importance of watershed management was recognized, but better management was constrained by the limitations of the contemporary knowledge of watershed hydrology.

Another serious concern was storage losses through evaporation. One experimental approach was to treat reservoir surfaces with "cetyl alcohol, and related compounds, which formed a thin film on a water surface and thereby substantially reduced evaporation..." (Dixey, 1956, p. 131). While conceptually sound, these treatments are largely ineffective because of the problems of keeping them in place. Inevitably, winds move films to the lee of a reservoir, exposing the upwind surface area to evaporation.

3.1.2 Groundwater Development

Despite the prominence given to groundwater in the questions posed in *The Future of Arid Lands*, there was little sustained or substantial effort to address the topic in the book. Groundwater was not ignored, but it was discounted to a major degree. As noted by Bailey (1956, p. 173), "... virtually all the readily accessible groundwater supplies have already been located and put to use ... consensus is also that we are not likely greatly to increase the water supply by new discoveries of underground sources."

Rather than promoting major efforts to find new sources of groundwater, the group considered the concept of managing groundwater as a resource and even using it as part of a more comprehensive water storage strategy. Kellogg (1956, p. 33) offered "the possibility of control of underground water storage in contrast to storage by dams". Storing some portion of retained water in the ground would drastically reduce evaporation losses. This concept of managing groundwater resources and even deliberately recharging them with surface waters was comparatively new and achieved in relatively few places, such as southern California (USA). Dixey (1956, p. 133) noted: "If the methods of artificial [groundwater] recharge now commonly applied in humid and semi-humid countries could be employed in arid regions they would be of untold benefit, but so far there has been only limited scope for such application."

But the science of groundwater hydrology was in its relative infancy. It is true that methods for determining water flow through porous media and subsequent yields had been developed a century earlier (Darcy, 1856). Yet, more complete assessments of groundwater resources and understanding of regional groundwater movement and recharge were not yet common. Hydrology in general and groundwater hydrology in particular were still considered to be underdeveloped, and there was concern about both the state of knowledge and the state of the field (Batisse, 2005). Kellogg (1956), for example, focused a good part of his paper on the challenge of establishing the age of groundwater. Reliable isotope dating techniques were still being developed and had been applied on a limited basis; only later would they unlock understanding of natural rates of recharge and the movement of groundwater. Perhaps in recognition of some of these profound needs, the International Association of Hydrogeologists was created in 1956, 100 years after Darcy's groundbreaking work.

Given this incomplete understanding, it is not surprising that the focus then was on basic scientific understanding rather than on management considerations. As a result, issues such as ownership of the resource and regulation of its use went essentially unaddressed in 1956. Yet the exploitation of groundwater resources was beginning to boom at that time, particularly in the subhumid Great Plains of the U.S.A.

Much of the Great Plains had lost population during the Dust Bowl and droughts of the 1930s. Even then, irrigation was seen as an insurance against uncertain rainfall rather than a fundamental production strategy. Renewed drought pressure, the existence of the very large and comparatively shallow Ogallala aquifer, the development of pumps that could raise water from greater and greater depths, inexpensive fuel, and little regulation of the water resource all converged to unleash an explosion of irrigation in this large region during the 1950s (Opie, 2000). Irrigation required three times the investment that rainfed dryland farming did, but yields also tripled (and were assured), as did land prices. Groundwater development made economic sense.

Given that groundwater was a topic of such intense interest among US farmers and developers, it is surprising that more attention was not paid to groundwater development in 1956. Perhaps these developments were still "below the radar" of the scientists gathered in Albuquerque. Regardless, groundwater became a significant element of dryland development from that point onward.

3.1.3   Water Harvesting

"Water harvesting" – as it has come to be known – was also discussed in *The Future of Arid Lands* (Evenari and Koller, 1956). Agricultural water harvesting includes a number of different techniques, all of which involve the capture of rainfall runoff from catchments to irrigate crops or water livestock. On a smaller urban scale, runoff from rooftops and other impervious surfaces is captured and stored to meet household and municipal needs (Section 3.2.6).

Evenari and Koller (1956) described the field study and experimental revival of the techniques that had been developed 2,000 years before by the Nabateans and Byzantines, who had created a network of isolated stations to sustain trade routes in the Negev Desert. This involved inducing runoff from the upper slopes of a catchment, often through the removal of soil and stones, and either channeling the flow through stone spillways into cisterns or tanks, or spreading it in fields behind terraces and dams for crop production (Kadar, 1956). Thus, to cope with very low rainfall amounts, they showed that it was possible to "trade land area for water", concentrating the runoff of a comparatively large area into a cistern, small plot, or field. Through these very labor-intensive efforts, it was possible to grow forage, food crops, and orchards for more than 1,000 years.

The work Evenari and Koller (1956) reported showed that these ancient techniques, found in a very arid area, were technically sound and feasible, and could be scientifically described, and replicated in a modern setting.

3.1.4   Desalination

Water quality often stymies dryland development as much as water availability. Seawater and terrestrial brackish groundwater are often available in abundance and have thus posed a persistent and often frustrating potential for providing water for municipal, industrial, and perhaps agricultural uses. The idea of developing a technology that might remove salts from saline water efficiently and cheaply was compelling. Powell (1956, p. 258) wrote that "There is every indication that demineralization of saline waters, through research and development backed by adequate financial support, and by pooling of knowledge, will help solve the water shortage problem in many arid regions and at a cost commensurate with the resulting benefits."

At the time, it was recognized that there were very serious obstacles to overcome, but even that skepticism was tempered by a great deal of optimism (Dickson, 1956, p. 57):

> [S]uccess in producing large quantities of fresh water economically from salt water is not just around the corner. There is no magic wand, but research is going on in many parts, and there is little doubt that the day will come when in some arid areas it will be possible to provide desalted water at lower cost than, for example, water transmitted over great distances.

Production and delivery costs of high-quality water were primary considerations, and attention centered on inherently high energy inputs, but by 1956, the technology for desalination had been demonstrated, and there was every reason to judge that energy costs would decline with the development of new energy alternatives. The use of alternative energy and coproduction was also considered, even though these were comparatively new concepts. Powell (1956, p. 266) quoted Davis S. Jenkins, Director of the Saline Water Conversion Program, as saying that "... it becomes important that nonconventional energy sources such as solar energy, wind power, and geothermal energy be explored vigorously".

The optimism surrounding desalination at the time was understandable. The potential sources of water were tantalizingly obvious and vast, the technology was just then being put to use on a fairly large scale, and almost unlimited nuclear energy was just around the corner. The first large facilities for desalination of seawater became operational in Kuwait in the mid-1950s (Hamoda, 2001).

3.1.5   *Water Reuse*

Little was said on the use of wastewater (or water reuse) in 1956. Opportunities for more deliberate water reuse were acknowledged but not emphasized. Reflecting the views of many, Hayward (1956, p. 280) argued for "the reuse of drainage and return flow water from irrigated land and the use of sewage effluent and industrial wastes whenever possible". The reuse of municipal sewage was touched upon elsewhere, but appeared to be more of an unpleasant afterthought than one element of a comprehensive water strategy. Koenig, the would-be economist, identified the need to manage effluent as a resource but noted that (1956, p. 325), "there is no possibility that even combined municipal and industrial reclaimed effluents can make more than a fractional contribution to irrigation supplies." This was consistent with his opinion that using water to grow crops in the drylands was imprudent.

The lack of overall emphasis given to water reuse in 1956 was not representative of the wider opinion. The use of urban wastewater for agriculture, particularly in the drylands, is probably as old as urbanization and the development of sewers to collect and carry wastewater from cities. As urban populations grew and science advanced, linkages were established in the mid-nineteenth century between wastewater disposal in rivers and epidemics of cholera and typhoid. Steps had been taken since then to dispose of wastewater in more "sanitary" ways, to begin to treat water before disposal, and to relocate water intakes upstream and wastewater discharges downstream of cities. As the cost of treating larger volumes of wastewater increased, the possibilities of reusing wastewater for agriculture to offset the costs of water treatment began to be exploited. By the mid-1950s, wastewater treatment was becoming a major activity, even though this was not much reflected in *The Future of Arid Lands*.

3.1.6   *Water-Use Efficiency*

Much of the content of *The Future of Arid Lands* was framed by the developments in the western USA. As suggested by Koenig, if water is a required, but finite element of development, the question becomes what kind of return to expect on water investment. In response to Koenig's position, McClellan (1956, p. 193) argued that:

> [I]rrigation may be criticized as an extravagant use of water. Nevertheless, the construction of irrigation works that are efficiently planned and soundly financed is justified by the increase in food and fiber which this kind of agriculture produces. …One major justification for irrigation is the contribution it makes to the wealth of the nation.

This position was countered by a contemporary reviewer of the book who observed that: "… agriculture is an economically marginal user of water, that cities and industries are the most efficient users of the arid realm, that intensive agriculture can best solve the world's food problems by shifting to the better-watered lands" (Borchert, 1957, p. 391).

Other reviewers' comments foreshadowed much of the current discussion related to water and the use of the drylands. Reviewing Koenig's paper, Billings (1958, p. 564) found that:

[his] paper ... brings scientific theory down to practicality with some eye-opening figures concerning the costs of increasing water use in climates with high evaporation losses. His conclusion: agriculture, with its high water need may not be as efficient a use of these regions as would be provided by some types of industry in these days of relatively abundant transportation.

Other reviewers argued along similar lines. Logan (1957, p. 282) noted that Koenig "challenges the present practice of evaluating land in conformance with humid land principles and has the audacity to question the advisability of using water for irrigation in arid lands".

Koenig's comments highlight the fundamental differences among sectors in terms of their demands with respect to water quantity and quality, and also their respective ability to pay. This understanding should have prompted a concerted effort to address efficiencies among sectors and how they might respond to differences in price and adjustments that might be made on the demand side of the equation. Indeed, Powell (1956) aimed his summary at both energy or production efficiency and allocation or use efficiency. Regarding the latter, he proposed that water should be graded by quality and distributed among sectors according to the nature of their need (municipal, industrial, and agricultural), clearly a fact of life even then. The notion of "water markets" or the mechanism by which each of these sectors might compete for this scarce resource was not reflected in the general tenor of the book. Considering the optimism of the time, it is possible to conclude that in 1956 the general belief was that the greatest advances would come on the supply rather than the demand side of the water balance equation.

3.2   The Situation Today

The years between 1956 and 2006 have seen much of what was discussed in 1956 come to pass. The 1950s marked the beginning of an unanticipated period of growth in water consumption, and this continues. Some of this increase is due to both economic and population growth, but most of it results from the Green Revolution and gains in agricultural production, primarily in Asia (Figs. 3.3 and 3.4; Chapter 5).

Undoubtedly there are links between this rapid growth in consumption and fundamental changes in perceptions about water development. Most of these links result from increased understanding of what development actually entails and improved ability to predict consequences that might result from a particular course of action.

While cost–benefit analysis was and has been done for most water development projects for some time, the scope of such analyses has broadened significantly. For example, it is now recognized that diversion of surface waters from streams has other costs that were not previously reckoned. Goods and services provided by downstream environments, such as wildlife habitat, may be preempted by upstream diversions and thus incur environmental costs. Similarly, while most people would agree that the costs of community relocation because of reservoir construction include the costs of purchasing new land, buildings, and equipment, it is now

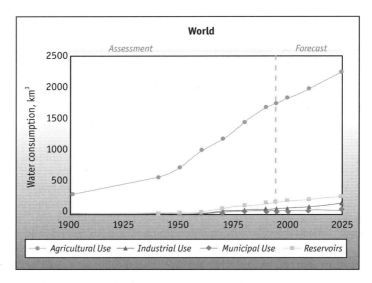

Fig. 3.3 Global water consumption by region. (From UNESCO IHP, http://webworld.unesco. org/water/ihp/db/shiklomanov/summary/html/figure_8.html)

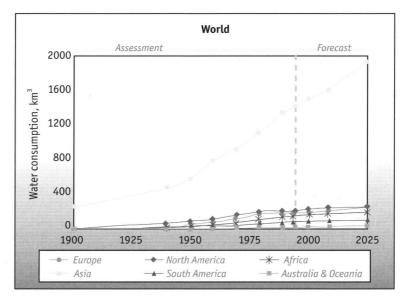

Fig. 3.4 Global water consumption by sector. (From UNESCO IHP, http://webworld.unesco. org/water/ihp/db/shiklomanov/summary/html/figure_9.html)

recognized that there are also other, sometimes major, "social costs", such as losses in human productivity and social upheaval.

The questions put forward now are quite different than those posed 50 years ago. Today, they include:

- What are the most effective ways to manage water demand among competing sectors in drylands?
- At what scales can integrated water resource management be most effectively achieved?
- How might global climate change affect water resources (availability and quality) in drylands?

3.2.1 Surface Water Development

Many large surface water development schemes have been put in place since 1956. Today worldwide, there are an estimated 45,000 large dams, with a 700% increase in storage capacity since 1950 (Revenga et al., 2000). Most of these facilities include massive infrastructure for the delivery of water both near (e.g., Aswan High Dam) and quite far (e.g., Kara Kum Canal in Turkmenistan; Central Arizona Project in the USA). While the Aral Sea offers one of the most notorious examples of the struggles that occur among sectors, similar conflicts center around other dryland lakes from which irrigation water is drawn, e.g., Lake Balkhash in Kazakhstan, Lake Qinghai in China, the Salton Sea in California – all examples of the difficulties of maintaining ecosystems while meeting growing water demands for agriculture and urban development.

Even though they were considered "inevitable" at one time, large-scale water transfers from river basins with surplus water to those with deficits have come and gone mostly unfulfilled. For example, the proposed North American Water and Power Alliance (NAWAPA) was intended to take many of the water resources of the North American continent that were being "wasted" through flow to the Arctic Sea and redistribute them to dry places in the western USA (Thomas and Box, 1969), but this has never materialized.

However, in the former Soviet Union, plans first put forward in the 1980s, to divert flow from Siberian rivers southward to the Aral Basin, are being resurrected (Pearce, 2004). Like large development programs elsewhere, the earlier plan was intended to support continued agricultural expansion and restore the Aral Sea. The current proposal pursues these same objectives but also seeks to reduce inflow of fresh water to the Arctic Sea in order to maintain salinity gradients that help drive the Gulf Stream, thus offsetting, to some degree, the effects of global warming.

As noted in Section 3.2.1, surface water development accelerated from the 1950s through the 1970s and has slowed since. Part of the declining rate of dam commissioning can be attributed to the shrinking pool of opportunities: the most suitable sites have already been developed. But part might also be attributed to an improved understanding of the true costs and benefits associated with surface water development.

The trade-offs in streamflow management have been well documented. For example, Mainguet (1999) described some of the consequences that accompanied the Aswan High Dam on the Nile in Egypt. On the plus side of the ledger were: (1) hydroelectric power generation; (2) flood control; (3) drought impact mitigation; (4) improved shipping; (5) expanded cultivation beyond the Nile valley and the delta; and (6) three crops per year rather than one. Negative impacts were: (1) lowering of the downstream riverbed; (2) erosion of the delta because of reduced sediment load; (3) sedimentation of Lake Nasser; (4) evaporation losses from Lake Nasser; (5) increased fertilizer requirements due to elimination of fallow periods; (6) rising water tables in cropped areas; (7) increasing incidence of water-borne diseases; and (8) displacement of 50,000–60,000 Nubians due to the creation of Lake Nasser.

Partly in response to some of the negative impacts of dams, another movement has emerged since 1956 that seeks to remove them from rivers. Removal may be necessary because of impaired storage due to sedimentation or damage to the structure itself, but it can also be undertaken to restore river ecosystems (Poff and Hart, 2002). Dams dramatically alter rivers by changing seasonal flow and sediment regimes, changing water temperature, and restricting the movement of organisms upstream and downstream.

While the movement for dam removal has gained some momentum, mainly in the USA, it has become clear that more dams may be needed in the future rather than fewer (Service, 2004). Some, it is argued, will be required to provide developing countries, especially in Africa, with the infrastructure necessary to reduce risk to populations and livelihoods, and the resources needed for economic growth (Grey and Sadoff, 2006).

More than one sixth of the world's population relies on meltwater from glaciers and winter snowpack for its water supply (Barnett et al., 2005). Glaciers and snowpacks also give rise to more than half of the world's rivers, maintaining flow throughout the summer season (Beniston, 2003). In low latitudes, snowpack continuously contributes to streamflow and often provides the only water source during the dry season (WWF, 2005).

Yet, as minimum temperatures continue to rise due to global warming, the amount of water stored in snowpack will diminish (Chapter 4). The Intergovernmental Panel on Climate Change (IPCC, 2001c) projects average global temperature increases of 1.4–5.8% by the end of this century. These changes will significantly affect how much precipitation falls as snow, how long snow cover lasts, and the rate and timing of both snowmelt and long-term storage in glaciers (Barnett et al., 2005). Even if the total amounts of precipitation remain unchanged, more precipitation will arrive as rain than as snow. This will result in earlier peak runoff in the winter and spring – potentially causing floods followed by reduced flows in the dry season when demand is highest – potentially creating periodic and chronic water shortages that could affect billions of people (Arnell, 1999; Barnett et al., 2005; Watson et al., 1998). To make effective use of these waters will, therefore, require corresponding increases in storage capacity within a given drainage basin. Thus, perhaps ironically, more dams may be needed in industrialized countries, such as the USA, where the dam decommissioning movement is most active.

Water supply shortfalls in regions that already experience water scarcity will create additional intersectoral competition. Especially with increasing global demand for water because of population growth, these problems will become ever more important. Developing countries in drylands are the most vulnerable to climate change and, due to limited technical, financial, and management resources, will face an enormous challenge in adapting to water shortages. This will create a heavy burden for their economies (Watson et al., 1998).

3.2.2 Groundwater

Over the last 50 years, the general dimensions of the groundwater resource and its importance to development – particularly in the world's drylands – have been appreciated but not fully assessed. Surprisingly, only one global assessment has been done on groundwater, in the 1980s, and it has not been updated (Mönch, 2004). Based on that survey it was estimated that 96% of the world's nonfrozen fresh water supply occurred as groundwater (Shiklomanov, 1993).

Despite *The Future of Arid Lands'* underestimate of groundwater development in 1956, exploitation of groundwater resources grew rapidly from the 1950s onward, reflecting both increasing awareness of its availability and increasing ability to tap it. Most exploitation took place between 1960 and 1980 – an exceptionally short period of time – and this was certainly not foreseen in 1956 (Fig. 3.5). However, unlike the attitude and thought given to understanding and managing groundwater in 1956, this later development was more concerned with immediate returns on investment than with sustainability (Burke et al., 1999).

While US farmers in the 1950s had pursued strategies for developing and using groundwater primarily in situ, Libya used a fundamentally different approach in the 1970s. In the Great Man-made River Project, large and deep fossil groundwater resources have been tapped in the hyperarid south of the country and pumped 600 km north to the more favorable, populated coastal area to support agriculture and other development. Geohydrologists predict 100–500 years of life for this project, which offered planners a stark, but probably unique, opportunity to choose between the merits of: (a) developing and transferring water over long distances; or (b) desaliniz-ing seawater adjacent to the areas of use (Gijsbers and Loucks, 1999).

What these and most other groundwater developments in drylands have in common is lack of sustainability. The fossil waters that such development projects exploit were put in place from 10,000 to often more than 400,000 years ago, during times that were far wetter than today (Sultan et al., 1997). As with petroleum, most of these waters were exploited with the goal of positive and immediate returns on investment, and they will only be replaced in geologic timescales. It might be argued that such consumption for current gain is both economically and socially appropriate. However, countervailing arguments about the intergenerational equity of this approach are much more common now. Nonrenewable resources consumed today are denied to future generations, thus limiting the options available to them (Portney and Weyant, 1999). Perhaps an even more ominous shadow of the future

Fig. 3.5 Drilling for groundwater on the edge of the Kalahari in Botswana (2003). (Courtesy of Frau Dr. Susanne Stadler)

is the fact that globally, since 1950, exploitation of groundwater has grown exponentially, and it clearly represents a major part of the water balance on which life on earth is based. However, a shortage of data makes any assessment difficult (Mönch, 2004). Regardless, if groundwater is removed from the total water supply as it is exhausted, the water crisis that looms on the horizon may be in fact much more severe than currently anticipated (Postel et al., 1996).

3.2.3 Water Harvesting

Water harvesting for domestic use in drylands was not a major focus in *The Future of Arid Lands*. Yet, water harvesting, in the strictest sense, has been used since there were buildings to provide water for domestic uses, by gathering runoff from rooftops or other surfaces and storing it in cisterns or in the ground for later use.

These practices will continue in those areas where water is especially difficult or expensive to secure (Heggen, 2000).

As in so many other things, water harvesting has never been implemented on a large scale during the modern era. The success of the Nabateans from 200 BC to AD 700 was due, in large part, to the circumstances that prevailed in the Roman and Byzantine Empires. The Negev formed part of the inhospitable fringe of the empire that had to be traversed for trade (Rubin, 1991). "Trading land for water" was not much of an issue in the desert where there was little demand for land. However, it was the critical role that these settlements played in commerce and trade that justified the considerable investment in labor required to create and maintain large water harvesting systems to support the demands of caravans. This also explains why these systems were ultimately abandoned when trade flow diminished or alternate routes opened.

Over the last 50 years, large-scale "industrial" water harvesting for agriculture, such as might have been the logical extension of Israeli experiences in reviving the Nabatean techniques in the Negev, has apparently not proven to be economically sustainable. Ultimately, the viability of such large-scale commercial ventures will be constrained by their ability to invest in the labor required. Nonetheless, water harvesting has been of continuing interest in the drylands. Smaller-scale water harvesting techniques – those that rely on catchment areas of around $100\,m^2$ or less – have proven to be valuable tools for increasing and sustaining production in semiarid regions, particularly in traditional or isolated settings (Dutt et al., 1981; Droppelmann et al., 2000; Tabor, 1995) For example, traditional agricultural methods for managing soil and water, such as simple stone lines or bunds built on contours, are very effective at slowing runoff, reducing erosion, and promoting infiltration (Fig. 3.6). Furthermore, they can be put in place over relatively large areas by villages, using essentially no tools and very small investment (Reij et al., 2005). Smaller-scale urban applications have also been done successfully for the millennia.

3.2.4 *Desalination*

Desalination on an industrial scale has been slower to develop than was hoped in the 1950s. Today there are about 12,500 industrial-scale desalination units operating worldwide, primarily in the Middle East; the Gulf States account for about 50% of total global capacity (Ettouney et al., 2002). Advances in the technology have been incremental, and costs have fallen from about US$6/$m^3$ to as little as US$1/$m^3$ for seawater, and US$0.50/$m^3$ for brackish water. The prevailing judgment is that desalination is still too costly for agricultural use in all but a few applications and should thus be used only to provide drinking water (FAO, 2005).

As demonstrated in the Gulf States, desalination is the only economically viable option for providing municipal water in areas where sufficient population is concentrated, where saline or brackish waters are freely available, and where other competing sources of fresh water are far removed and thus expensive to transport. However, even when the need for potable urban water is extreme, as in much of the

Fig. 3.6 Water retention by stone bunds in the Central Plateau of Burkina Faso. (Courtesy of Melchior Landolt and Terra-Verde e.V [http://www.terra-verde.de])

developing world, technical complexity and maintenance requirements make desalination plants a challenge that many countries are unable or unwilling to accept (Alghariani, 2003).

In contrast, small, household-scale desalination technology – the solar still – has found some acceptance. However, frequent maintenance and relatively low production remain as obstacles to wider adoption.

Today as in 1956, maintenance and energy costs remain primary barriers to wider use, even as membrane and distillation technologies continue to become more efficient. In addition, concern about the environmental consequences of disposing of brines that contain mineral solutes is a challenge that did not exist then. In the end, the niche that desalination technology can occupy is probably narrower than might have been imagined 50 years ago.

3.2.5 Wastewater

The attention given to wastewater treatment in the 1950s led to the "era of wastewater reclamation, recycling, and reuse" that began in 1960 and continues today (Asano and Levine, 1995). Today, a wide range of wastewater reuses exists, determined by need and the ability to pay for treatment. For example, in Windhoek, Namibia, virtually all urban wastewater is recycled and reused as drinking water. Although this practice was judged to be somewhat extreme when it was begun in

1968, the quality of surface waters since then has also declined as a result of urbanization that both surface and wastewaters are now being blended and treated together (Haarhof and van der Merwe, 1996).

In many settings in the developed dryland countries, secondary treated wastewaters are used for irrigation in agriculture or for landscaping. The intent is to replace potable waters in agriculture with reclaimed wastewater, reserving the higher quality water for municipal uses (Friedler, 1999). The US city of Tucson, Arizona (USA), for example, uses treated effluent to irrigate golf courses, parks, and schools, thereby meeting about 8% of its total current water demand (City of Tucson Water Department, 2004).

Worldwide, however, only about 35% of wastewater is treated and, understandably, very little of this occurs in developing countries because of its cost. As a result, the use of untreated effluent for agriculture around cities is common. Obviously, this poses health risks to farm workers and consumers. However, as shown in a study that included drylands in Mexico, Tunisia, and Pakistan, in the developing world, the potential benefits of using wastewater may outweigh the risks. This is because urban areas provide a ready and constant supply of wastewater, a supply of labor that would otherwise be underemployed, and a ready market for high-value crops such as vegetables (Martijn and Redwood, 2005).

Most countries place restrictions on the use of effluent. In developing countries, enforcement is uneven at best and nonexistent more often than not. Nonetheless, wastewater can be an extremely valuable commodity in agriculture and will grow in significance as urban centers continue to expand (Scott et al., 2004). It has value not only as water per se, but also because of the nutrients it carries and because of its continuous availability, permitting year-round production. In Pakistan, land parcels with access to wastewater for irrigation are 3.5 times more valuable than those without. Another indirect benefit of using wastewater for irrigation is that pollutants are also deposited in fields rather than in surface waters (van der Hoek et al., 2002).

Outcomes of effluent use may not be all positive. Farmers are exposed to obvious and immediate health hazards (Martijn and Redwood, 2005). Wastewaters carry various pathogens (e.g., bacteria like *Escherichia coli* and parasites like hookworm) that can cause health problems such as diarrhea, skin and nail diseases, typhoid fever, cholera, and hepatitis. There is also the potential for long-term soil contamination through the use of waters that contain heavy metals. Once introduced to the soil, they can then enter the food chain and ultimately endanger the health of consumers. If the sources of wastewater are large with industrial sources of heavy metals, concern is obviously warranted. However, in smaller population centers without industry, loadings of heavy metals may be low and derived from the existing water infrastructure (i.e., copper pipes and joinings) and pose little threat of long-term accumulation (van der Hoek et al. 2002).

Given the realities of limited water supply and the attractive economics of peri-urban agriculture, the use of wastewater in developing drylands should be acknowledged and accommodated in development planning. At the very least, attention should be given to finding low-cost means of treatment, or providing training for farmers in managing wastewater, and insuring that there are means for dealing with issues of access to both land and wastewater (Martijn and Redwood, 2005).

3.2.6   Stormwater

Like wastewater, stormwaters have been managed and used for millennia (Angelakis et al., 2005). Again, in urban areas, water from impervious surfaces such as rooftops and paved areas may be collected and stored for subsequent use. The quality of stormwater is highly variable, depending on the nature of the surfaces from which it is collected and the materials (e.g., gasoline, dust, fertilizer) that are deposited on those surfaces. However, collected stormwater has been and continues to be used for human and animal consumption, or for nonpotable uses (e.g., washing, toilets) in many parts of the world, not only drylands (cf. Herrmann and Schmida, 1999). Recently, there have been arguments for more focused and intentional management of stormwater as a resource; in an Australian case study, for example, the average annual urban stormwater runoff was almost equal to average annual water use (Hatt et al., 2006). Integrated management of this resource is only just beginning and best practices are yet to be established. If water quality issues can be dealt with economically, stormwater will probably become an attractive water source for urban areas in drylands.

3.2.7   Conservation

While largely ignored 50 years ago, conservation – managing the "demand" side of the water equation – is the most cost-effective way to make better use of the supply and provide for growth. In many countries, more than 30% of domestic water supply never reaches its intended destination because of transmission losses through leaky pipes, faulty equipment, and poorly maintained distribution systems. Moreover, if water consumption is not measured and charged for, there is no incentive to conserve it. As a consequence of poor distribution and a failure to manage consumption, the quantity of water "lost" in Mexico City would be enough to meet the water needs of a city the size of Rome (Gleick, 2001).

3.2.8   Integrated Water Resource Management

In *The Future of Arid Lands*, water development opportunities were dealt with individually, focusing largely on the science and technology on which they were based. While there might have been a tendency to rely on future technology to solve the problems that then existed and would grow in the future, the notion that new technology might somehow bring forth unlimited supplies of inexpensive water was then and is still largely a fantasy. In reality, each element on both the supply and the demand side of the equation makes a contribution to the total amount of water available, and it is this realization that is driving an increasingly integrated view of water management (Bouwer 2000). Integrated water management requires consideration of linkages between urban and rural water use, as well as between the domestic, industrial, and agricultural sectors (Waser, 1999).

The Aral Sea in Central Asia (Box 3.1) provides a cautionary lesson about favoring one sector over another in water allocation (agricultural over fisheries and environment). Meanwhile, the Salton Sea, located in the agricultural Imperial Valley of southern California (USA), offers a case study of how water markets might work on a comparatively large scale (Box 3.2). In this case, the dry coastal cities are buying water rights from farmers, so that water once used to irrigate crops is being diverted to municipal uses. As this story unfolds, it is clear that agriculture in the Imperial Valley will either disappear entirely or be transformed (e.g., by more water-efficient greenhouse production). What remains unclear is what the environmental outcomes will be for the Salton Sea itself, in terms of its fishery or, more important, its function as critical habitat for migratory birds.

Box 3.1 The Aral Sea

During the Soviet period, particularly in the 1960s in Turkmenistan and Uzbekistan, the Aral Sea basin in central Asia saw huge gains in agricultural production through the development of irrigated cotton. While wildly productive, there were drastic and largely unforeseen economic and particularly environmental costs. The Aral Sea has become the world's prime example of the kind of ecological catastrophe caused by unrestricted water diversions for agricultural expansion (Kobori and Glantz, 1998; Micklin, 2000).

Water for this ambitious development was diverted from the Syr Darya and Amu Darya rivers, the primary tributaries of the Aral Sea. Little attention was paid to water management in these massive projects. Most canals were unlined, and transmission losses often exceeded 90%.

By the 1980s, there was essentially no inflow to the sea and it began to shrink rapidly, increasing fivefold in salinity. In addition, cotton required high inputs of fertilizers and pesticides. These chemicals were dissolved in irrigation waters and collected in drainage waters that were returned to streams. Surface flow that managed to make its way to the Aral Sea was thus laden with chemicals. The subsequent decline in water quality eliminated the fish populations of the sea, thus ruining a thriving fishery. As the sea disappeared, the toxic materials that had been precipitated from the brine were exposed to wind erosion. The resulting dust has been a severe hazard for both human health and agriculture in the region, especially in the Autonomous Republic of Karakalpakstan in Uzbekistan. Altogether, the Aral Sea came to be labeled one of the "major human-induced environmental disasters of the twentieth century" (Glantz, 1999, p. 1; Fig. 3.7a–d). Since then, with assistance from the World Bank, there has been a modest recovery, thanks to the construction of a dike between the northern and

(continued)

Box 3.1 (continued)

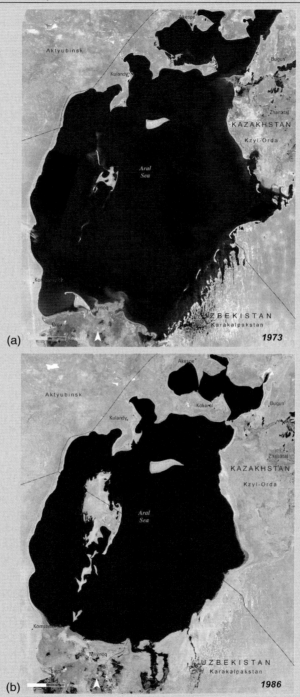

Fig. 3.7 (**a**) Extent of the Aral Sea in 1973. (From UNEP/GRID-Sioux Falls.) (**b**) Extent of the Aral Sea in 1986. (From UNEP/GRID-Sioux Falls)

Box 3.1 (continued)

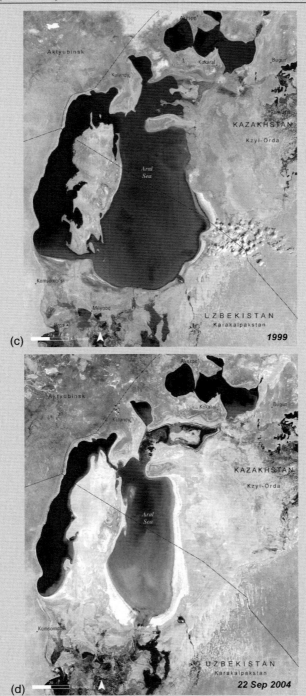

Fig. 3.7 (**c**) Extent of the Aral Sea in 1999. (From UNEP/GRID-Sioux Falls.) (**d**) Extent of the Aral Sea in 2004. (From UNEP/GRID-Sioux Falls)

Box 3.1 (continued)

southern parts of the Aral Sea and to the repair of deteriorated irrigation works upstream along the Syr Darya. However, the outlook for rehabilitation is not altogether promising. Kazakhstan has been able to invest in improving water management as a result of high oil and mineral prices. How long the Kazakh government can resist the temptation of tapping these waters for agricultural development is unknown. Moreover, decades of fighting had denied Afghanistan its share of water from the Amu Darya, which feeds the southern part of the Aral Sea. For all these reasons, the future of the Aral Sea is in doubt (Pala 2005; Pala, 2006).

Box 3.2   The Salton Sea

California's Salton Sea was created by an engineering debacle in 1905, when heavy rainfall caused the waters of the Colorado River to rise and eventually break through the headworks for a planned irrigation project in the Imperial Valley. The sudden influx of water and lack of natural drainage filled the previously arid basin over the course for more than 1 year. Since then, the sea has been sustained almost entirely by the inflow of agricultural runoff from the Imperial Valley, also derived from the Colorado River.

Without agricultural drainage, the Salton Sea would evaporate completely within about a decade. However, with no outflow, declining water quality is affecting the ecology of the lake. In particular, salinity, nutrient loading, selenium and pesticide residues present challenges to water quality and animal life (Cohen et al., 1999). As water evaporates, these constituents are concentrated in the lake water and sediments. The quality of agricultural drainage feeding the lake has caused a steady rise in salinity. Increased fertilizer runoff has led to algal blooms that resulted in die-offs of fish populations and fish-eating birds (Fig. 3.8) (Kaiser, 1999).

The future of the Salton Sea is uncertain. To allow it to disappear and expose the lakebed would be both damaging to the environment and dangerous to human health (as witnessed with the Aral Sea). Its fate depends on water politics and the directions they drive agriculture in the Imperial Valley. The 2003 Colorado River Water Delivery Agreement enabled large-scale agriculture-to-urban water transfers, which will supply San Diego with water from the Imperial Valley Irrigation District for the coming 75 years (Norton, 2003). In this scenario, some part of agricultural production might be sacrificed to provide water both for urban uses in San Diego and for the environmental preservation of the Salton Sea itself.

Box 3.2 (continued)

Fig. 3.8 Salton Sea Tilapia mass die-off. (Courtesy of Jeff Alu)

If only a finite amount of water is available, decisions must be made about how to allocate it among competing uses. Decisions about allocation may be made by a central authority, particularly in planned economies, or through some political process negotiated among stakeholders. Increasingly, water "markets," in which competing interests buy water, are offered as a more efficient mechanism in making water allocations (Bjornlund, 2003). The argument is that water markets will ultimately define water prices and will assure, to some degree, the most efficient allocation and use of this limited resource.

As suggested by the Salton Sea case, one intended outcome of market-based water pricing has been and will continue to be a sustained focus on water-use efficiency. This applies not only between sectors, but also within individual sectors as the prices they pay converge. The rapid development and diffusion of drip irrigation and other irrigation technologies was a predictable outcome of rising water prices. Because agriculture accounts for more than 70% of water consumed in the drylands, comparatively small increases in agricultural efficiency can significantly affect water availability for other sectors. As noted above, high prices have also fueled research and development in water reuse, desalination, and the search for optimal matches between water quality and water use. Again, the experience of the Gulf States, such as Kuwait, shows how all of these water sources have been optimally merged, with the lowest quality water (e.g., treated effluent; brackish groundwater) being relegated to the lowest-value use (irrigation), highest quality water (i.e., distilled seawater) going to the highest use (human consumption), and blended waters going to other intermediate uses (industrial, household) (Hamoda, 2001).

As the value of water is increasingly realized, markets have emerged as a mechanism to address inequities in its distribution through the trade of commodities that it represents, or "virtual water" (Allan, 1997). The notion of "virtual water" accounts for the water used to produce a product, such as wheat or electricity, and echoes the earlier claim of Koenig (1956) that water was too valuable to be used for agriculture in the drylands. Countries or regions that face water shortages can purchase wheat, and the "virtual water" required to produce it, at far less cost than developing the water resources they would need to grow the same wheat crop.

Economically, the notion of water markets is an entirely reasonable position about where we might end in developing a rational system for allocating scarce resources, whether it is water or any other natural resource. However, this notion assumes that water resources are managed, available to all through an infrastructure that allows equal access, and that mechanisms exist that provide a transparent means to allocate water among competing demands. These requirements are well met in places such as Europe, North America, and Australia. However, as noted in the 2006 World Water Development Forum in Mexico, neither the infrastructure nor the institutional mechanisms exist in much of the developing world to ensure the "water security" of most of the world's citizens (Grey and Sadoff, 2006). Parallel to food and energy security, Grey and Sadoff (2006, p. 5) define water security as "the reliable availability of an acceptable quantity and quality of water for production, livelihoods and health, coupled with an acceptable level of risk to society of unpredictable water-related impacts".

Using the simple measure of water reservoir storage capacity, they go on to note that in the semiarid USA, the Colorado River basin has a storage capacity that can satisfy 1,400 days of demand. In dramatic contrast, the Indus River has about 30 days' capacity. When put into these terms, the meaning of both water security and the ability to negotiate price among competing demands is far different depending on whether you are in the Colorado or Indus basin. Put more simply, water security status looms large in determining the ability of any population, country, or region to play a meaningful role in the global economy.

In considering water development and water use as a whole, there are some fundamental differences between 1956 and today. Then, more attention was paid to developing water supplies. Today, while the supply side is certainly not ignored, there is more focus on managing all water sources from an integrated perspective, both on the supply and the demand sides.

Chapter 4
Weather Modification:
More Than Bargained For?

Throughout history, humans have tried to modify weather and climate, or at least to understand them more fully. Particularly in the drylands, where rainfall is scarce and variable, there has been a keen interest in: (1) understanding and being able to predict this variability; or even better, (2) finding ways to "make it rain" when natural rainfall is inadequate.

While great faith was placed in the ability to control climate and create more favorable weather conditions in the drylands in the 1950s, this optimism about ultimate control has largely given way to concerns about undesired human impacts on global climate. Rather than purposeful weather modification, strategies of mitigation and adaptation to the consequences of inadvertent climate change dominate the scientific and political discourse some 50 years later.

Furthermore, with the growing awareness of large-scale atmospheric and environmental interrelationships, the focus of scientific interest has shifted from local and regional impacts to changes at a global scale.

4.1 The Situation in the 1950s

Issues of weather and climate appeared in two sections of *The Future of Arid Lands*: "Variability and Predictability of Water Supply" and "Prospects for Additional Water Sources". The first described the nature of variability as it was understood at that time and addressed questions such as:

- How predictable is precipitation in an arid region?
- Are there distinct drought cycles? (White, 1956, p.65)

The second section addressed means of supplementing natural water supply, among others by modifying the weather, and was guided by the questions:

- How practicable is it to induce precipitation?
- What are the social and economic implications of these programs? (White, 1956, p. 255)

45

C. F. Hutchinson and S. M. Herrmann, *The Future of Arid Lands – Revisited.*
© Springer 2008

4.1.1 Understanding Climate Variability

In the 1950s, it was already well understood that arid climates were highly variable and uncertain by nature; their climatic problems were not just a matter of simple lack of rainfall. As Thornthwaite (1956, pp. 77–78) pointed out: "variability is one of the main characteristics of dry climates. The reliability of precipitation becomes less as the amount decreases, so that in dry regions one might expect great yearly changes in the extent of the arid and semi-arid zones."

However, an understanding of the variability of dryland climates seems to have been ignored beyond climatology itself, particularly in policy and management, and many continue to perceive drought as a transient phenomenon rather than as a recurrent, ever-present constraint to drylands development and management.

Because the year-to-year fluctuations in rainfall were recognized by climatologists in the 1950s to have important economic repercussions, affecting both harvests and the rise and fall of water tables, there was a great interest in determining the probabilities of occurrence of dry and wet periods. A simple method for doing this, though then hampered by lack of data, was "to try to deduce periodicities from the analysis of past observations and to suppose that they will continue in the future" (Tixeront, 1956, p. 93).

More reliable forecasting of rainfall variations over time, however, would require a better understanding of the underlying causes of the observed variability. In *The Future of Arid Lands*, Tixeront (ibid.) postulated that:

> [V]ariations in climate are the result of causes which themselves fluctuate. Thus one proceeds to a study of the fluctuations in climate and to a study of the fluctuations in all the geophysical or cosmic phenomena capable of varying in a concomitant manner, choosing those phenomena whose fluctuations can be forecast, such as cycles of sunspots.

Apart from sunspot cycles, potential explanations of natural rainfall variability that were offered then were rather limited. Although the existence of "cycles or variations of widely different amplitude" (Dixey, 1956, p. 123) was acknowledged, few forcing factors that would correlate with these different cycles had been discovered. Very few data sources then available described changes or variability in the major features of climate: the circulation and temperature of the oceans and atmosphere. Addressing this lack of data was one major focus of the 1955 conference.

Another important part of the discussion in *The Future of Arid Lands* that has not lost any of its relevance is the distinction between climate variability and climate change. In the drylands particularly, this was expressed in concerns over progressive desiccation, such as that which had been observed in southern Africa since the beginning of European occupation (Dixey, 1956) – a region that today has indeed been categorized as particularly vulnerable to global climate change (IPCC, 2001a). However, with the short observation record available in the 1950s, it was not possible to definitely ascribe increasing aridity either to progressive climate change or to the downward leg of a recurring natural cycle. In the southern African example, opinions also differed as to the cause of the observed drying trend and whether to attribute it to climatic or anthropogenic factors (Dixey, 1956) – another question which has not been fully resolved even today.

It was further recognized in 1956 that the ability to reconstruct past climates would be a key to understanding rainfall variability. Smiley (1956) saw a great potential in geochronology, particularly the study of tree rings, to reconstruct records of rainfall through these proxy data. By that time, thousands of samples from living trees as well as historic and prehistoric specimens analyzed in the Laboratory of Tree Ring Research at the University of Arizona had allowed the construction of "tree ring indices", which provided a local chronology of tree growth across the southwestern USA. However, absolute rainfall quantities corresponding to differences in tree growth could not be ascertained at the time. Another important limitation articulated by Smiley (1956, p. 161) was that "geochronology can aid in understanding the effects of climate although it cannot help in determining the cause". Nevertheless, Smiley put forward the thesis that geochronology might develop predictive powers with respect to climate.

Hopes were high in 1956 that by understanding variability, it might be possible to predict and adapt to it. Another less passive approach was also advocated, in which this understanding would produce a prescription for interventions that would reduce variability and make it rain "on demand".

4.1.2   Weather Modification: Making It Rain

Rainmaking had been pursued for centuries. In some quarters, such efforts were guided by spiritual beliefs or fringe science. Wilhelm Reich's rainmaking operations in the desert outside Tucson in the early 1950s are an example: he used his "cloudbuster", a metal contraption of his own design, to attempt to bring benevolent rain clouds (Reich, 1954).

By the time of the publication of *The Future of Arid Lands*, the first scientific approaches to weather modification, even large-scale alteration of the climate, had emerged. Significantly, these were paralleled by the beginnings of the numerical weather modeling made possible by the use of increasingly powerful computers. The general view held in the 1950s was that modifying weather and climate was a promising and appropriate means of furthering societal and even military goals: securing your own good harvests and creating droughts for your enemies (as witness, e.g., John von Neumann in testimony before the US Senate, 1956; quoted in Kwa, 2001, pp. 141–142):

> Our knowledge of the dynamics in the atmosphere is rapidly approaching a level that will make possible, in a few decades, intervention in atmospheric and climatic matters. It will probably unfold on a scale difficult to imagine at present. There is little doubt one could intervene on any desired scale, and ultimately achieve rather fantastic effects.

The scientists attending the Arid-Lands meetings in New Mexico seemed to share this optimism. Based on scientific understanding of cloud physics and precipitation processes of that time (such as the Bergeron–Findeisen process), experiments to increase precipitation by cloud seeding had been under way since the mid-1940s at General Electric's laboratories, Schenectady, New York, and had produced some initial success (Box 4.1). Cloud-seeding experiments were also carried out under the auspices of

Box 4.1 Project Cirrus (1947–1952)

Physical chemist Irving Langmuir (1881–1957) and his colleagues set out to find ways to hasten the formation and growth of ice crystals in supercooled clouds and so to artificially initiate rainfall. Their starting point was an understanding of natural cloud and precipitation formation mechanisms through the nucleation of ice crystals or water droplets. Out of their activities grew the US government-sponsored *Project Cirrus*, an extensive cloud study program. While laboratory studies on materials that might function as artificial ice nuclei were carried out in the General Electric Research Laboratory in Schenectady, New York, the project's most comprehensive field experiments, including cloud seeding from airplanes, were conducted over semiarid New Mexico over a 3-year period (Table 4.1).

Table 4.1 Results from cloud-seeding experiments (Schaefer, 1956, p. 303)

Flight No.	Date	Seeding agent	Results
45	October 1948	CO_2/AgI	Development of large storm
106	July 1949	CO_2	Removal of large cloud from line of cumulus
108	July 1949	CO_2	Towering, followed by consolidated rainstorm
110	July 1949	$AgICO_2$	Development of large storm
168	July 1950	CO_2	Development of cirrus overcast
172	July 1950	CO_2	Towering, followed by consolidated rainstorm

The team experimented with a range of seeding agents – mostly dry ice (solid CO_2) and silver iodide (AgI) – and documented their results in descriptive protocols of observed impacts and photographic series of the treated cloud areas. Although there was controversy over whether the rainfall observed after operations was due to the cloud seeding or to natural variability, "the impact of this project on the science of cloud seeding, cloud physics research, and the entire field of atmospheric sciences was similar to the effects of the launching of Sputnik on the US aerospace industry" (Cotton and Pielke, 1995, p. 8). The project's growing body of evidence did not directly lead to more cloud seeding, but rather fueled a new era in weather modification research. By the close of *Project Cirrus* in 1952, 30 countries around the globe had weather modification programs.

CSIRO in Australia (Kraus and Squires, 1947) and by a growing number of commercial cloud-seeding companies worldwide. Although positive effects seemed to result from both aerial and ground-based release of seeding agents, the cause-and-effect relationships were difficult to establish. The response variability – increase, decrease, or no change in rainfall both inside and outside the targeted areas – remained uncertain, but appeared to be linked to the choice of clouds and the execution of seeding (Cotton and Pielke, 1995). However, improvements in cloud-seeding techniques were expected to solve the remaining uncertainties, particularly with respect to finding optimum concentrations of effective seeding agents (Bowen, 1956).

Despite some controversy about the ambiguity of results and lack of replicability of the more successful experiments, optimism about the ultimate success of this technology prevailed in 1956. Schaefer (1956, p. 311; italics original), for example, stated that: "Although it must be admitted that there is no currently available *easy* solution to the tapping of unlimited water from the sky rivers which flow over arid lands, there are still many research angles to probe." Part of the continued interest in the science of weather modification can be explained by a sense of Cold War urgency and desire to be the first to "control the weather" (Keith, 2000).

Remarkably, there were a few environmental, legal, or ethical concerns then about interfering with the atmosphere as if it were a private research laboratory, without advising or even obtaining the consent of the people affected by such experiments (Standler, 2002). Negative side effects, such as the possibility of suppressing rainfall in adjacent areas, were not discussed. Another potential problem that was overlooked was the lack of coordination between scientific and commercial cloud-seeding operations, the latter possibly affecting the results of the former.

This seemingly careless attitude towards the natural environment reflects the zeitgeist of the 1950s, which was characterized by an unshakable belief in the merits of technological progress. In fact, there were even plans then to make the climate warmer, with deserts considered as suitable candidates for large-scale artificial albedo changes of the earth's surface, to be induced by laying down a layer of carbon dust (Wexler, 1958). However, troubling questions were about to emerge, beginning with a landmark paper by Revelle and Suess (1957), which found no evidence to support the prevailing assumption that the oceans would absorb any excess CO_2 from human activities. This finding led to the beginning of Keeling's systematic measurement campaign that has documented so dramatically the steady increase of atmospheric CO_2 (Keeling, 1960; Keeling et al., 1995).

4.2 The Situation Today

Since the 1950s, our continuously improving scientific understanding of the global climate system has also brought about important advances in our understanding of dryland weather and climate. This understanding has been supported by large, and growing, numbers of data and improved technological capabilities for monitoring global-scale climatic and biophysical phenomena. Furthermore, public awareness of and attitudes towards the environment, including the climate, have changed radically since the 1970s (Glantz, 2003). Enthusiasm about weather modification schemes has been tempered with time. Today, concerns about the negative impacts of anthropogenic global warming dominate contemporary climate science as well as the debate about climate policy.

With respect to drylands, the following questions define the research foci of modern climate science:

- How does global warming affect the drylands of the world, particularly their
  rainfall variability?
- Can drought prediction using satellite-driven early warning systems help us to
  better cope with climate variability in drylands?
- What options of mitigating and adapting to the impacts of global climate change
  are most suitable for drylands?

4.2.1   Advances in Understanding Climate Variability

Growing interest in climate variability in drylands was sparked by recurrent news
of droughts around the globe in the early 1970s. The central Soviet Union (1972),
Australia (1972–1973), and most dramatically the West African Sahel (several
occurrences between the late 1960s and the 1990s) were all suffering from severe
rainfall shortages, and this received increasing media coverage (Weart, 2006a).
Since then, the level of research into climate variability has risen considerably, and
major progress has been made in understanding, modeling and, consequently, ability to predict the occurrence of seasonal and interannual variability (Navarra,
1999). The spatial aspect of climate variability in drylands – the spotty distribution
of rain due to the convective nature of rainfall events – (particularly in the tropical
drylands) has been addressed much less and is more difficult to predict. Studies
from a few dryland sites, which were equipped with a dense network of rain gauges
for research purposes, show significant differences in the amount of rainfall
received at gauges located as little as 10 km apart (Sicot, 1991; Goodrich et al.,
1995; Graef and Haigis, 2001). Outside these research sites, and particularly
throughout much of the drylands of the developing world, both the network of rain
gauges and the resolution of satellite estimates are too coarse to capture the considerable variation of rainfall over relatively small distances, let alone to incorporate
this variation into predictive climate and meteorological models.

Compared to the 1950s, the availability of climatological data – then considered
insufficient for obtaining a more complete understanding of climate – has increased
dramatically. Not only are traditional instrumental time series growing ever longer;
a greater variety of atmospheric and oceanic variables is being routinely measured,
including aerosols, cloud cover, and sea surface temperatures. While satellite observations account for much of this progress, conventional climatological data acquisition
remains indispensable for validation purposes and as complementary measurements
(Nicholson et al., 2003a, b; McCollum et al., 2000). Yet, rain gauges are still sparse and
reports irregularly in many of the remote dryland regions, and the number of upper air
measurements has been declining in some countries since the 1950s (S. Nicholson,
2006, personal communication).

With the synoptic perspective offered by satellite remote sensing, emphasis has
shifted from regional-scale analyses of variability in individual drylands to attempts
to understand global-scale interrelationships and complexities. A major break-
through in understanding the coupled atmosphere–ocean mechanisms and their

contributions to drought cycles was achieved through the scientific study of the El Niño–Southern Oscillation (ENSO) phenomenon, first observed by Walker in 1923 and later explained by Bjerknes (1969; Philander, 1983). ENSO occurs in cycles of 3.5–6 years and comprises two interrelated components: changes of sea surface temperatures in the tropical Pacific Ocean (El Niño) and changes in atmospheric pressure at sea level across the Pacific basin (Southern Oscillation). During an ENSO warm episode, the weakening or even reversal of the atmospheric pressure gradient between Darwin in Australia and Tahiti causes warm surface water to appear in the central and eastern Pacific Ocean near the equator, a region normally dominated by upwelling of deep cold ocean water (Glantz, 2001; Fig. 4.1a–c). Apart from bringing unusually wet or dry conditions to the adjacent coastal areas of western equatorial South America, ENSO is associated with climate variability and extremes around the globe; such associations are referred to as teleconnections. Thus, during El Niño years, droughts are likely in the drylands of southern Africa (Richard et al., 2001), Australia (Chiew et al., 1998), and northeastern Brazil (the *Nordeste*; Andreoli and Kayano, 2005; Giannini et al., 2004). By contrast, during

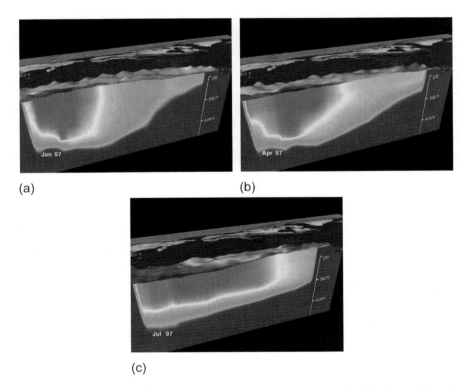

(a)   (b)

(c)

Fig. 4.1 East–west surface water temperature gradient decreases in the Pacific Ocean during the onset of an El Niño (January–July 1997). (**a**) January 1997; (**b**) April 1997; (**c**) July 1997. (From NASA Visible Earth, http://visibleearth.nasa.gov/)

an ENSO cold episode (or La Niña), in which opposite anomaly patterns prevail, the likelihood of droughts increases along the west coast of tropical South America (Kayano et al., 2005), in the southwestern USA (Sheppard et al., 2002) and in East Africa and the Horn of Africa (Anyamba et al., 2002), while southern Africa and the Brazilian *Nordeste* are likely to experience unusually wet conditions.

While ENSO is the most prominent and well-documented example of global-scale ocean–atmosphere dynamics, it is not the only such dynamic event and does not capture the full complexity of rainfall anomalies in drylands (Kayano et al., 2005). There is evidence of similar interannual fluctuations of atmospheric pressures and sea surface temperatures in the smaller Atlantic and Indian Ocean basins; the influences of these fluctuations on regional rainfall variability are still not fully understood. Rainfall regimes in drylands have also been found to undergo decadal and longer-term fluctuations. The most striking example is the West African Sahel, where below-average rainfall persisted for two decades and only recently has shown a "recovery" (Nicholson, 2005; Box 2.1). Although still incompletely understood, this phenomenon has been associated with the Tropical Atlantic Variability (TAV), a covarying fluctuation of tropical Atlantic sea surface temperatures and trade winds, which in turn is strongly linked with the North Atlantic Oscillation (NAO). Both of these phenomena oscillate at decadal scales (Marshall et al., 2001). Their Pacific counterpart, the Pacific Decadal Oscillation (PDO), has also been found to affect rainfall variability in drylands, modifying the impact of the shorter ENSO cycles (Barnett et al., 1999). By contrast, in the monsoon regime that governs rainfall variability in the Asian drylands, the influence of ENSO on rainfall appears to be modified by shorter, quasi-biannual fluctuations (Slingo, 1999). While the basic mechanisms governing how sea surface temperatures and the atmosphere affect each other have gradually come to be understood, much remains to be explained, particularly with respect to decadal-scale fluctuations. Most reanalysis datasets – continuous climate records reconstructed from quality-controlled data from different observing systems – currently reach back to the late 1940s (NOAA CDC, 2006). This period is long enough to include several ENSO cycles but captures only a few of the longer cycles (Folland et al., 1999).

Research on correlations and dynamic relationships among atmospheric pressure conditions, sea surface temperatures, and regional rainfall regimes using reanalysis datasets has formed the basis of seasonal prediction systems. Unlike the 1950s, the evolution of sea surface temperatures can now be monitored in real time, and numerical climate models have reached a level of complexity which permits simulations of interannual variability (Navarra, 1999). Our advancing understanding of the complex interrelationships governing rainfall variability, coupled with these new technological tools, holds great promise for drought forecasting. In particular, regions like southern Africa, where ENSO events play a major role, have benefited from early warning information (Box 4.2). However, despite the great scientific progress of the last two decades, the challenge of chaotic behavior, inherent in drylands as in many other environmental systems, will put an ultimate limit to the amount of predictability for which we might hope (Vogel and O'Brien, 2003).

Finally, advances in our understanding of climate variability have helped modify our perspectives on desertification, or land degradation in drylands (Herrmann and

---

Box 4.2 Use of ENSO information for southern Africa

Much of southern Africa has a semiarid climate with high year-to-year rainfall variability; this presents a challenge to agriculture. Much of the climate variability experienced in the drylands there is strongly correlated with the ENSO phenomenon in the tropical Pacific and with sea surface temperatures in the South Atlantic and Indian Oceans (Vogel and O'Brien, 2003). Partly because of this ENSO connection, seasonal rainfall variability is fairly predictable, making southern Africa a good pilot region for ENSO forecasting. Droughts tend to occur there in the year following the onset of an El Niño (Dilley and Heyman, 1995). Armed with this knowledge, ENSO forecasting technology was put to a test and refined during three El Niño events in the 1990s.

1991–1992. Droughts in southern Africa associated with an El Niño event led to a major regional disaster, which required massive food aid. ENSO forecasts had been issued by two sources (the Climate Analysis Center of the US Weather Service and the Australian Bureau of Meteorology), but they were accessible to only a few specialists in the region. Ultimately, the information was not used because: (1) its potential users had not been identified; and (2) there was no formal mechanism for disseminating it. Thus, even with a reasonably reliable forecast, coordinated drought mitigation efforts were not possible (Glantz et al., 1997).

1994–1995. A minor El Niño event caused a smaller emergency. Again, ENSO forecasts did not play a major role in preparing for the drought, because of a considerable lag between information availability and the initiation of the response. However, the need for international aid intervention was reduced because a liberalization of the grain market had allowed for more flexible import and distribution response by the private sector. Increasing awareness of the ENSO–drought linkage spurred development of a systematic process for disseminating and applying seasonal climate forecasts (Dilley, 2003).

1997–1998. Plans were in place for production and distribution of climate outlook guidance for southern Africa. As a result, public and government meetings on drought risks and appropriate response strategies began in August 1997. Bulletins warning of high probabilities of below-average rainfall were issued, and El Niño became a daily topic in the local news. Recommended preparations included shifting to more drought-tolerant crop varieties and reconsideration of new animal purchases. However, the expected severe drought did not materialize, except in Namibia. Drought preparedness in the region was so high that some farmers had reduced the area planted, which resulted in economic setbacks (Dilley, 2003).

Hutchinson, 2005). Since the notion of desertification was introduced by Aubréville (1949) to describe the transformation of productive land into desert, the phenomenon has alternately been attributed to anthropogenic or climatic processes. While the relative contributions of climate and human agency remain controversial, progress in climate science has contributed to a greater appreciation of the extent and causes of rainfall variability at different temporal and spatial scales. These insights have challenged earlier hypotheses, which stressed the importance of land cover changes in modifying climate in drylands (Charney et al., 1975; Otterman, 1974). In contrast, satellite observations of the West African Sahel, for example, show that changes in vegetation greenness follow rainfall variability and not vice versa (Tucker and Nicholson, 1999; Tucker et al., 1991). The relationships between climate and land degradation in drylands are much more complex and less well understood than initially assumed, with major uncertainties revolving around the roles of surface albedo and atmospheric dust and the mechanisms of ocean–atmosphere interactions.

4.2.2   Revisiting Weather Modification

The optimism of the 1950s about the ability of weather modification to increase rainfall continued for another two decades. This optimism was sometimes accompanied by inflated statements of success that were eventually overshadowed by fears of the possible negative consequences of human interference with climate. The early 1970s saw a radical shift in perception regarding the role of humans and their relationship with the natural environment. Technologies aimed at actively manipulating the environment to suit human needs came to be seen as transgressions rather than triumphs, particularly given the mounting evidence of inadvertent and potentially fatal environmental degradation and global climate change (Weart, 2006a).

Changing environmental attitudes are not the only explanation for the declining interest in weather modification. Funding for weather modification research decreased drastically in the 1980s as a result of lack of scientific rigor, unsubstantiated claims of success, and unrealistic promises (Cotton and Pielke, 1995; Fig. 4.2). The engagement of the World Meteorological Organization (WMO) in weather modification also began to wane. The WMO's "Precipitation Enhancement Project" intended to demonstrate planning, execution, and evaluation of weather modification experiments was terminated in 1984; in the same year, meetings of the WMO "Panel of Experts on Weather Modification" began to be held only every 4 years rather than annually (List, 2003). At the beginning of the twenty-first century, funding for rainfall enhancement research had reached its lowest level since the beginning of weather modification after World War II (Terblanche, 2005).

The technological and scientific breakthroughs that, in the 1950s, were expected to enable full control over the weather, failed to materialize. However, knowledge of cloud microphysics made it possible to estimate under which circumstances cloud seeding might work. For example, seeding clouds formed by air flowing over mountains seem to promise the best results (AMSC, 1998). However, cause-and-effect relationships are still not fully understood, and the intrinsically variable climate of drylands makes it difficult to detect the results of weather modification, which almost always fall within the range of natural variability.

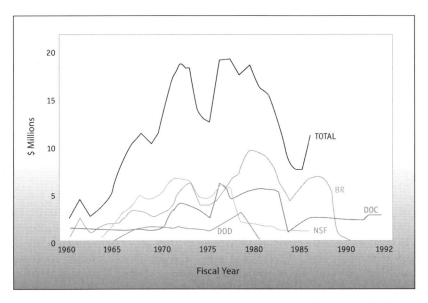

Fig. 4.2 Federal spending levels in the USA for weather modification. [BR (Bureau of Reclamation), DOC (Department of Commerce), DOD (Department of Defense), and NSF (National Science Foundation)]. (Redrawn after Cotton and Pielke 1995)

Nonetheless, hundreds of operational – as opposed to research – weather modification programs are currently being carried out in dozens of nations and regions, particularly in drylands (WMO, 2005). These programs appear to be buoyed by the belief that the marginal benefit of any additional precipitation – whether rigorously proved or not – justifies investment. Apart from China and South Africa, national operational programs exist in Libya (Al-Fenadi, 2003), Morocco (Mokssit and Grana, 2003), Burkina Faso (Traoré and Ouattara, 2003), India, and Australia (Terblanche, 2005); state-run programs exist in Utah (USA) (UDWR, 2005) and Colorado (USA) (Zaffos, 2006), with new programs being initiated around the world. Often suffering from a shortage of experienced practitioners to provide guidance, their results are not always convincing. This tendency to move directly into operational projects without strengthening their scientific basis is a concern. As List (2003, p. 8) put it in a summary paper for the 8th World Meteorological Scientific Conference on Weather Modification:

> While there is no shortage of papers for the 8th Conference [on Weather Modification] I recognize a noticeable reduction in hard-nosed scientific contributions. When it comes to the state of the sciences, then I would have to say that only statistics is in good shape. Cloud physics, the forecasting skills, and the numerical modeling are lagging behind and it seems that most countries are coasting along with standard operations, with evaluations at best by historical comparisons.

In contrast to the civil sector's general disillusionment about weather modification, the military continues to devote funds to developing tools for "climatological warfare", often behind a curtain of secrecy (Weart, 2006a). In a research paper presented to the US Air Force, House et al. (1996) developed a scenario in which technological development would enable the Air Force to "own the weather" by 2025. They assumed that advancements in five major areas – (1) nonlinear modeling techniques; (2) computational capability; (3) information gathering and transmission; (4) a global sensor array; and (5) weather intervention techniques – would enable "anyone who has the necessary resources" to modify the weather.

Even assuming that the ability to truly modify and control weather eventually emerges, the questions regarding its social, political, legal, and ethical ramifications remain unanswered.

4.2.3   Global Climate Change and Drylands

Although hypotheses about man's interference with climate have been in the air for some time (Brönnimann, 2002), the current climate change debate gained momentum only in the decades following the publication of *The Future of Arid Lands*. Research activity has accelerated rapidly since then, making climate change a prominent theme in the growing field of global environmental change. Advances in telecommunications since the early 1950s had, by 1956, allowed near-instantaneous transmission of meteorological observations and thus enabled the compilation of near-real-time synoptic charts. Since then, three developments difficult to foresee in the 1950s have fundamentally improved our understanding of the global climate system and our ability to detect and predict climate change: (1) significant gains in complexity of computer models; (2) the synoptic perspective offered by the vantage point of outer space; and (3) progress in the reconstruction of past climates.

Climate modeling has been an important step towards integrating our knowledge of the climate system. Computer models made it possible for the first time to study the effects of various climatic processes together, occurring simultaneously and interacting with one another (Harries, 1990). They brought insights into the general circulation of the atmosphere – the global pattern of air movements, only crudely known up to the 1960s. With growing computing power, increasingly complex models could be constructed, handling more data and more complex sets of equations.

Over the last 30 years, submodels of different components of the climate system have been developed separately and then progressively incorporated into comprehensive climate models (Fig. 4.3). Early models included feedback mechanisms between the land surface and the atmosphere. With the realization of the crucial role that oceans play in shaping global climate and an increase in the availability of oceanographic data, three-dimensional models of ocean circulation were developed and integrated into models of the general circulation of the atmosphere (Anderson and Willebrand, 1992). The impacts of aerosols on the global radiation budget have increasingly been included in climate modeling, particularly since the eruption of Mount Pinatubo in 1991, even though uncertainties about their effects on atmospheric heating or cooling and on precipitation still limit the applicability of such modeling (Gaffney and Marley, 1998). Similarly, methods for incorporating land and ocean carbon cycle feedbacks into global climate models and for linking climate models with vegetation change models are still being refined.

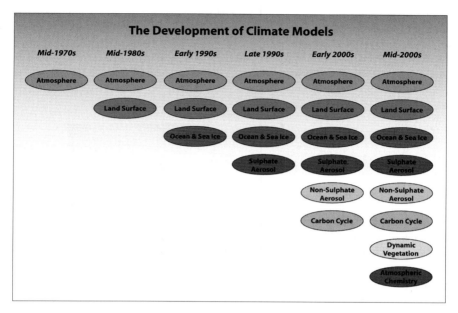

Fig. 4.3 Increasing climate model complexity since the 1970s. (Redrawn after IPCC, 2001c)

Regardless of these remaining gaps, climate models today are able to reproduce current climate with some confidence. Results of comparisons between different models converge to show an overall agreement with reality (Weart, 2006a). Modeling results and climate observations also indicate an increase in global average surface temperatures of about 0.6 °C over the twentieth century, accompanied by changes in precipitation, cloud cover, sea level, and the extent of sea ice (IPCC, 2001c). There is strong evidence that most of the warming observed can be attributed to human-induced increases in atmospheric greenhouse gases. Latest measurements show that CO_2 levels have reached 381 parts per million (ppm) (Shukman, 2006) – 100 ppm above the preindustrial average and 66 ppm above the average value when Keeling started his CO_2 measurements atop Mauna Loa volcano in Hawaii in 1958 (Keeling, 1960; Fig. 4.4).

Confidence in the ability of models to project future climates has increased considerably over the past years, "the greatest uncertainty now [being] no longer ... how to calculate the effects of the greenhouse gases and aerosols that humanity poured into the atmosphere ... [but] how much of this pollution we would decide to emit" (Weart, 2006b, p. 34). To address this uncertainty, the Intergovernmental Panel on Climate Change (IPCC) has formulated a range of emission scenarios, which form the basis of different climate projections (IPCC, 2000).

Data acquisition (as input for climate modeling) has been facilitated by a growing fleet of satellites ever since the launch of the Soviet *Sputnik* in 1957 signaled the beginning of the Space Age. As of March 2006, 23 weather satellite sensors and 76 earth resource satellite sensors were in orbit (NORAD, 2006) and new and improved

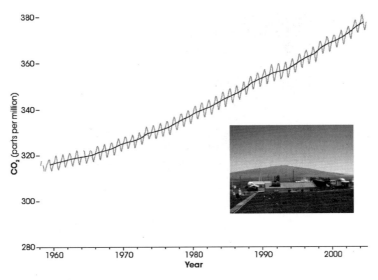

Fig. 4.4 Carbon dioxide measurements charted in the "Keeling curve". (FromNASA Visible Earth, http://visibleearth.nasa.gov)

sensors are continuously adding new capabilities to observe the status of the Earth. Remote sensing developed very rapidly, offering opportunities for climate research that were impossible to foresee in the 1950s. Being able to observe the distribution and movement of dust and clouds, land surface and sea surface temperatures, atmospheric water vapor, and winds, has contributed immensely to our understanding of global climate (Figs. 4.5 and 4.6). Like many developments of that time, our ability to observe the whole Earth derives in part from Cold War political and military goals; nonetheless, the scientific impact of this technology is immeasurable.

It would also have been difficult in 1956 to foresee the advances that have been made in our ability to reconstruct past climates from a variety of independent data sources. These datasets place the twentieth-century climate in a much longer temporal perspective and provide a more useful context to evaluate current conditions. Reconstructions also provide a record against which the performance of models can be measured. While instrumental records cover much less than 200 years for most of the world, Mann et al. (1999) reconstructed northern hemisphere temperatures for the second millennium from a combination of tree rings and ice core data (Fig. 4.7). This record showed that twentieth-century warming stands out against a millennial-scale cooling trend attributed to long-term changes in Earth–Sun geometry (Berger, 1988). These findings provide additional evidence of the role humans play in causing global warming.

Although scientists can now predict, with high confidence, a globally averaged temperature increase of 1.4–5.8 °C (depending on the assumed emission scenario) by the end of the twenty-first century, the regional and local-scale consequences of this warming trend are much less clear.

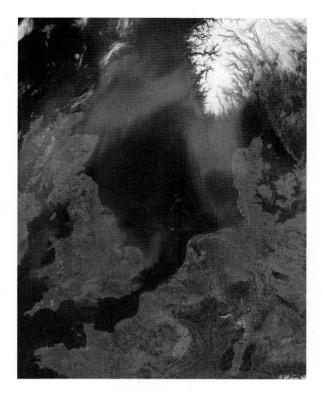

Fig. 4.5 Saharan dust over the North Sea. This Moderate Resolution Imaging Spectroradiometer (MODIS) image from April 16, 2003, shows African dust blowing over Scotland (left) and across the North Sea to Norway and even southward to Denmark.

Because the availability of water is a key factor in the abundance of vegetation, changes in precipitation are most critical for continued biodiversity and human livelihoods in arid and semiarid environments. While all climate models predict increases in global mean precipitation, some dryland regions are projected to become wetter and others drier. Furthermore, these projections differ widely among different climate models, due to uncertainties in boundary conditions (such as emission scenarios) and the processes included (such as respective roles of cloud cover, oceans, and greenhouse gases) (van Boxel, 2004). Regardless of average rainfall conditions, rainfall variability and extreme events have increased and are likely to further increase as a result of global warming (Hulme, 1996; Salinger, 2005). In addition, increases in evaporation and evapotranspiration resulting from higher temperatures will increase the potential for more severe, longer-lasting droughts. Water availability in drylands is also affected by climate change impacts outside the drylands, particularly in mountain areas. These constitute important water reservoirs (Box 4.3) and feed rivers that provide water for adjacent drylands (see, e.g., Barnett et al., 2005; Chapter 3).

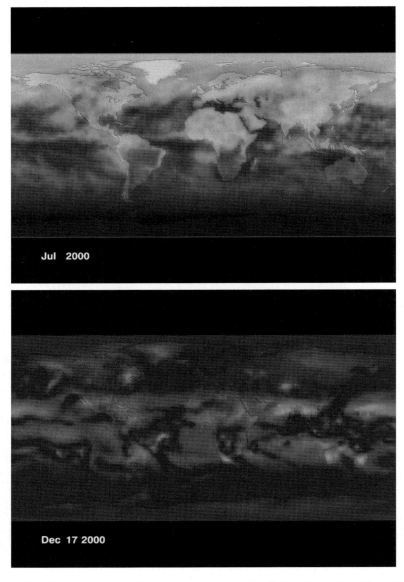

Fig. 4.6 Earth's energy balance. Top: average amount of sunlight reflected from Earth in July 2000 with clouds and high albedo surfaces being highly reflective. Bottom: average amount of heat emitted from the Earth in December 2000, with deserts emitting a lot of heat and cold cloud tops very little. (From NASA Visible Earth, http://visibleearth.nasa.gov/)

Dryland ecosystems are also sensitive to slight changes in atmospheric CO_2 when these are combined with changes in temperature, and this can alter the mix of plant species in any one place. Thus, in semiarid grasslands, increases in minimum temperatures shift competitive interactions between species using the C_3 photosynthetic

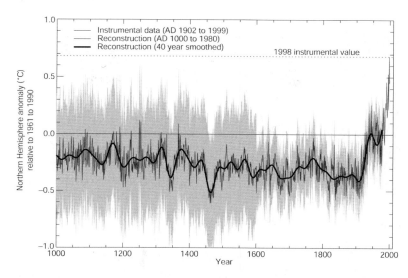

Fig. 4.7 Millennial Northern Hemisphere temperature reconstruction (blue) and instrumental data (red) from AD 1000–1999. (Adapted from Mann et al., 1999.) Smoother version of NH series (black), linear trend from AD 1000–1850 (purple-dashed) and two standard error limits (grey shaded) are shown. (Courtesy of IPCC, 2001c)

pathway and those using the C_4 photosynthetic pathway, favoring higher productivity of native and exotic forbs at the expense of drought-tolerant and grazing-tolerant grass species (Alward et al., 1999; Melillo, 1999).

This complexity and the uncertainties associated with it have made for a pitched debate over what action should be taken in response to climate change. Since the 1950s, our general relationship with, and attitudes about, climate have changed radically – from seeking to shape local weather to meet our immediate needs, to recognizing the necessity of preventing dangerous anthropogenic interference with the global climate system. In terms of policy, two approaches to addressing climate change are: (1) mitigation of climate change by limiting anthropogenic greenhouse gas emissions and enhancing greenhouse gas sinks; and (2) adaptation to the adverse effects of climate change (UNFCCC, 1992). In reality, both approaches are needed: adaptation remains necessary because mitigation efforts, though indispensable in the long run, will have little impact on climate change over the next few decades (Huq and Grubb, 2003). While mitigation must be a global-scale effort, adaptation happens at the local scale and would have to take different forms regionally, as will the impacts of climate change. Improvements in climate scenarios will allow us to move from responsive adaptation driven by extreme weather events to adaptation planning in anticipation of events (Dessai et al., 2005). However, as already noted, climate change projections often vary widely for individual drylands as a result of uncertainties about boundary conditions and processes involved. Thus, for example, Held et al. (2005) expect a drying trend in the Sahel

Box 4.3 No Snows of Kilimanjaro – a threat to water resources in the adjacent drylands?

Due to their extreme sensitivity to climate change, glaciers in low latitudes have become important sources of proxy data in climate-change research. The ice fields of Mount Kilimanjaro in northeastern Tanzania lost over 80% of their area during the twentieth century and are likely to disappear completely between 2015 and 2020 – possibly sooner (Thompson et al., 2002). The high rates of melting due to global warming play a part in this recession. However, according to climatologist Douglas Hardy (Minarcek, 2003) inadvertent modification of local climate might be the more proximate cause of glacier retreat: vegetation loss due to deforestation on the lower mountain slopes leads to reduced evaporation; this, in turn, leads to decreased cloud cover and precipitation and increased solar radiation and snowmelt.

In addition, some argue that these lower-slope montane forests, rather than the glaciers, give Mount Kilimanjaro its high catchment value and ability to supply water to a broader region (Agrawala et al., 2003). If so, the disappearance of the ice field – though an immense aesthetic and symbolic loss – might have only limited the hydrological and socioeconomic impact in this particular region. A much larger factor affecting local water supply might be reduced atmospheric moisture (Kaser et al., 2004), leading to decreased precipitation in the forest zone that feeds springs and rivers. While this can be explained partly by long-term changes in large-scale ocean–atmosphere mechanisms, local-scale phenomena such as deforestation are likely to play an important role as well. (Fig. 4.8).

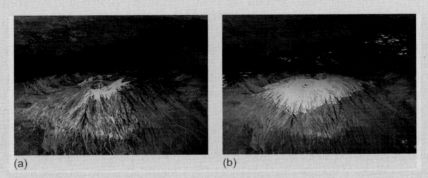

(a)   (b)

Fig. 4.8 Mount Kilimanjaro in February 1993 and 2000. Encroachment of agriculture into the forest zone can be observed in the background. NB: appearance of the summit does not indicate rate of loss of ice. (From NASA Earth Observatory, http://earthobservatory.nasa.gov/)

over the next 50 years, whereas Haarsma et al. (2005) predict increased rainfall. Such discrepancies make concrete adaptation to climate change difficult and put the focus on increasing adaptive capacity and reducing vulnerability as part of socio-economic development strategy (Tschakert, 2006).

Chapter 5
Plant and Animal Alternatives

Beyond water, humans need food, fiber, energy, and shelter to survive. Agriculture – the generation of many of the products that satisfy these needs from plants and animals – was the primary land use considered in *The Future of Arid Lands* (Chapter 7). As noted elsewhere, it was argued even in 1956 that this view of the potential uses of drylands was far too restricted.

A handful of strategies might be pursued for improving drylands agriculture: (1) exploit the plant and animal resources that were already there; (2) introduce crops and/or animals from other similar regions that might perform better than natives; or (3) improve crops or animals for dryland environments through breeding or more advanced forms of genetic manipulation.

The Future of Arid Lands dealt directly with these individual challenges. Since then, more in line with the general thinking of the editor Gilbert White, increasing attention has been given to the broader issues that surround agricultural production. Agricultural research has come to address not only the technical issues that confront agricultural systems but also the economic, legal, institutional, and social environments in which they operate.

5.1 The Situation in the 1950s

The section of *The Future of Arid Lands* titled "Better Adaptation of Plants and Animals to Arid Conditions", dealt largely, but not exclusively, with strategies for doing better than the status quo. Some of the questions addressed included (White, 1956, p. 329):

- What are the economic possibilities in the development and utilization of arid lands plants and animals?
- What screening procedures would lead to the selection of more productive plant and animal species for arid regions?
- What are the prospects of increasing drought resistance through genetic research?

C. F. Hutchinson and S. M. Herrmann, *The Future of Arid Lands – Revisited.*
© Springer 2008

5.1.1   Exploiting What Is There

One approach strongly advocated for rangelands was to encourage plants that were useful for forage and remove those that were not. These useful plants could be spread through practices such as reseeding, or reducing grazing pressure long enough to allow them to recover (Kellogg, 1956, p. 38):

> Along with selection and reseeding, where possible, is the usually overriding matter of management, or controlled use. Almost phenomenal effects of temporary rest or "guarding" of the range to bring it to a high state of production have been reported from many part of the world ...

A highly selective technique of vegetation manipulation to complement reseeding was also discussed by Kellogg (1956, pp. 38–39):

> Many differential plant-killing hormones and other chemicals are in practical use, and testing is going forward with thousands of new kinds. We can confidently expect continued improvement in arid land management through our ability to remove the useless plants that waste water so that we may conserve it for the good ones.

As has been noted, most of the management alternatives, discussed in 1956 were considered in the context of the developed world. Moreover, aside from briefly examining the economics of many of these treatments, essentially no attention was given to understanding or suggesting how individual land managers might be convinced to adopt them. Both this problem and the lack of solutions for it were recognized (Kellogg, 1956, p. 42): "Although we have made much progress in the basic and applied research among the natural sciences related to range management, much less has been done in the social sciences aside from production economics."

Israel presented a different situation. As a new country, Israel was intent on extracting as much as possible from its limited land resource. This offered some fundamental challenges for a region where even the prime agricultural land near the Mediterranean was at best semiarid (Evenari and Koller, 1956, p. 390): "Consequently, our agriculture had, from the very beginning, to deal with arid zone problems, and we can consider the whole country as a large-scale experiment in problems of aridoculture."

The evolution of dryland exploitation in Israel followed a path similar to other regions in that the potential uses of local plants and sites were discovered largely through trial and error over a long period. In Israel, however, the period of this search was greatly compressed and it was far more systematic. Outside of irrigated areas, the search focused on native local or regional plant species that could provide: (1) pasture; (2) shade; (3) dune fixation; and/or (4) industrial and pharmaceutical products (Evenari and Koller 1956, pp. 397–403). Dune fixation may be a comparatively unique objective, but in general this range of uses largely circumscribes the agricultural options available in drylands. The first two uses – pasture and shade – are concerned with direct ecosystem management, but the last – plants that might yield valuable products – suggests that wild plants with economic promise can be brought into routine production in an agricultural setting.

5.1.2   Developing New Crops from Dryland Plants

Four different paths for the development of new crops have been proposed and are outlined here with some familiar examples (Paarlberg, 1990). Attention was already being devoted to the first three in 1956, but the potential for the fourth was just being realized.

- Domesticated from the wild: the oil palm and natural rubber
- Imported from abroad: the soybean
- Changed by conventional breeding: high-yielding wheat
- Developed by gene-splicing: maize with resistance to certain herbicides

Domestication – the notion of making productive use of wild native species, particularly plants, based on their inherent properties – has been an enduring theme in drylands research. There are compelling reasons for pursuing this line of attack. First, it seems obvious that the persistence of dryland plants and animal species is testimony to their being well adapted to the stresses the environment imposes on them: high temperatures and periodic drought, saline or brackish waters, competition with other plants and animals for scarce resources. Second, earlier dryland cultures exploited the unique properties of many dryland plants and animals; this could point to likely candidates for agricultural development. Finally, the very mechanisms that have evolved to allow these species to succeed may have not-yet-discovered value that will be important in the future.

Shantz, in particular, focused part of his chapter, "History and Problems of Arid Lands Development", on the argument that more attention should be paid to better determining the products that might be extracted from dryland plants. He pointed out that "we have by no means fully utilized the highly adjusted plants of the arid lands so rich in fibers and valuable chemical components." (Shantz, 1956, p. 22)

This line of reasoning was more fully explored in Pultz's chapter, "Problems in the Development and Utilization of Arid Land Plants". To provide a general framework of analysis, he reviewed the economic demands that must be met for any new crop to succeed. First was value. To have value, a plant must provide a product that is either (1) scarce or unique; or (2) cheaper than similar products derived from other sources. Second was supply. The plant or plant product "must be available in sufficient quantity to furnish a fairly continuous supply to commercial users" (Pultz, 1956, p. 414). Pultz touched on several previously used plants – often called "new" crops – to support his arguments.

Guayule (*Parthenium argentatum*) is a rubber-producing shrub found in the drylands of Mexico and the USA. Its rubber has been used since pre-Columbian times in Mexico (Bonner, 1991). Conforming to Pultz's value rule, guayule has seen periodic spikes of interest as a potential new crop (Box 5.1). Pultz also described jojoba (*Simmondsia chinensis*) and candelilla (*Euphorbia antisyphilitica*), both of which produce waxes that satisfy his value rule. Both have been used traditionally and have found some measure of commercial success. For a time, candelilla was able to outcompete other waxes (e. g., carnauba) in terms of cost because its natural stands were claimed to be "inexhaustible". However, excessive harvesting led to its economic decline by violating Pultz's second, or continuous supply rule (Pultz, 1956).

Pultz saved most of his discussion for canaigre (*Rumex hymenosepalus*), a source of tannins used to process leather. He described ongoing research and speculated that the crop might meet with commercial success in the future. The fact that it did not suggests that it may have violated his value rule by failing to offer a product at a lesser cost than competing sources.

Box 5.1 Guayule: A "new" drylands crop

Guayule (*Parthenium argentatum*) is native to the arid and semiarid parts of the southwestern USA and northern Mexico. Guayule produces rubber very similar to that produced by the tropical tree *Hevea brasiliensis*, used in automobile tires and other products. Investment in guayule peaked four times during the past century, in response to developments in the rubber market. The first pulse in the early twentieth century was driven by high prices of *Hevea* rubber as tire manufacturers looked for less costly alternatives. Prices eventually came down as more *Hevea* plantations were established and production increased. The second period of interest followed the threat of interruption to rubber supplies during World War II. Similar threats triggered by the 1970s oil embargo caused a third wave of interest in guayule. The fourth began in the 1990s when it became apparent that many people had allergic reactions to *Hevea* rubber medical and personal hygiene products. Each of these spikes in interest spurred investment in research which, among other advances, has led to increases in guayule rubber yield of over 250% since the 1940s (Ray et al., 2005; Fig. 5.1). Despite this, the advantages in price or uninterrupted supply guayule enjoyed during each of these periods were short-lived. In the most recent round of interest, however, guayule did establish a unique advantage over *Hevea* due to its hypoallergenic properties. This has resulted in modest but sustained demand for guayule rubber, but uses must be found for the other 90% of the guayule plant if it is to become a viable economic alternative for farmers (Nakayama, 2005). Other potential products from guayule include the resins that remain in the bagasse (plant matter) after rubber extraction, and the bagasse itself, which can be converted into termite-resistant wood products (composites), or fuel pellets for burning. The guayule experience shows that the path to commercial viability for new crops in drylands is difficult.

Box 5.1 (continued)

Fig. 5.1 Cultivated guayule in Arizona. (Courtesy of Bob Roth, Maricopa Agricultural Center)

Animals presented similar opportunities. However, rather than searching for "new" species of animals that might offer some advantages, attention was focused on widely distributed domesticated animals (i.e., goats, sheep, cattle, camels) and on breeds that had been developed locally over millennia. Draz's view, summarized by Dickson (1956, p. 61), was that "it is shortsighted to look down on local animal breeds which have become adapted to the conditions of living in the environment".

The rules laid out by Pultz apply equally well today. Most of the plant species then discussed as potential new crops for drylands have resurfaced from time to time and have had some marginal success. None, though, has really provided a viable alternative to traditional crops for farmers in most of the world's drylands (Box 5.1).

5.1.3 *Importing New Resources from Other Drylands*

The second avenue for developing a new crop is to bring successes in from somewhere else – Paarlberg (1990) used the soybean as an example. In a dryland agricultural setting this is fairly straightforward; the environment can be changed through irrigation to ensure that the new crop can thrive. However, even outside the agricultural field setting, it is possible to take uncultivated wild species and introduce them into dryland ecosystems with the intent of increasing production. This involves the deliberate introduction of plants – often from another continent – for use as animal forage, to supply wood, to control erosion, or to serve some other productive use.

In his chapter, "Adaptation of Plants and Animals", Draz (1956, p. 335) listed three methods recommended by the Food and Agriculture Organization (FAO) for improving breeds: (1) selection within native types; (2) grading up with improved breeds from other countries; and (3) development of new types. To this list, Draz (ibid., p. 336) added "introduction of preadapted species". This neatly summarizes the general approach that was pursued in much of *The Future of Arid Lands* and that seems to have been common at the time.

Animals received a good deal of attention, and there was speculation about strategies that might improve returns. Some authors suggested selecting for smaller breeds that might more efficiently harvest widely dispersed plant resources (Draz, 1956). Others argued that larger animals were inherently more efficient and judged the camel to be especially attractive; for example, Schmidt-Nielsen (1956, p.380) stated that "From the theoretical considerations it seems amazingly clear that the camel offers a most obvious solution to increased meat production in arid zones with a low natural vegetation density that cannot easily be increased."

While the comparative advantages of different breeds and stocking strategies served as points of discussion, it was generally agreed that increasing animal production in rangelands depended less on the type of livestock than on the quantity and quality of forage available to feed them. Describing the findings of extensive research in New Zealand, Draz (1956, p. 331) reported that "... raising the plane of nutrition among the animal population caused more production ... than [animal breed] selection. ..."

In the end, aside from the camel, no other animal species were identified in 1956 that would provide any kind of revolutionary change in rangeland management. There were locally developed breeds that might fit particular situations and, in fact, great emphasis was placed on making site-dependent selection of both plants and animals. But opportunities to manipulate animal resources did not approach the potential gains of working with plant resources. Because of the fundamental importance of primary production – that is, production of organic matter by plants through photosynthesis – the search narrowed to finding plants that could produce more rangeland forage or generate new products that might be useful for humans in a cropping system. In either case, it was assumed that there were new plant species to be found or created that could do better than what was currently in place.

While optimism generally prevailed, there also was ambivalence about the wisdom of introducing exotic plants into dryland environments. This was underscored, for example, by Kellogg (1956, p. 38), who pointed out that "... useful plants (and useless ones) are distributed unevenly over the world. One need think only of the great value of subterranean clover to Australia, and of the great harm done to Australia by the prickly pear cactus from the United States. ..."

The potential for "renegade" plants to cause disaster was still vivid in 1956, with control of the prickly pear outbreak in Australia dating only to the 1930s (Box 5.2). Obviously influenced by this experience, Kellogg (ibid.) went on to caution that "although we must be on the outlook for good exotics, greatest progress is being made with local varieties that have persisted for a long time".

5.1.4 Improving Crops for Dryland Environments

Because water is a primary constraint to agricultural production in drylands, interest persists in making more efficient use of the water that is available, particularly with respect to water use by plants. Then, there was an underlying and often explicit assumption that it would be possible to find or engineer plants that were more water efficient. However, it was recognized that fundamental limits to water-use efficiency

---

Box 5.2 The prickly pear menace in Australia

The prickly pear cactus (*Opuntia inermis*) that was introduced to Australia from Brazil in 1787 was intended to form the basis of a cochineal dye industry. This never materialized because the project's backers had imported the wrong species of prickly pear. Nevertheless, it was found to be useful for creating living fences and producing edible fruit, qualities that led to its dispersal. By the 1870s, the plant had gained a foothold in the clayey soils of the subhumid interior of Queensland and New South Wales in eastern Australia. Originally viewed as a pest but also a source of forage for cattle during droughts, by the 1920s it covered more than 250,000 km^2, an area larger than Great Britain. About one fifth of this area was so densely infested as to be useless. Initial efforts to clear land of the cactus relied on poisons or physical removal, both of which were expensive and ineffective for large areas. Moreover, treated lands were quickly reinvaded. By 1911, it was agreed that a biological control agent would likely be more effective, even though the use of biological agents had rarely been successful up to that time. After several unsuccessful beginnings, in 1927 the larvae of a moth – *Cactoblastis cactorum* – from Argentina were found to be both effective in attacking this prickly pear species and well adapted to the Australian environment. The results were astounding (Figs. 5.2 and 5.3). In less than 2 years, 220 million eggs of *Cactoblastis* and been distributed to settlers. By 1930, 2,000 km^2 had been cleared of prickly pear and by the end of 1931 most of the infestation had been eliminated. Eventually, a balance of sorts was achieved in which the prickly pear was restricted to about 1% of its former maximum range. The control of prickly pear in eastern Australia bordered on the miraculous, but the infestation itself delayed development of the region by 50 years (Freeman, 1992).

(continued)

Box 5.2 (continued)

Fig. 5.2 Prickly pear in Australia before release of *Cactoblastis* moths (National Archives of Australia, Image Series A1200, No. L58278)

Fig. 5.3 Prickly pear in Australia after release of *Cactoblastis* moths (National Archives of Australia, Image Series A1200, No. L58277)

might be prescribed by the physical consequences of gas exchange at the leaf and cell level. As Kellogg (1956, p.39) noted:

> We know that most of our plants are highly inefficient in their use of water and light. As plants proceed with their basic function—the manufacture of plant food by photosynthesis in sunlight—they are required to take in carbon dioxide. In most of them, as they take this in, water can escape. ... Basic researches on these processes can give our plant breeders new plant material.

While there was significant interest in overall water-use efficiency, Kellogg showed that it was only one of the many plant characteristics that might be manipulated to create crops that would be successful in a variety of dryland environments. It was generally thought that plant breeding could create plants that were higher yielding, more drought resistant (as contrasted with water efficient), more responsive to fertilizers, less vulnerable to diseases and pests, and less variable in their performance across different environments. The potential for more conscious and precise genetic manipulation was foreseen. Kellogg (1956, p. 39) stated that "The newly emerging discipline, sometimes called 'physiological genetics', holds great promise for giving us far greater potentialities than can be had from plant selection alone."

There was good cause for this optimism. In 1943, at the request of the Mexican government, the Rockefeller Foundation had begun the program that ultimately became the International Maize and Wheat Improvement Center (CIMMYT). The purpose was to create a locally focused crop improvement program based on plant breeding that would increase production to meet the needs of Mexico's rapidly growing population. The dramatic results – which led to the development of the "Mexican dwarf" wheat varieties that became a cornerstone of the Green Revolution – were just becoming apparent in 1956, when Mexico achieved self-sufficiency in wheat production (Borlaug, 1972).

What was just then emerging was an era in development in which research would transform agriculture, tripling agriculture production over the next 40 years and thus "foiling Malthus, again and again" (Trewavas, 2002).

5.2   The Situation Today

As always, water is a basic constraint to the occupation and productive use of drylands. As populations have grown, competition for water has correspondingly intensified. With irrigated agriculture accounting for about 70% of all water consumed in drylands, farmers are caught between the pressure to maintain or improve economic returns from agricultural production and the need to reduce water consumption in the face of competing demands. It is easy to imagine that, 50 years ago people hoped that technology would immediately and dramatically increase water supplies by tapping "new" sources (Chapter 3) or by discovering or engineering new crops that would use less water.

The many dramatic advances made early on led to what became known as the Green Revolution. However, with time it became apparent that those dramatic leaps did not benefit all people and regions equally. In fact, it has been argued that outside of the irrigated regions, the drylands were largely bypassed by the first waves of the Green Revolution, due to their risky climate and the inability of poor farmers to invest in the necessary technology (Whitman and Meyer, 1990). Until the 1990s, improvements in dryland agriculture were more evolutionary than revolutionary, advancing incrementally on a number of fronts. It appears that advances in water productivity (grain yield per unit of water consumed) will continue along this evolutionary path, with cultivars becoming increasingly finely adapted to local environments and irrigation amounts and timing becoming more precise to better meet crop demands during flowering and to reduce water use overall (Passioura, 2006).

5.2.1   Exploiting What Is There

Our understanding of ecosystem function and behavior, especially in drylands, has advanced significantly in the last 50 years (Chapter 6), and this has – or should have – changed our policies. When considering opportunities other than cropping, livestock is a first option. However, it is also understood now that such activities should be developed in a way that enhances, rather than reduces, other crucial goods and services provided by dryland ecosystems. Thus, rather than livestock production alone, corollary management objectives are to provide wildlife habitat, protect biodiversity, and conserve soil resources. It is also understood that managed systems may change due to human use, climate variability, fire, or other pressures, and that management objectives may have to be adjusted in response to these changes. All of this represents significant evolution in our view of natural resources and how they should be managed.

5.2.2   Developing New Crops from Dryland Plants

Optimism about the potential for discovering new crops was balanced by skepticism, even in the 1950s. Whaley (1952, p. 229), for example, stated that "The potentialities of the world's flora seem sufficiently well known to enable the conclusion to be drawn that the likelihood of finding crops of economic significance that can be grown commercially on a large scale in the arid regions, without irrigation, is only slight."

Nonetheless, events have often fueled interest in new crops during the last half-century, largely in response to periodic emergencies (Box 5.1). In the early 1970s, the US National Academy of Sciences established a committee to investigate the potential for new crops, with an emphasis on drylands (NRC, 1975). While much of the committee's attention went to potential food crops, interest also increased in industrial crops (i.e., waxes, oils, resins), as well as plants that produced medicinal products (Thompson, 1990; Vietmeyer, 1986; Wickens et al., 1985). There was also growing realization that, for new crops to be competitive, revenue-generating uses must be found for by-products previously considered as waste (Hinman, 1984). In short, every effort must be made to make new crops economically competitive.

The history of dryland crop development shows how risky these efforts can be (Box 5.1). Pultz's rules regarding the need to establish demonstrable value and provide a more-or-less uninterrupted supply of the plant product are unforgiving. Yet, two crops mentioned by Pultz have found comparatively small but consistent niche markets: guayule in medical and personal rubber products, and jojoba in cosmetics. However, even though these and other such plants are adapted to arid environments, some may require irrigation for maximum production, thus diminishing their initial allure (Foster and Cofelt, 2005). Moreover, many crops – guayule and jojoba included – require some processing to extract the product from the plant material. This requires investment in infrastructure, presenting an additional obstacle to widespread adoption (Hinman, 1984). All of these factors make it difficult for farmers to commit to new crops, particularly when conventional cropping options are less risky. As Arnon (1992, p. 342) pointed out, "With an assured water supply, there is a great choice of mesophytic crops, with high-yielding potentialities and commercial value; the native desert plants can rarely compete under these conditions."

As a result, considerable attention has been devoted to exploring and exploiting the comparative advantages that some dryland species possess. First is the ability to exploit water resources that are unavailable to essentially all other terrestrial plants. Halophytes are a class of plants that grow in both coastal and dryland habitats where the available saline waters are toxic to other plants. Many are widely used for livestock fodder (e.g., saltbush, *Atriplex* spp.), some have been proposed as sources for oil (e.g., *Allenrolfea* spp., *Salicornia* spp.), and others primarily for land reclamation or restoration, with secondary forage value (e.g., *Distichlis spicata* to stabilize dry lake beds near Mexico City) (Aronson, 1985). Each occupies a niche, but they are limited.

The other approach – and the first suggested by Pultz as a way to create value for drylands plants – is to find a unique product that they alone can provide. It is in this approach that a truly new alternative has emerged over the last 50 years in the search for resources among dryland plants and animals.

An analysis by McLaughlin (1985) suggested that dryland crops could not compete with crops from other zones when water was assured. Instead, a more fruitful path for dryland agriculture would be production of chemicals. Dryland plants and other organisms are often comparatively rich in the production of secondary metabolites, also known as "natural products". These metabolic products (chemical compounds) are secondary in that they are not essential for normal growth, development, or reproduction of an organism. Instead, they may help the organism deal with environmental stresses, such as herbivory by grazing animals or attack by pathogens. Many of these compounds may also have medicinal or other human uses that may or may not have been discovered. For example, the plant genus *Ephedra*, found in many drylands in both the new and old worlds, produces a number of secondary metabolites that have been used medicinally for millennia. The Asian *Ephedra* produces ephedrine, useful in treating asthma (Caveney et al., 2001). Certain bacteria and fungi that grow in the root zone in close association with specific dryland plants also produce useful chemicals. One fungus found in the root zone of a Sonoran Desert cactus yielded several chemical compounds that were effective in controlling human cancer in the laboratory (Wijeratne et al., 2003). Other "endophytic" fungi are found within plants in the spaces between cells, where they generate secondary metabolites that provide benefits to the host plant (symbiosis). One such fungus, found in a species of *Ephedra*, also produced a compound effective against cancer in the laboratory (Bashyal et al., 2005).

Efforts to isolate and test chemical compounds from this wide array of sources are still at a relatively early stage, and the ultimate benefit they might bring to those who rely on drylands for their livelihood is unclear. However, these potential benefits appear significant and are thus worthy of attention. The recent FAO International Treaty on Plant Genetic Resources for Food and Agriculture is aimed at protecting indigenous farmers' intellectual property rights to their knowledge of plants and plant secondary products and ensuring that they recieve equitable benefits from any products developed through that knowledge (Mekouar, 2001). However, many of the major food crops and, more important to this discussion, industrial crops, are not included in the treaty. This leads to speculation that some countries may wish to keep certain plant resources outside the treaty so that they can negotiate bilateral arrangements for developing them (Falcon and Fowler, 2002).

5.2.3   Importing New Resources from Other Drylands

The kinds of unintended consequences that concerned Kellogg with the introduction of new species 50 years ago remain. The number of "problem" species has grown as a result of both intentional and inadvertent introduction of species into new environments (IUCN, 2004). As the importance of maintaining biodiversity has been increasingly recognized (e.g., United Nations Convention on Biological Diversity in 1992), concern has grown that species introduced into new environments may become invasive, causing serious problems (Mack and Lonsdabe, 2001). This concern has led to the creation of a subdiscipline for the ecology of invasions and the establishment of new centers for research (Richardson et al. 2004; Sax et al., 2005).

The story of buffelgrass in the USA–Mexico border region illustrates some of the complexities of the issue beyond mere contrasts in land use (Box 5.3). First is differing perceptions of value. Some studies have suggested that forage production of buffelgrass pastures in Mexico is two to three times greater than that of nonconverted rangelands (Martin et al., 1995). This would make the introduction of the species attractive to ranchers. However, more recent research suggests that, in addition to a loss of biodiversity, total primary production may actually be lower for buffelgrass pastures than for adjacent nonconverted areas (Franklin et al., 2006). Second, it suggests that perception of value may change over time. For example, the low woody mesquite tree (*Prosopis juliflora*), common throughout the Sonoran Desert region, has been widely used in agroforestry because its leaves and pods provide forage for animals and it also produces high-quality firewood. However, in many places it can become seriously invasive. For example, mesquites introduced into Rajasthan with support by Indian government programs, over time largely replaced local species that produced a wider variety of products. As a result, the tree that was initially valued eventually came to be viewed as a problem (Gold, 1999). These findings underscore the need to objectively assess both: (1) how the introduced species is likely to interact with native species in the broadest sense; and (2) what the benefits are likely to be to the farmer or rancher (Krause, 2004). This prudent and obvious guidance, however, is not easily followed because of the difficulty of resolving the sometimes basic conflicts between conservation and economic development (Ashley et al., 2006).

Box 5.3 Buffelgrass: boon or bane?

Buffelgrass (*Pennisetum ciliare*), a native of Africa, has been deliberately introduced into rangelands in the USA and Australia. In these new habitats it has proven to be an aggressive colonizer. Based on its high productivity and resistance to fire, drought, and heavy grazing, it has been judged very useful in raising the productivity of semiarid rangelands (Dixon et al., 2002).

In North America, buffelgrass was introduced during the 1930s to the state of Sonora in northern Mexico. It proved to be very popular among ranchers. Since then, it has been promoted by government programs in both Mexico and the USA (Arriaga et al, 2004). By 2000, almost 2 million hectare in northern Mexico had been converted through a process termed *desmonte*, in which native desert vegetation is mechanically removed and the area reseeded to buffelgrass (Franklin et al., 2006; Fig. 5.4).

Fig. 5.4 View of a buffelgrass pasture north of Hermosillo, Mexico, characterized by "chorizos" or rows where native vegetation has been bulldozed into piles to make way for the cultivation of buffelgrass. The photograph was made possible by the kind assistance of Dr. A. Burquez at UNAM and S. Lanham at Environmental Flying Services. (Courtesy of Todd Esque, USGS.)

(continued)

Box 5.3 (continued)

Fig. 5.5 A rocky southwest-facing talus slope invaded by buffelgrass at Saguaro National Park, near Tucson, Arizona, USA. Should a fire occur on this slope, many of the giant saguaro cactus (>100 years old) would die. (Courtesy of Todd Esque, USGS.)

Even outside areas where *desmonte* is practiced buffelgrass establishes itself easily, generally leading to replacement of native grasses and major changes in vegetation structure and species diversity (Arriaga et al., 2004; Fig. 5.5). In addition, buffelgrass drastically alters fire regimes because of its increased fuel load and spatial continuity that respond well to high ignition opportunities. This increased fire frequency and intensity favors buffelgrass even more, because fire was a rare feature in the Sonoran Desert and thus native species have very limited capacity to withstand it (Clarke et al., 2005).

In the 1970s buffelgrass began to appear in the Sonoran Desert region of Arizona (USA) (Burgess et al., 1991). Here, though, economic and environmental sensibilities were different. A good part of Arizona's economy is based on tourism which is drawn to the unique vegetation of the Sonoran Desert. The very emblem of the region is the giant saguaro cactus (*Cereus gigantea*); its importance is symbolized by Saguaro National Park, which straddles Tucson, the second largest city in the state. Ironically, the spread of buffelgrass could cause the saguaro to disappear completely, because it is not tolerant to fire (Clarke et al., 2005; Fig. 5.6).

The buffelgrass situation highlights the nature and magnitude of the problems that are encountered in manipulating natural resources. On one hand, it is considered a highly valuable resource for local ranching economies in semiarid regions, like those in Mexico. On the other, it directly threatens biodiversity and a prized vegetation resource that is central to a tourist economy in the USA.

Box 5.3 (continued)

Fig. 5.6 Burned saguaros and yuccas, 1995 Rio Fire in the Phoenix area. Note: This particular fire was the result of red brome (*Bromus madritensis*), a Mediterranean annual grass. However, a fire resulting from buffelgrass would cause similar or worse damage because of higher fuel loads. (Courtesy of Todd Esque, USGS.)

5.2.4 Improving Crops for Dryland Environments

Most of the world's drylands, particularly in Africa, did not benefit much from the Green Revolution. As should have been expected, the peculiar challenges offered by the drylands continued to make them marginal in most parts of the world. Research focused on the main cereal crops that did best in more humid regions. This meant that the Green Revolution only benefited those dryland settings where irrigation could minimize crop stress or "add" another growing season. Interest and investment in the drylands was discouraged by their unreliable climate conditions and the inability of poor farmers to invest in the inputs, particularly fertilizers, that modern crop varieties demand. Reflecting the general lack of research focused on the world's drylands, it has also been suggested that much of the Green Revolution's failure there resulted from unwillingness to invest in the exploration of local plant resources or to establish appropriate local plant breeding programs suited to marginal dryland environments (Evenson and Gollin, 2003a).

To address part of this issue, new international agricultural research centers – such as the International Center for Agriculture in the Dry Areas (ICARDA), the International Center for Research in the Semi-Arid Tropics (ICRISAT), the International Institute for

Tropical Agriculture (IITA), and others – were specifically directed to marginal environments that were not within the mandates of the earlier centers (CIMMYT and IRRI). Good measures of success were finally achieved as they began to focus on traditional plant breeding programs that were built on local resources and responded to local needs. These efforts, which began to produce results in the 1990s, have been called a "lite" Green Revolution (Evenson and Gollin, 2003a).

Even while recognizing such successes, there remains a great deal of debate over genetically modified crops and their potential future role in the world's drylands. Much has been learned already about the genetic structure of many important crops and how they can be manipulated to be more resistant to the effects of stresses – drought, pests, and diseases. Much of this knowledge has been generated in the private sector, which seeks to develop new improved crop varieties that are then sold as improved seed to farmers. However, as already noted, the performance of such crops is closely tied to the application of sufficient water, fertilizer, and pesticides. Crops perform very well, especially as monocultures, in the "optimal" settings that can be provided by farmers with fairly large operations and the capacity to invest in required inputs. Many farmers in drylands, though, are poor, cultivate small areas, and typically plant fields to more than one crop. Even if they can afford improved seed, they cannot afford to apply inputs at the rates required for optimal performance. Thus, even though seed companies may be capable of engineering crop varieties that would outperform those currently grown in suboptimal settings, there are very few incentives for them to do so if farmers do not need to buy seed every year (Serageldin, 1999).

To resolve this conundrum, it has been proposed that public–private partnerships (PPPs) should be established, similar to those that have been created to deliver modern treatment to two tiers of HIV/AIDS patients: one tier in the developed world where higher prices can be charged, and a second in developing countries where lower cost or subsidized alternatives are pursued. In the case of agricultural PPPs, it has been suggested that the private-sector partner develop traits of general interest (e.g., drought and disease resistance) that can be packaged and sold to large-scale farmers. The public-sector partner would concentrate on developing and maintaining breeding programs that utilize local varieties better suited to low-input operations, but would also work to introduce traits developed by the private partners into the local populations (Delmer, 2005).

As this was being written, the Rockefeller Foundation, which initiated the Green Revolution more than 60 years ago, and the Bill and Miranda Gates Foundation jointly announced a new Alliance for a Green Revolution in Africa (AGRA) aimed at addressing this very need (Gates Foundation, 2006).

5.2.5   Livestock

Along a climatic gradient of increasing aridity, as rainfed cropping becomes riskier, animals are increasingly important in agricultural production systems (Sere and Steinfield, 1995). Much of the discussion regarding livestock in *The Future of Arid*

Lands addressed systems in which ruminants (cattle, sheep, goats, and camels) played a central role. Generally, these were either the subsistence-oriented, extensive pastoral systems practiced in most of the developing world or the more market-oriented, less land-intensive but more capital-intensive ranching systems found in the developed world. As noted in Section 5.1.2, in the 1950s there was some discussion about improving animal breeds while preserving locally well-adapted ones, but the greatest attention was given to improving forage production.

Two related factors led to changes in this general approach. First and foremost was what has come to be called the "Livestock Revolution" (Delgado et al., 1999). Between 1967 and 1997 there was a 50% increase worldwide in the per capita consumption of animal products (meat, milk, and eggs); more specifically, per capita consumption increased 100% in East Asia and the world's developing countries (Hall et al., 2004). Unlike the technology-driven Green Revolution a generation earlier, the Livestock Revolution was and is being driven by increased demand resulting from higher rural incomes and rapid urbanization in the developing world.

Second, as the demand for animal products has increased, livestock production has become increasingly oriented towards markets rather than subsistence. As a result, it has come to be viewed less as a discrete agricultural activity than as one aspect of a far broader and more complex economic system within which households are embedded. In this perspective, livestock can increase local resiliency, playing a greater or lesser role in generating income for farmers – or more accurately rural households – as shifting opportunities may dictate (Sere and Steinfeld, 1995).

It appears that we are still in the midst of the Livestock Revolution and that these trends will continue for some time. Between 1997 and 2020, demand for animal products is expected to increase another 50% , worldwide, and more than 100% in Asia and sub-Saharan Africa specifically. Also, by 2020, it is projected that more than 50% of livestock products will come from developing countries (Delgado et al., 1999). Obviously, this offers significant opportunities for the developing world.

The degree to which the drylands may benefit from this major trend is not entirely clear. In the developed drylands, there has been a shift in livestock production – particularly cattle – from rangeland-based to "landless" systems (i.e., pens and feedlots) in which animals are controlled and fed with trucked-in forage or specially prepared rations (Sere and Steinfeld, 1995). In the developing world, livestock production has historically provided the only activity that many drylands could support; they are thus potentially in a good position to take part in this new shift. The move away from subsistence to market orientation will present challenges, but can also provide unexpected opportunities. For example, a recent news story described how seminomadic camel herders in Mauritania traditionally supplied milk "on-demand" to travelers alongside roads but made only uncertain profits due to relatively limited demand and recurring quality and health issues. Now, herders have increased their income by delivering milk to collection points where it is taken to the capital city, processed, packaged, and sold locally, and in much larger quantities, as safe long-life milk (Smith, 2006).

It has been argued that, where capital is more readily available than land (i.e., in urban and peri-urban areas), the tendency will be to concentrate animals in pens and stalls. Such settings provide opportunities to enrich livestock diets with readily available agro-industrial waste products like tomato pulp and olive oil waste. In addition, low-cost feedblock equipment is often easily purchased or manufactured and can further reduce livestock pressure on the resource base (Thomas et al., 2003). However, higher concentrations of animals can also create threats to both public health and the environment. In those areas where land is essentially "free" and animals range widely (e.g., the Sahel) the tendency to overstock and degrade the resource base is high (Delgado et al., 2001).

While there are major opportunities, they will also be accompanied by major potential obstacles. Health concerns on the part of consumers will create demands for food safety, guarantees of animal health, and the corresponding need to track animal products. Perhaps even more important, the considerable investment that has accompanied the Livestock Revolution in developing countries seems to have been made mostly on the production side. However, in the long term, developing countries, and particularly the drylands, are likely to suffer because of poorly developed indigenous scientific, financial, and information technology resources on which they must build this production (Henson and Loader, 2001).

5.2.6   Changes in the Scope of Research

Both the scope and orientation of research being pursued now would have been unimaginable 50 years ago. However, as envisioned then, the sweep of research required by the complex issues of dryland development and management has indeed led to international cooperation. There are national research programs that support only national interests, but the most robust of these tend to be found in the developed world. Problems of the developing world were largely left to the international community; the response was the creation of the family of international research organizations known as the Consultative Group on International Agricultural Research (CGIAR). A recent assessment suggested that, among many other impacts, crop production in the developing world would have been at least 20% lower than it is today, and food prices more than 60% higher, without international agricultural research (Evenson and Rosegrant, 2003; Evenson and Gollin, 2003b).

The nature of research has changed fundamentally over the last 50 years. As noted, initially, attention was largely restricted not just to crops but even more specifically to major cereal grains. In the 1970s, though, agricultural technologies began to address a larger set of issues that encompassed both the entire farming production system in which crops were produced, and the other needs confronting the farmers who managed these systems (Bertram, 1993). Part of this shift might simply reflect the adoption of a "systems" perspective by those involved in development and agricultural research (Chapter 7). It may also, at least in part, reflect a growing realization that the Green Revolution's benefits did not reach many dryland farmers outside of irrigated areas. This reasoning suggests that, in drylands, pursuing multiple incremental changes that can be implemented on a small scale by local farmers might ultimately have an impact comparable to that of the Green Revolution's more overtly dramatic impact in humid regions (Simmonds, 1985).

The failures of the Green Revolution to reach the poorest of the poor – especially those in the drylands – and its tendency to overlook environmental considerations were also tackled by the Brundtland Commission (WCED, 1987). Specifically, the commission was critical of research conducted by CGIAR member institutions both for its tendency to address a limited range of crops and for considering only the biophysical dimensions of research at the expense of environmental and social issues. In response, the CGIAR (CIFOR, 1999, under "Introduction") acknowledged that, prior to 1990:

> [S]ignificant increases in food production – however successful – had been limited to a few crops, leaving many plants nutritionally important for poor people without major research efforts, and with only very limited input into animal husbandry and fish production, [suggesting] that the knowledge gained from farming systems research in the 1980s had not been integrated significantly in the CGIAR agenda.

The *Review of Priorities and Strategies* (CGIAR, 1992) confronted those criticisms even more directly, moving toward a more holistic and integrated view of development. Based on ecoregions, this view was more sensitive to the environment and more in tune with the needs, capacities, and aspirations of local populations. Today, multiple levels and whole domains of research extend from the genetics that determine crop traits through the agricultural production systems that support crop production from field to market. They encompass research into the social fabric of farm households, communities, and whole economies as well as the specific forces that drive production from individual farm to global commodity markets.

As suggested above, the systems approach that has emerged in agricultural research allows for incremental improvements to multiple facets of the environment in which farmers, ranchers, and pastoralists are embedded. The coining of terms like "agrosilvopastoral" is testimony to this recognition that all these different components are inextricably linked together in a livelihood system (Chapter 7). Approaching them as such has resulted in development strategies that, in turn, have brought improved standards of living in many of the world's drylands. This is also one path that must be maintained in the future. Although they framed their arguments regarding agroecosystem management within the context of a severely limited energy future, the suggestion by Edens and Koenig that (1980, p. 701): "We are truly entering the age of closed system management – in agriculture as in industry", has become truer and more useful with time, particularly in the drylands of the world.

Chapter 6
Ecosystems

Ecology, maybe more than any other discipline, offers some insight as to how schools of thought, or paradigms, develop. The process is not necessarily chronological, with a new paradigm invariably replacing an older one. Instead, paradigms fall into and out of favor with communities of practice. In ecology, the two most relevant paradigms for understanding dryland ecosystem behavior are the equilibrium ("balance of nature") and the nonequilibrium ("flux of nature") models, which describe two poles between which other viewpoints are arrayed.

Ecology began to come into its own in the 1960s, with the rise in concern over the degree to which humans had altered the structure and functioning of global ecosystems (Worster, 1977). This chapter elaborates on a few recent topics in ecology that are now seen as particularly relevant to drylands but that were not explicitly addressed in *The Future of Arid Lands*.

6.1 The Situation in the 1950s

Ecology did not receive much explicit attention in *The Future of Arid Lands*. This seems peculiar in that the field had been established as a scientific discipline decades earlier. The British Ecological Society, the first professional society for ecologists, was founded in 1913 and began publication of the *Journal of Ecology* that same year; the Ecological Society of America was established in 1915 and began publishing *Ecology* in 1920. Around the time of the publication of *The Future of Arid Lands*, Dice (1955, p. 346) stated that: "The science of ecology has now approached, if it has not already reached, an early state of maturity ... [as] ... the science that deals with the relationships between organisms and their physical and biotic environments." The marginal treatment of ecology in the 1956 book might have been due to the lack of agreement among ecologists and other scholars about the precise scope of the field, as well as the lack of a well-developed set of functional concepts of ecosystems before the 1960s. Another reason might have been that the realm of ecology at that time was more concerned with theoretical relationships that might prevail in "pristine" environments than with environments that had actually been perturbed by human intervention. An agricultural field, for example,

C. F. Hutchinson and S. M. Herrmann, *The Future of Arid Lands – Revisited.*
© Springer 2008

was not considered worthy of the attention of ecologists. The environment–development nexus had not yet surfaced in the 1950s.

It is also puzzling that there was not more mention of ecosystem change in *The Future of Arid Lands*. The landmark publication *Man's Role in Changing the Face of the Earth* (Thomas, 1956) clearly acknowledged the importance of such change; it was the product of a similar conference, also held in 1955, and contained work by some of the same authors. Furthermore, Thomas's work had been inspired in turn by a much earlier work, *Man and Nature; or, Physical Geography as Modified by Human Action* (1864) by George Perkins Marsh.

Despite its marginal treatment in *The Future of Arid Lands*, ecology is implicit as an underlying theme in the book section "Better Use of Present Resources". This section addresses the following questions of ecological relevance that, seemingly, represent the fundamental conundrum of managing the highly variable and dynamic dryland ecosystem – reconciling the desire to increase production with the need to protect the environment.

• What are the consequences of utilizing arid lands beyond their capabilities:?
• What are the possibilities of increasing and maintaining sustained production from grass and forest lands without accelerating erosion:? (White, 1956, p. 177)

6.1.1   Ecological Balance as Guiding Principle

Although not elaborated on, the assumption that dryland ecosystems operated under the equilibrium model was implicit in *The Future of Arid Lands*. This is apparent in Whyte's (1956, p. 185) statement that: "If the biotic factor [i.e., grazing] could be limited for some 5 or 10 years, it would be possible to make full use of the remarkable capacity of degraded types of vegetation to revive, to climb again up the ecological ladder, and to provide a superior type of vegetation."

The equilibrium paradigm emphasizes internal ecosystem regulation through negative feedback mechanisms that will move the system toward stability (Briske et al., 2003). This was the dominant view in much of ecology during the 1950s; it was heavily influenced by the tradition of the nineteenth-century ideas about a "balance of nature" in which nature obeyed laws and was predictable and controllable (McIntosh, 1985). In ecology, it was formalized in the "Clementsian" model of plant succession, developed to explain vegetation dynamics in the North American temperate grasslands (Clements, 1916). The succession model is based on the hypothesis that any particular site will have a single equilibrium state, the climax, which is determined by climate and soil. When the climax state of a particular site is disturbed (as by heavy livestock grazing, clearing, or fire), the vegetation is progressively pushed back in the successional sequence to an early successional state that represents poor condition. After removal of the disturbance, the vegetation is assumed to return to its predisturbance climax state, once again following the natural successional path towards that state (Parker, 1954). Thus, vegetation of a particular site at a particular time is viewed as one point along a linear trajectory from poor (very disturbed) to excellent (climax) (Dyksterhuis, 1949).

Although there were competing hypotheses in the 1940s and 1950s, the succession model became widely accepted as the scientific basis for the range management profession in the USA: "Range condition classes are in reality successional stages of plant communities described in terms to make them readily available for use by range administrators and stockmen" (Parker, 1954, p. 14) (Box 6.1). Under this model, the objective of range management was – and still is in many drylands where the model has persisted among range managers – to balance grazing pressure with successional tendency (Westoby et al., 1989; Fig. 6.1). The stocking density at which this balance could be achieved is practically expressed in the concept of "carrying capacity", defined as "the upper level beyond which no major increase can occur – assuming no major changes in the environment" (Odum, 1953, p. 122). Stocking densities above

---

Box 6.1 Succession and The Classification of Range Condition

Sustained drought, wind-blown, dust and agricultural decline in the southern Great Plains of the USA in the 1930s marked the beginning of the soil conservation movement in the USA; this led to the creation of the Soil Conservation Service (SCS) in 1935. The work of the SCS contributed to a growing appreciation of the role of range management in livestock production. As knowledge of the condition of a particular range is a prerequisite for good range management, such as deciding on appropriate livestock numbers, the SCS used a quantitative system of range condition classification based on the Clementsian concept of plant succession progressing toward a climax (Helms, 1990).

Range condition of a particular site might be defined as "the percentage of the present vegetation which is original vegetation for the site" (Dyksterhuis, 1949, p. 105). Since the 1950s, the SCS has used a categorization system known as the Quantitative Climax Method, which arbitrarily divides the scale from 0% to 100% into four range condition classes: poor (0–25%), fair (26–50%), good (51–75%), and excellent (76–100%). As the percentage of original or climax vegetation is a rather abstract measure, Dyksterhuis developed a field method that used the proportion of plant species groups as a quantifiable indicator of range condition. Depending on their response to grazing, he grouped range plant species into "decreasers", "increasers", or "invaders", building on work done by Sampson in the early decades of the twentieth century (Dyksterhuis, 1949; Fig. 6.7). Decreasers were defined as species that dominated in the undisturbed climax communities and decreased with progressing deterioration of the range condition. Increasers at first increased under grazing pressure before decreasing, whereas invaders were species not indigenous to a particular site, and which increased with progressing deterioration (Pendleton, 1989). The novelty of Dyksterhuis' quantitative approach lay in its classification of all plant species by ecological criteria, resulting in a continuous and measurable temporal change of group prevalence (Joyce, 1993).

Since the 1950s, the Quantitative Climax Method developed by Dyksterhuis has been adopted for rangeland assessment by many organizations such as the Society for Range Management (SRM) and the Food and Agricultural Organization (FAO). Despite criticism, it is still widely used around the world (Pendleton, 1989).

Box 6.1 (continued)

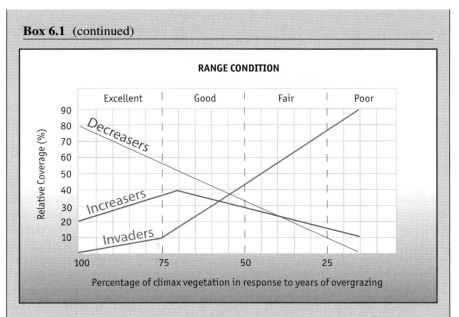

Fig. 6.7 Diagram illustrating a quantitative basis for determining range condition (Dyksterhuis, 1949, p. 109. Copyright Society for Range Management. Reprinted by permission of Alliance Communications Group, a division of Allen Press)

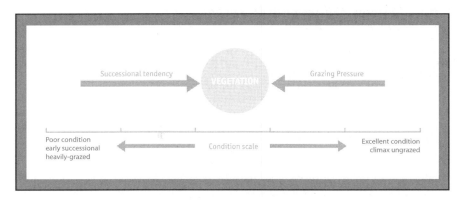

Fig. 6.1 Schematic representation of the succession model: grazing pressure counteracts successional tendency in moving vegetation along a gradient from poor to excellent condition. (Redrawn from Westoby et al., 1989, p. 267. Copyright Society for Range Management. Reprinted by permission of Alliance Communications Group, a division of Allen Press.)

the carrying capacity, a number that could be calculated for each particular site, presumably led to the problem of overgrazing. Kellogg (1956, p. 41) stated that: "[O]nce serious overgrazing has taken place, the carrying capacity falls far below normal and its recovery depends upon a temporary sharp reduction in stocking…." His statement reflects the equilibrium thinking and the carrying capacity concept for drylands that were so prevalent then. While the carrying capacity concept entered scientific ecological literature in the 1950s in the form of the theoretical value K in Odum's logistic population growth equation (Odum, 1953), the mathematical model behind it is credited to Verhulst's logistic growth function (1838), which was inspired by Malthus (1798). It describes the theoretical maximum population that might be sustained by a given rate of resource production.

Ecologists, or certainly many resource managers, of that time operated under the understanding that drought affected vegetation much as livestock grazing did, counteracting the successional tendency in a continuous and directional manner. In contrast, good rainfall years were understood as advancing the trajectory towards the assumed climax state (Westoby et al., 1989).

Clements was a dominant plant ecologist of the first half of the twentieth century. His model of plant succession, published in many textbooks, became widely accepted as the scientific basis for range management and guided the management philosophy for many agencies. Nevertheless, the applicability of this model in highly variable drylands was disputed among ecologists from its first publication. A few Americans and many leading European plant ecologists rejected the Clementsian emphasis on succession (McIntosh, 1985). Forrest Shreve, ecologist at the Desert Laboratory of the Carnegie Institution, found the principles of succession and climax to be inappropriate for the Sonoran Desert by the early 1950s (Bowers, 1988). As Shreve operated almost exclusively in desert environments, his disagreement with Clements centered on the latter's interpretation of the behavior of desert vegetation (Clements, 1936).

6.1.2   Systems Thinking in its Infancy

The term "ecosystem" has been attributed to the British ecologist Arthur Tansley, who defined it as comprising (Tansley, 1935, p. 299):

> the whole system (in the sense of physics), including not only the organism-complex, but also the whole complex of physical factors forming what we call the environment of the biome – the habitat factors in the widest sense. Though the organisms may claim our primary interest, when we are trying to think fundamentally we cannot separate them from their special environment, with which they form one physical system.

This concept of the interaction of living organisms with their physical environment became one of the most influential ideas in ecology, but only some decades later. Most ecologists in the 1950s understood that organisms and their environment were interrelated, but continued to treat them as separate entities, with the environment unilaterally acting on its component organisms (McIntosh, 1985). Thus, in *The Future of Arid Lands*, water, soil, grazing resources, plants, and animals were analyzed individually as discrete entities, with no section or chapter devoted to the functioning and dynamics of the ecosystem as a whole.

Systems thinking – in which systems are viewed as a whole rather than as a conglomeration of discrete parts – emerged in the middle of the twentieth century across a wide range of fields as disparate as engineering, physics and biology, and social and behavioral sciences (Ashby, 1956; von Bertalanffy, 1968). It represented a basic shift in thinking, which occurred in all fields of knowledge, from considering single entities in isolation to placing them in complex webs of interrelationships. This shift which began to occur as traditional analytical approaches proved inadequate for the study of many complex phenomena, particularly those including multiple interactions and nonlinear relationships. Human–environment interactions in the biosocial sciences are but one noteworthy example.

However, actually applying the systems approach to theoretical and applied science required large amounts of data and considerable computing power, which, were not generally available in the 1950s. This constraint slowed the full development of systems thinking in ecology as well as other disciplines.

6.2 The Situation Today

Since the 1950s, ecologists have profoundly changed their view on ecosystem functioning, as it has become increasingly obvious that previously assumed equilibrium conditions are rare and occur only at particular temporal and spatial scales (Picket et al., 1994). Today, it is well understood that disturbance, from local perturbations to regional climate variability to global climate change, is so inevitable that ecosystems most likely never reach a climax stage (Turner and Dale, 1998). Rather, the global environment is recognized as highly dynamic at multiple temporal and spatial scales, and transitional, not climax, stages are an important part of these dynamics (Paine, 2002).

Whether this change in mainstream ecological perception qualifies as what Kuhn (1962) called a paradigm shift – that is, a sweeping transition from one paradigm to another through a revolutionary process – remains a matter of perspective (McIntosh, 1987). In any case, new thinking in ecology had far-reaching impacts on our interpretations of environmental change in drylands, particularly on our view of desertification – that is, land degradation in drylands (Gillson et al., 2003).

The developments since the 1950s that have helped to advance ecological understanding beyond traditional ecological concepts, particularly with respect to dryland ecosystems, include:

1. Major international research initiatives such as the International Biological Programme (1964–1974) with its focus on "the biological basis of productivity and human welfare" (Goodall and Perry, 1981; Worthington, 1975), the UNESCO Man and the Biosphere Programme (ongoing since 1970) and the Millennium Ecosystem Assessment (2001–2005)
2. The growth of the environmental movement in the 1970s, which spurred a general interest in ecology, particularly in nature conservation (Worster, 1977)
3. A human and environmental crisis in the Sahel, sparked by a series of long and severe droughts, which raised questions about the "balance of nature" notion and caused a fundamental and continuing debate about land degradation and desertification (Herrmann and Hutchinson, 2005)

4. Advances in global-scale assessment of land cover, facilitated by a growing number of satellite sensors and increasingly comprehensive satellite data sets (e.g., surface temperature, vegetation greenness, land cover) which helped refine concepts of ecological change in drylands (e.g., Prince et al., 1998; Tucker and Nicholson, 1999)

In the 1950s, questions of maintaining or restoring ecological balance were dominant. Today, ecological research in drylands is primarily guided by questions such as the following:

- How can sustainability be defined and achieved in a nonequilibrium system?
- Which indicators can be used to determine different states and thresholds? How can the theoretical nonequilibrium model fit into a managerial context?
- What exactly is degradation? How resilient are drylands; that is, when is degradation irreversible?
- How are climate, land use and management and land degradation related?

In the following, the development of ecological thinking is not traced chronologically, but is considered in terms of various developments that happened more or less simultaneously and stimulated one another.

6.2.1 "New Ecology" and the Nonequilibrium Paradigm

The traditional views of a "balance of nature", on which the ecological succession model was based, had been challenged by individual scientists and rangeland managers even before *The Future of Arid Lands* (e.g., Shreve, 1951; Watt, 1947). The early challenges concerning the limitations of these views became more credible and widely discussed in the 1970s (see, e.g., Lauenroth and Laycock, 1989). The new thinking in ecology, described by the metaphor "flux of nature", became known as the nonequilibrium paradigm or "New Ecology" (Scoones, 1999). Interestingly, these changes in thinking were initiated mostly on abstract grounds, such as in the works on resilience and stability of ecosystems (e.g., Holling, 1973; Noy-Meir, 1973; Walker et al., 1981). Much of the paradigm controversy has been concerned with the functioning of rangeland ecosystems, which are predominantly grasslands (e.g., McClaran and Van Devender, 1995), hence its direct relevance to the semiarid drylands. Although a majority of scientists came to acknowledge the nonequilibrium paradigm, some have argued that it remains largely theoretical, with empirical validation and application in rangeland management still lagging (Jelinski, 2005).

The nonequilibrium paradigm rejects the concept of a single equilibrium point to which an ecosystem tends in a successional sequence. It holds that dryland ecosystems in particular have great potential to transit among multiple equilibrium points as a function of an inherently variable climate (Briske et al., 2003). Periodic and stochastic climatic events, such as severe droughts or floods, can result in discontinuous and possibly nonreversible ecosystem changes through a complex set of feedback mechanisms among climatic events, primary productivity and consumers at different levels in the food web (Holmgren et al., 2006). Because ecological processes are not necessarily linear at different spatial and temporal scales, and are subject to the influence of outside processes, there is no "natural state" to which an ecosystem returns after a disturbance. This prompted Jelinski (2005) to assert that "there is no Mother Nature".

Unlike the equilibrium hypothesis, which is represented mainly by a single model (the succession model), nonequilibrium models can be grouped into at least three types, which describe different patterns of vegetation change (see also Gillson, 2004):

(1) State-and-transition models (e.g., Westoby et al., 1989) hold that systems, when disturbed, may cross thresholds to transit to any one of a number of alternative states. These states can be distinguished on the basis of vegetation composition, plant growth forms, or soil properties. The idea of thresholds suggests that changes can be irreversible, even after the removal of the disturbance that caused the change. For example, encroachment by woody plants has been observed in many dry grasslands, possibly induced by heavy grazing. However, the increase in woody vegetation is not necessarily reversed after removing grazing pressure (Bestelmeyer et al., 2004) (Fig. 6.2; Box 6.2)

(2) Cyclical models (e.g., Caughley, 1976; Pellew, 1983) have been invoked to describe periodic fluctuations of tree abundance in savanna ecosystems.

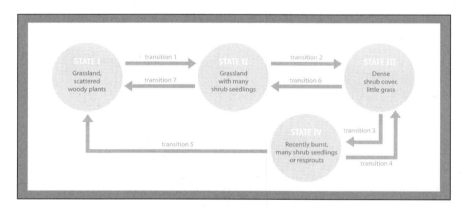

Fig. 6.2 Schematic representation of state-and-transition nonequilibrium model (example of a semiarid grassland/woodland in eastern Australia): A few very good rainfall years produce many shrub seedlings (transition 1). Shrub seedlings grow and establish a seed bank (transition 2). Sufficient rain produces enough vegetation for destructive fires, after which a cover of ephemerals develops (transition 3). Shrub regeneration grows to maturity (transition 4). Fire before transition 4 has reestablished the regeneration capacity of the shrub population (transition 5). Sufficient rain produces a cover of ephemerals, which provide fuel for fire (transition 6). Fire or competition from grasses kills shrub seedlings (transition 7). (Redrawn after Westoby et al., 1989, p. 270. Copyright Society for Range Management. Reprinted by permission of Alliance Communications Group, a division of Allen Press.)

Box 6.2 Santa Rita Experimental Range (SRER)

The Santa Rita Experimental Range (SRER) is a rangeland research facility on the western alluvial fan of the Santa Rita Mountains in the Sonoran Desert, south of Tucson, Arizona (USA). Today the vegetation of the range consists of short trees, shrubs, cacti and other succulents, perennial grasses and other herbaceous species (McClaran, 2003). Established in 1903, the SRER is one of the oldest continuously operating facilities of its kind worldwide and the site of more than one hundred years of experiments and systematic observations. Important techniques of monitoring vegetation change, such as repeat photography and the line intercept transect method (Canfield, 1942), as well as key concepts in range ecology, such as nonequilibrium-based models of vegetation dynamics (Sayre, 2003), were developed or refined on the SRER. This strong contribution to our evolving understanding of ecosystem behavior is amply documented; by 1988 there were already more than 400 publications based on research carried out on the SRER (Medina, 1996). The century-long record of observations shows a steady increase of velvet mesquite (*Prosopis velutina*), four cycles of burroweed (*Isocoma tenuisecta*), one cholla cactus cycle, and both interannual and interdecadal changes in perennial grass composition and abundance (McClaran, 2003). Because of the unparalleled length and continuity of its record, the SRER provides ideal condi tions for evaluating theoretical concepts of long-term ecosystem change. Since the baseline descriptions from the early 1900s, the transformation of grasslands

Fig. 6.8 Repeat photography looking looking north into Rothrocks grama range (pasture 6 of SRER) (location marked on Landsat TM false color composite). Increasing abundance of mesquite in the grasslands (McClaran, 2003).

> **Box 6.2** (continued)
>
> ands into mesquite–grass savanna has been observed. The purposeful suppression of potential driving forces of this change – livestock grazing and fire – has not reversed this trend, which either (1) undermines the validity of the succession model; or (2) suggests that other processes (e.g., climate change) are at work. Whether this transformation represents a transition in the sense of the state-and-transition model, however, remains to be established and depends on the definition of both state and transition for this particular site.

Plant–herbivore interactions have been suggested as the main driving forces for such changes. Although tree abundance seems to oscillate about a central tendency, the environment is in a constant state of flux so that equilibrium conditions are never reached (Box 6.3)

(3) Stochastic models (e.g., Ellis and Swift, 1988; Holmgren et al., 2006) assume persistent nonequilibrium conditions with unpredictable changes determined mainly by abiotic variables, such as extreme climate events or fires. The variability and unpredictability of rainfall in drylands leads to a complete decoupling of herbivores and vegetation. Both herbivore numbers and vegetation condition are so strongly controlled by climatic pulses that interactions among them are negligible in comparison (Fig. 6.3).

> **Box 6.3** The Elephant Question in Tsavo
>
> Tsavo National Park, located in semiarid savanna zone of southeastern Kenya, was established in 1948 on just over 21,000 km^2 of land considered unsuitable for agricultural or pastoral use. As a result of increasing human pressure outside the park, most elephants of the area were confined within the park's boundaries by the late 1960s; this made it one of the largest concentrations of elephants in the world (Sheldrick, 1999a).
>
> As an ecosystem in which natural processes were allowed to evolve without human intervention, the park came to play a key role in the "elephant debate" – the question of how to best manage elephants. The impact of elephants on their habitat is often perceived as destructive; damage to woodland and scrubland appears catastrophic at first glance. Fears of losing biodiversity as a result of severe elephant overpopulation have frequently been used to justify large-scale elephant culling (Gillson and Lindsay 2002). Assumptions of a "natural balance" and a constant carrying capacity are implicit in this argument (e.g., Rensberger, 1973).

(continued)

Box 6.3 (continued)

While changes in thinking within the field of ecology have brought equilibrium assumptions into question on theoretical grounds, monitoring and scientific documentation of the trends of elephants and vegetation cover in Tsavo provide supporting "real world" evidence of an equilibrium. Despite the fears of vegetation loss as a result of elephants overpopulation of Tsavo did not irreversibly destroy their habitat or endanger the survival of other species (Sheldrick, 1999b). Rather, they came to be recognized as a keystone species in this semiarid environment, on which many other species depended. For example, they recycle nutrients and trace elements locked in wood, expose subsurface water by tunneling into dry watercourses with their trunks, bring browse to a lower level by breaking down branches, seal waterholes against seepage by their weight, and provide large amounts of dung.

The disturbance of vegetation caused by elephants is now considered a normal part of savanna ecology, which is characterized by natural cyclic changes between woodland and grassland as well as fluctuations in the abundance of different species. Thus, elephant populations in Tsavo were controlled naturally in 1970, when a severe drought triggered adjustments of birth rates and mass die-off of selected female age groups, creating generation gaps necessary to relieve pressure on the land and allow establishment of a new generation of trees. Paleoecological studies show that such changes have occurred many times during past centuries (Gillson, 2004).

The limited availability of data on long-term vegetation dynamics constrains the evaluation of these alternative paradigms and models. At present, empirical evidence of species replacement after grazing has been excluded and is used to distinguish between equilibrium and nonequilibrium patterns; that is, vegetation is examined to determine whether and after how much time fenced-off areas return to their pregrazing species composition. However, emphasis on vegetation species composition alone might be insufficient for evaluation, since plant species fluctuations could be a compensatory mechanism actually contributing to overall ecosystem stability (Briske et al., 2003; Schlesinger et al., 1990). Moreover, most ecosystems in semiarid regions exhibit both equilibrium and nonequilibrium characteristics, depending on spatial and temporal scale (Illius and O'Connor, 1999). Therefore, the appropriate question might not be whether equilibrium or nonequilibrium dynamics apply, but rather which dynamic applies in a given situation (Briske et al., 2003).

Although nonequilibrium views have become widely accepted among ecologists since the 1980s, equilibrium thinking persists both in other professional circles and in society at large, and "the balance of nature" remains an appealing notion (e.g., Pimm, 1991). Thus, when interviewed about preferences in environmental policies, more than half of the respondents from a group of professionals involved in science, policy and

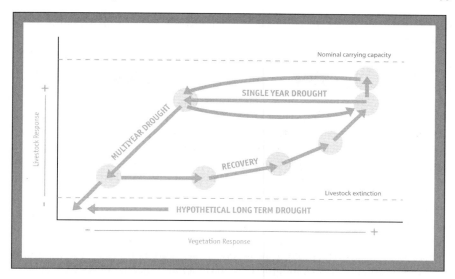

Fig. 6.3 Schematic representation of stochastic nonequilibrium model (example of Turkana, Kenya): Drought perturbations regulate livestock populations independent of livestock density. Single-year droughts affect livestock condition but do not cause livestock mortality. Multiyear droughts result in livestock mortality and reduction of reproductive rates. (Redrawn and simplified after Ellis and Swift, 1988. Copyright 1988 Society for Range Management. Reprinted by permission of Alliance Communications Group, a division of Allen Press.)

management fell back on a "balance of nature" argument at least once during their interview (Hull et al., 2002). It is unclear whether this reflects simple bureaucratic inertia and outdated training curricula or a basic failure to grasp the fundamental differences between these alternative models and their respective management implications.

6.2.2 Complex Systems Science

Advances in the ecological sciences, particularly our understanding of the mechanisms that govern equilibrium and nonequilibrium in ecosystems, are intertwined with developments in the somewhat fuzzily defined academic domain of complex systems science (von Bertalanffy, 1968). Unlike traditional branches of science, complex systems science is a worldview, or way of thinking, that cuts across disciplinary boundaries. Examples of complex systems – defined as any set of interdependent components – can be found in disciplines as diverse as climate (e.g., global circulation in the atmosphere and oceans), biology (e.g., anthills), economics (e.g., national economies), psychology (e.g., family relationships) and ecology (e.g., ecosystems). Though they appear to have little in common at first glance, these systems can all be viewed as networks and can be mathematically modeled (Heylighen and Joslyn, 2001).

The study of complex systems dates to the middle of the twentieth century, when systems ideas emerged simultaneously in research groups working independently on different problems and in different locations (Umpleby and Dent, 1999). The International Society for the Systems Sciences was founded in 1954 to encourage greater integration of disciplines through "development of theoretical systems which are applicable to more than one of the traditional departments of knowledge" (Bailey, 2005, p. 356). Ross Ashby's classic book on cybernetics (Ashby, 1956), an approach closely related to systems science, was published in the same year as *The Future of Arid Lands*. However, systems thinking was still in its infancy then and did not gain a firm foothold in general consciousness until the late 1960s and 1970s.

The essence of complex systems science lies in its holistic perspective: Rather than breaking a system down into a study of its individual components (analytic approach), systems scientists seek to understand the relations and interactions that connect these components into a whole (systemic approach) (Table 6.1). For dryland ecology, that means examining the interrelationships among soil, vegetation, herbivores, and climate along with decisions made by human managers (e.g., McNaughton, 1985). As in climate science, the systemic approach in ecology only became practicable with progress in computing power and numerical modeling.

Ecosystems ecology

The development of ecosystems ecology – the study of flows of energy and matter among organisms and the environment – has been greatly influenced and perhaps driven by complexity thinking. Interestingly, the ecosystems approach in ecology has encompassed both equilibrium and nonequilibrium thinking throughout its history. Thus, the early ecosystem concepts of Eugene Odum, the founder of ecosystems ecology in North America, refer to balanced systems structured by energy flows within clearly defined boundaries (Odum, 1959), but his later work acknowledges ecosystems as "thermodynamically open [and] far from equilibrium" (Odum, 1992, p. 542).

Contrary to earlier ecological approaches, which saw humans as separate from nature, the ecosystems approach in ecology explicitly integrates biotic, including human, and abiotic components. As such, it has been promoted as a scientific foundation for natural resource management by entities such as the Convention on Biological Diversity (CBD) (Hartje et al., 2003). The adoption of the ecosystem approach requires that resource management be based on an ecosystem unit rather than an administrative unit. An example is integrated watershed management (Chapter 7) as practiced for example by the OMVS (Senegal River Basin Organization) in the transboundary basin of the Senegal River since 1972 and by the Nile Basin Initiative since 1999 (Box 7.2). Global-scale and regional-scale environmental assessments now also prefer ecosystems as the basic unit of study. The most extensive of these is the Millennium Ecosystem

Table 6.1 Summary table comparing characteristics of analytic and systemic approaches in science (simplified after de Rosnay 1997)

Analytic Approach	Systemic Approach
• isolates and concentrates on the elements	• unifies and concentrates on the interaction between elements
• emphasizes the precision of details	• emphasizes global perception
• modifies one variable at a time	• modifies groups of variables simultaneously
• remains independent of duration of time; the phenomena considered are reversible.	• integrates duration of time and irreversibility
• validates facts by means of experimental proof within the body of a theory	• validates facts through comparison of the behavior of the model with reality
• efficient approach when interactions are linear and weak	• efficient approach when interactions are nonlinear and strong
• leads to discipline-oriented education	• leads to multidisciplinary education
• leads to action programmed in detail	• leads to action through objectives
• knowledge of details; poorly defined goals	• knowledge of goals; fuzzy details

Assessment (2001–2005), which assesses the current and projected ability of ecosystems to provide "goods and services" and focuses on both the consequences of ecosystem change for human well-being and on options for responding to those changes. It is anticipated that such integrated assessments will be repeated at regular 5–10 year intervals.

Although ecosystems ecology entered mainstream scientific thought relatively late (see, e.g., Eugene Odum's *Fundamentals of Ecology*, 1971), its beginnings can be found much earlier. Ecosystem-like concepts have been an important part of traditional ecological knowledge in a number of ancient and contemporary non-Western societies. For example, integrated floodplain management was practiced in the inland delta of the Niger River in the nineteenth century, with the exploitation of natural resources codified in the "Dina" of Peulh leader Sékou Amadou (Moorehead, 1989). Another example is the collective grazing reserve or "Hema" system in the Arab world (Draz, 1978). The understanding of nature underlying such traditional resource management systems is compatible with the emerging view of ecosystems in two ways: (1) geographical ("ecosystem") boundaries are used to define units of nature; and (2) within these units, abiotic components, plants, animals, and humans are considered to be interrelated (Berkes et al., 1998).

Biogeochemistry

Biogeochemistry is another research field in ecology that emerged from, and then developed concurrently with, complex system science. Originating in the 1920s, biogeochemistry has matured as a science only since the 1950s (Gorham, 1991). It involves the study of chemical, geological, and biological processes, particularly their cycling of nutrient elements (carbon, oxygen, hydrogen, sulfur, nitrogen, and phosphorus), within and among ecosystems. Global biogeochemical cycles play an important role in global environmental change, which has often been incorrectly considered to involve climate change alone. In reality, there is ample evidence of chemical changes, such as changing concentrations of biogenic gases, that precede climate change (Schlesinger, 1997). Thus, biogeochemistry has become a major field in the study of human impacts on the global environment (Schlesinger, 2004) and was identified as one of the "Great Challenges in Environmental Sciences" by the US National Research Council (NRC, 2001).

The biogeochemical topics that are relevant to drylands, and that have been studied extensively since the 1950s, include (1) patch-mosaic dynamics in dryland ecosystems; (2) the role of biological soil crust in soil conservation, redistribution of water resources and nutrient cycling; (3) local-scale and global-scale dust transport; and (4) changes in these processes over time.

With the exception of some grasslands, which appear relatively homogeneous, many dryland ecosystems are characterized by a great deal of spatial heterogeneity, expressed as a mosaic in which some patches function as sources and others as sinks (Safriel, 1999). According to this concept, source patches contribute water, soil, and minerals to sink patches, thereby augmenting productivity in the latter. The spatial distribution of sources and sinks is mostly determined by geomorphology, with rocky and compacted surfaces acting as sources because of their low infiltration, and vegetated patches, usually located in depressions, acting as sinks. These sinks constitute islands of fertility, with higher soil moisture and nutrient availability than the source patches (Schade and Hobbie, 2005). Through the generation of litter, soil organic matter, and protection from wind, vegetated source patches create favorable conditions for the germination of seeds, thus causing a positive feedback mechanism (Whitford, 2002). Patch dynamics have been found to contribute to ecological sustainability at a small scale, by redistributing and concentrating scarce resources (Safriel, 1999). The spatial heterogeneity is overlain by a marked temporal variability, as precipitation in drylands occurs in pulses, triggering pulses of plant production (Noy-Meir, 1973). Temporal dynamics also influence the distribution of sources and sinks; establishment of higher plants can turn source patches into sinks and removal of plants can turn sinks to sources.

Biological soil crusts, which are frequently found on source patches, are an important component of biogeochemical cycling in deserts. Rare in hyperarid deserts, they are very common in arid deserts and the drier parts of the semiarid drylands. Despite their widespread occurrence, their crucial role in the desert ecosystem has only been discovered in the last two decades (e.g., Belnap, 2003; Harper and Marble, 1988; Williams, 1994; Zaady, 2005). Biological soil crusts are composed of communities of nonvascular organisms, dominated by cyanobacteria, mosses, and lichens (Fig. 6.4) (West, 1990), which can tolerate high solar radiation, extreme temperatures, and dehydration. Forming a thin film on the soil surface, biological soil crusts create cohesion among soil particles and thus provide stability and resistance to wind erosion. Depending on soil and crust type, they improve water availability on sink patches by preventing infiltration on, and generating runoff from, source patches, thereby sustaining vegetation growth on the former.

Fig. 6.4 Close-up of seedling in biological soil crust (USGS Canyonlands Research Station, http://www.soilcrust.org/gallery.htm/)

In addition to their effects on soil stability and water regulation, biological soil crusts also play a major role in the nutrient cycle: cyanobacteria and lichens are photosynthetic organisms that fix carbon and nitrogen from the atmosphere and release them upon wetting (Belnap, 2003). As a result, rainfall pulses are accompanied by pulses of nutrient availability for vascular plants. Moreover, the presence of biological soil crusts decreases the reflectance of shortwave radiation, thus affecting the surface energy balance (Fig. 6.5).

Due to their sparse vegetation, drylands, and particularly deserts, are sources of aeolian dust – fine soil particles rich in minerals and nutrients as well as organic residues. Desert dust is dispersed by wind over short and long distances. Although dust received some attention in *The Future of Arid Lands* in connection with the 1930s Dust Bowl problem in the central USA, its biogeochemical role came to be acknowledged only later. On a local scale, nutrient-rich dust is trapped by biological soil crusts and higher vegetation, adding to the fertility of sink patches and depleting source patches. Offer et al. (1998) and Zaady et al. (2001) used dust collectors to measure the amount of aeolian deposition and its nitrogen content in the northern Negev Desert. They found that up to $100\,mg/m^2/year$ of nitrogen had been added to their study plots through dust deposition.

Much of the finest dust generated in deserts (particles of less than $2\,\mu m$ in diameter) travels great distances and thus affects biogeochemical processes in regions far away from its origin (Safriel et al., 2006). Dryfall of dust in downwind areas can be spectacular. Saharan dust has been found in Europe, North and

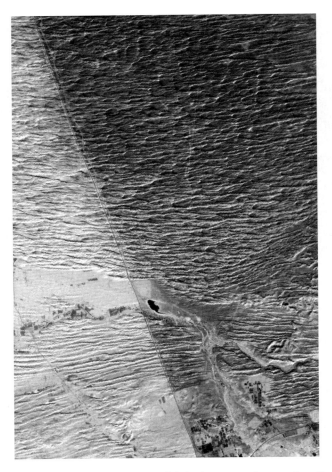

Fig. 6.5 Biological soil crusts in the Negev and their absence on the more heavily grazed Sinai Peninsula make for a sharp contrast in reflectance between the two sides of the Negev–Sinai border as observed from SPOT (Courtesy Arnon Karnieli)

Central America, and the Amazon basin; Asian dust has been found in the Pacific islands and North America. Dust adds nutrients to the marine and terrestrial ecosystems in which it is deposited, enhancing phytoplankton production in nutrient-poor oceans (Jickells et al., 2005) and replenishing nutrient pools in terrestrial ecosystems (Okin et al., 2004). Potential negative effects of dust deposition include the decline of Caribbean coral reefs, to which Saharan and Sahelian dust might have significantly contributed (Shinn et al., 2000). Human health concerns arise when desert dust is enriched with toxic pollutants, such as in the case of the Aral Sea (see Box 3.1) or in eastern Asia and the Pacific, where dust originating from Central Asia and Inner Mongolia is mixed with air pollutants from the industrialized eastern Chinese urban centers.

Dust loading in the atmosphere is thought to influence global climate by affecting radiation balance and rainfall. Satellite remote sensing has contributed considerably to our understanding of large-scale dust–climate interactions; however, the exact mechanisms involved remain controversial, as atmospheric dust modifies both incoming shortwave solar radiation and outgoing longwave radiation (Nicholson, 2001) and can potentially either increase (Yin et al., 2000) or suppress rainfall (Rosenfeld et al., 2001). Long-term surface concentration measurements in Barbados and satellite imagery suggest the intensification of dust emissions from the Sahel region and of their transport across the Atlantic (Moulin and Chiapello, 2006). In contrast to other recent studies which argue that less than 10% of the dust is man-made (Tegen et al. 2004), Moulin and Chiapello (2006) attribute much of this increase to anthropogenic impacts (i.e., human-induced soil degradation).

Biogeochemical issues have also been raised in connection with land cover changes, particularly desertification. Otterman (1974) and Charney et al. (1975) were among the first to propose the idea that modification of land cover characteristics in drylands might affect regional climate by way of positive feedback mechanisms among plant cover, albedo, and precipitation. Their hypothesis – that decrease in plant cover leads to atmospheric subsidence and desiccation via increasing albedo – has been refined by more recent work, which has benefited from advances in remote sensing and numerical modeling and has shown that relationships are more complex than at first assumed (Ba et al., 2001; Hulme, 2001; Schlesinger et al., 1990; Williams and Balling, 1996). For example, if semiarid grassland is transformed into shrubland or bare ground as a result of desertification, albedo might increase; but soil surface and air temperatures would increase as a result of reduced transpiration, and not decrease, as would be expected from the increase in albedo alone. Hot, dry soils enhance nitrogen volatilization and consequently reinforce the spread of shrubland (Schlesinger et al., 1990). With increased spatial heterogeneity of vegetation cover, below-ground resources such as organic matter and nutrients tend to concentrate, reinforcing patchiness (Asner et al., 2004).

6.2.3 Panarchy

The concept of "panarchy" emerged in the early 2000s as an extension of thinking that developed in the 1970s about change in complex adaptive systems – systems that are constantly adapting to and coevolving with their environment and are characterized by a high degree of connectivity and feedback among their components (Allison and Hobbs, 2004). This concept has been used to identify and explain structures, patterns and causes of change in ecological systems (e.g., Box 6.3); however, its primary applications to date have been interdisciplinary, integrating ecological, economic, and social systems across a range of scales (Holling, 2001; Gunderson and Holling, 2002).

The adaptive cycle, a heuristic model for understanding the process of change in complex adaptive systems, describes continuous change through four phases in an eco-

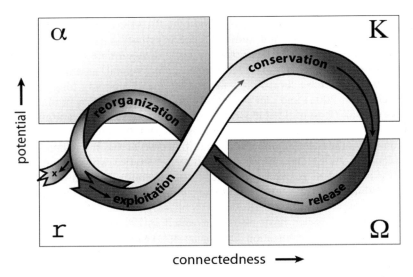

Fig. 6.6 A stylized representation of the four phases of the adaptive cycle. (Gunderson and Holling, 2002)

system (Fig. 6.6). In the traditional view of ecosystem succession, only the exploitation or *r* phase (i.e., the rapid colonization of a disturbed area), and the conservation or *K* phase (i.e., slow accumulation and storage of energy and material) were considered. In the adaptive cycle, they are usually referred to together as the "foreloop". The adaptive cycle adds two more phases referred to as the backloop: the release or Ω phase (i.e., the release of accumulated biomass and nutrients by drought, fire, or grazing) and the subsequent reorganization or α phase (i.e., the appearance and expansion of pioneer species that capture opportunity). The α phase prepares the site ground for exploitation by other, more permanent, species, as the cycle begins again (Holling and Gunderson, 2002). Although elaborated for an ecosystem in this context, these four phases can also be applied to social and economic systems.

Each phase displays characteristic levels of three system properties: potential, connectedness, and resilience. The potential available for change is high during the reorganization phase, with rapid exploitation of available resources (e.g., nutrients in biological systems; capital in economic systems), and also during the conservation phase when resources are most fully concentrated. The degree of connectedness among elements of a system, which defines its sensitivity to external influences, is high in the conservation and release phases. That is, these phases are characterized by high internal control, which mediates the influence of external variability. By contrast, connectedness is low in the reorganization and exploitation phases, which are highly affected by external variability (Holling and Gunderson, 2002). Resilience is not seen as a fixed system property but as a quantity that expands and contracts as the adaptive cycle moves through the four phases. The comparatively high resilience characteristic of the reorganization and exploitation phases, when connectedness is low, is a condition that facilitates creative experimentation without jeopardizing the integrity of the system as a whole. Change and stability of a system are brought about by the interactions between the slow and the fast variables, in which the slow variables (e.g., accumulated resources) set the conditions for the faster variables (e.g., forest fire) to operate; fast variables may affect or periodically change slow variables.

The adaptive cycle has provided a framework for the study of socioecological systems, such as the Western Australian agricultural region (Allison and Hobbs, 2004) and the interplay between environmental problems and famines in different parts of the world (Fraser, 2006), and has served as a basis for sustainable natural resource management in socioecological systems (Turner et al., 2003; Walker, 2005; Walker et al., 2002). Desertification, as a complex socioecological problem affecting drylands, lends itself particularly well to a panarchy approach of analysis.

To date, there are very few examples of practical applications of the panarchy concept. One of them is the "Dahlem Desertification Paradigm" (Reynolds and Smith, 2002), which attempts to integrate elements of the panarchy concept, resilience theory, and adaptive cycles into a new interdisciplinary framework for assessing desertification. The framework focuses on interrelationships among biophysical and socioeconomic factors at multiple scales, which determine the dynamics of degradation and recovery. Its main points are summarized in nine assertions (Table 6.2).

Table 6.2 The nine assertions of the Dahlem Desertification Paradigm and some of their implications for management. (Reynolds et al. 2003, p. 2045)

Assertion	Implication
Assertion 1. Desertification always involves human and environmental drivers	Always expect to include both socioeconomic and biophysical variables in any monitoring or intervention scheme.
Assertion 2. Slow variables are critical determinants of systems dynamics	Identify and manage for the small set of 'slow' variables that drive the 'fast' ecological goods and services that matter at any given scale.
Assertion 3. Thresholds are crucial, and may change over time	Identify thresholds in the change variables at which there are significant increases in the costs of recovery, and quantify these costs, seeking ways to manage the thresholds to increase resilience.
Assertion 4. The costs of intervention rises nonlinearly with increasing degradation	Intervene early where possible, and invest to reduce the transaction costs of increasing scales of intervention.
Assertion 5. Desertification is a regionally emergent property of local degradation	Take care to define precisely the spatial and temporal extent of and processes resulting in any given measure of local degradation. But do not try to probe desertification beyond a measure of generalized impact at higher scales.
Assertion 6. Coupled human–environment systems change over time	Understand and manage the circumstances in which the human and environmental subsystems become 'decoupled'.
Assertion 7. The development of appropriate local environmental knowledge must be accelerated	Create better partnerships between local environmental knowledge development and conventional scientific research, employing good experimental design, effective adaptive feedback and monitoring.

(continued)

Table 6.2 (continued)

Assertion	Implication
Assertion 8. Systems are hierarchically nested	Recognize and manage the fact that changes at one level affect others; create flexible but linked institutions across the hierarchical levels, and ensure processes are managed through scale-matched institutions.
Assertion 9. A limited suite of processes and variables at any scale makes the problem tractable	Analyze the types of syndromes at different scales, and seek the investment levers which will best control their effects – awareness and regulation where the drivers are natural, changed policy and institutions where the drivers are social.

Since its development and initiation at the 88th Dahlem Workshop[1], the Dahlem Desertification Paradigm has grown into an ongoing initiative, the AridNet research network (http://www.biology.duke.edu/aridnet/), which aims to support the theoretical framework embodied in the paradigm with concrete regional case studies. A first series of workshops building on the paradigm has been conducted in Central and South America, bringing together ecologists and social scientists as well as local stakeholders (Huber-Sannwald et al., 2006). Further case studies on similar grounds are planned in the Asian–Australian and the European–African regions.

Apart from this attempt to bring together scientific theory and practical field-level application in the context of the Dahlem Desertification Paradigm, the panarchy concept has so far remained a largely theoretical construct that still requires much more empirical testing, particularly because of its broad scope. However, it has proven a useful tool for stimulating debate about nonlinear, complex systems and their interactions.

The science of ecology was not explicitly addressed in *The Future of Arid Lands*. However, equilibrium thinking – the assumption of an ecological balance – was implicit throughout the book and provided a guiding principle framework for designing and implementing land management interventions. Systems thinking, which only emerged in the 1950s and was not a topic in *The Future of Arid Lands*, has since then provided the most important drive in the evolution of the ecological sciences. The practical implications of the systems approach for the management of dryland ecosystems, however, are only beginning to be taken up by land managers and policymakers today, and the complexity inherent in systems thinking remains a fundamental challenge to its translation into applicable principles and concepts.

---

[1] Eighty-eighth Dahlem workshop, "An integrated assessment of the ecological, meteorological and human dimensions of global desertification"; Berlin, June 10–17, 2001

Chapter 7
Land Use and Management

Putting the drylands to productive use has proved to be a persistent challenge. Low rainfall amounts ensure that, generally, returns will be modest from most agricultural uses. Extreme interannual variability of rainfall presents a diabolical trap, which means that ventures aimed at maximizing agricultural returns tend to be short-lived and can lead to a degradation of the land resource.

Growing concern about land degradation and the depletion of natural resources has spurred increased interest in the ways humans live in and with drylands over the last 50 years. Land use and management options in drylands have evolved in conjunction with developments in climatology, plant sciences, and our understanding of ecological processes. They are furthermore determined by the economic value associated with the land and its natural resources; in drylands, this value has always been inextricably linked to water availability.

Agricultural uses – ranging from grazing to rainfed and irrigated agriculture, depending on water availability – were the only land use options considered in the 1950s, but a much broader range of land use alternatives has since emerged. In many drylands, priorities are shifting from exclusive livestock or crop production to mixed agricultural systems and various non-agricultural land uses.

This development is, in part, a result of the increasing importance attributed to environmental, social, and aesthetic values, as well as the pressures exerted on, and opportunities offered to, drylands by various aspects of globalization.

7.1 The Situation in the 1950s

Problems pertaining to land use and management in drylands were addressed in the Section "Better Use of Present Resources" in *The Future of Arid Lands*. The discussions of these problems were guided by the following questions:

- What are the possibilities of increasing and maintaining sustained production from grass and forest lands without accelerating erosion?
- What are the consequences of utilizing arid lands beyond their capabilities?
- Can irrigated lands be occupied permanently? (White, 1956, p. 177)

C. F. Hutchinson and S. M. Herrmann, *The Future of Arid Lands – Revisited.*
© Springer 2008

Although the need to withdraw some arid lands from agricultural production was already recognized in the 1950s (e.g., Whaley, 1952), few land use options other than agriculture were taken into consideration in *The Future of Arid Lands*. Instead, two themes dominated the discussions of land use and management strategies in the book: (1) optimizing resource use, ultimately with the aim of increasing food production for a growing population; and (2) concerns about overuse of dryland resources, resulting in their degradation.

7.1.1   Drylands As A Source of Food: The Malthusian Argument

Much of the reasoning in *The Future of Arid Lands* was dominated by Malthusian thought (Fig. 7.1). Meeting the food demands of a rapidly growing global human population by increasing agricultural output was a major concern (Sain, 1956, p. 252):

> One of the chief maladies of present day agriculture has been that in many countries the area under the plow has been decreasing instead of increasing owing to greater demand on land from other quarters like expansion of cities, highways, canal systems, industries, and other matters of defense or strategic importance. The world stands in great need of an increase in crop acreage…. This can be done by reclamation of arid waste, marginal and saline lands.

Drylands seemed to offer a vast potential for agricultural expansion, if only water resources could be provided, and the right technology and management strategies applied, to make them productive. As Kellogg stated (1956, p. 40), "…[O]ur soils are not yet used under anything like optimum sustained production. In other words, the potentialities of the arid lands of the world are very much higher indeed than our present realization."

Plans for exploiting this potential and bringing drylands under cultivation – with or without irrigation – sprang up not only in the southwestern USA, but also in the Soviet Union, where the agricultural sector had been severely neglected for

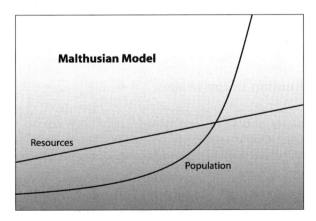

Fig. 7.1 Diagram of Thomas Malthus' prediction that unchecked population growth would eventually surpass agricultural production, leading to dwindling food supply per person. (Malthus, 1798)

the sake of developing the industrial complex (Box 7.1). In Israel, the conquest of the Negev desert by agricultural settlement became a declared aim of the Zionist enterprise following its occupation by Israeli troops in 1948–1949. In 1956, desert ecologist Michael Evenari and his team began reconstructing an ancient Nabatean runoff farming system, with its terraces and channels, in the northern Negev; this became the experimental farm Avdat (Evenari, 1987; Evenari et al., 1982).

While cropland – and irrigated cropland in particular – was considered of highest value, other uses were to be promoted where drylands were unsuitable for cultivation. Water availability determined how far a particular parcel of land could be moved up a value chain ranging from wasteland, to forestry, to grazing, to rainfed agriculture, to irrigated agriculture – all treated as discrete, unconnected activities at the time. Little, if any, consideration was given to land use for urbanization, open space, conservation,

---

Box 7.1 The Virgin Lands Programme in The Soviet Union

In the face of a worsening agricultural crisis in the Soviet Union, First Secretary Nikita Khrushchev placed great hopes on the exploitation of seemingly unused drylands as potential breadbaskets (Wright, 1954). In 1954, he launched his "Virgin Lands Programme" (*tselina*), an agricultural scheme to convert vast tracts of semiarid steppe in northern Kazakhstan and western Siberia into cropland. These "virgin lands" (in fact a misnomer, since most of them had already been used as pasturelands) were put under the plough at an unparalleled intensity and scale. By the end of 1954, 17.6 million ha had been converted to croplands; a total of 30 million ha was reached by the end of 1955, of which 20 million were cultivated (Durgin, 1962). Thousands of highly mechanized state farms and several hundred new rural settlements were hastily constructed to accommodate about 650,000 settlers, who immigrated to these lands in the first two years of the program (Zonn et al., 1994).

Dry farming was extended to the 150 mm isohyet [sic] (Kovda, 1961), where climate and soils are marginal at best for rainfed agriculture. Indeed, droughts in Kazakhstan led to a near disaster in 1955. Overall Soviet grain production that year was only maintained thanks to favorable weather conditions and excellent harvests in Ukraine and Moldavia. The 1956 harvest, by contrast, was the largest in Soviet history up to that point, with half of the 127 million t of grain produced coming from the virgin lands (Durgin, 1962).

During its first two years, the Virgin Lands Programme recorded both positive and negative impacts. Grain production sharply increased, but soil degradation processes, notably wind erosion on the sandy lands cleared of their natural vegetation, were already being noted (Zonn et al., 1994). In the long run, yields could not be sustained for a number of reasons: natural rainfall variability made rainfed agriculture a risky enterprise, the wheat monoculture drained soils of their nutrients, and problems of logistics and manpower recruitment only increased the difficulties encountered.

(continued)

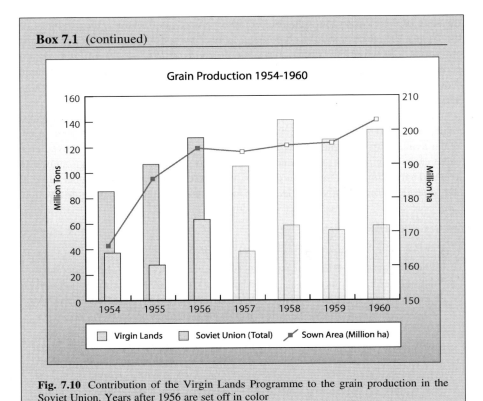

Box 7.1 (continued)

Fig. 7.10 Contribution of the Virgin Lands Programme to the grain production in the Soviet Union. Years after 1956 are set off in color

recreation, or other environmental goods and services. Woodlands and shrublands, although an important component of traditional livelihood systems in drylands (as sources for food, medicines, fiber, fuel, etc.), were considered to have little economic potential unless they were converted to higher-value uses (Price, 1956).

The great value attributed to agricultural uses in drylands in *The Future of Arid Lands* can partly be explained by Whyte's (1956, p. 188) postulation that "... [W]e have to accept the fact that peoples are living in these areas and have to produce their own requirements locally." While this assumption might have been true a few decades before *The Future of Arid Lands* appeared, improved transportation mechanisms rendered it partially obsolete, especially in the developed world, even as early as 1956. Only Koenig (1956, p. 328) questioned the appropriateness of using water resources to convert drylands into croplands, stating that "...[T]he use of irrigation in the arid lands of the twentieth century is not an appropriate use of that valuable resource, water, but it is an attempt to follow a historical precedent and increase the value of the land."

Concerns about "underutilization" of drylands – using lands at less than their highest economic value – also account in part for the low appreciation of pastoralist land use expressed in the book. The other factor contributing to this underappreciation was that pastoralists were considered to be responsible for overgrazing and land degradation – a concern that prevailed in the 1950s and was best captured in Hardin's *Tragedy of the Commons* a decade later (Hardin, 1968). Cultivation of fodder crops was a land use generally preferred over pastoralism (Whyte, 1956).

7.1.2   Concerns about "Overuse"

While most attention was paid to promoting increases in agricultural production, Sain (1956, p. 250) also voiced concerns about the "overuse" of dryland resources, pointing out that "[M]an has not used the resources properly; in his ruthless exploitation of land and water resources, man has violated the basic arrangements in a manner that upsets the fruitful balance which created and maintained the land and water resources."

These concerns referred primarily not only to the degradation of pastureland by overgrazing, but also to erosion and salinization in croplands. In particular, traditional grazing systems in the developing world were criticized for their tendency to overstock, leading to deterioration of the vegetation cover and desertification (Draz, 1956, p. 331):

> Continuous overstocking of arid or semi-arid zones has greatly reduced their productivity. Through ages of misuse, man has in the most unwise way exploited millions of acres by extensive and uncontrolled grazing. This has caused denudation of plant cover, which, hand in hand with erosion, produced aridity and in many cases man-made deserts.

Based on an equilibrium understanding of vegetation dynamics (Chapter 6), large surveying and mapping campaigns of natural vegetation and its livestock carrying capacity were under way, for example in India, where Indian Council of Agricultural Research was studying existing grass vegetation in relation to climax types (Whyte, 1956). The authors of *The Future of Arid Lands* recommended a modern range of management techniques, including the removal of undesirable vegetation, range reseeding, and the cultivation of fodder crops, in conjunction with reductions of stocking rates.

Soil erosion had become a widespread phenomenon in the semiarid dry farming region of the US Great Plains, where high rainfall variability made crop cultivation a risky enterprise. Droughts repeatedly caused crop failures and led to accelerated erosion of barely vegetated fields (Fig. 7.2). According to Shantz (1956, p. 19): "[T]he beginning of dry farming was greatly influenced by false conceptions and by propaganda. The most common misperception was perhaps the belief that 'rain follows the plow'", which had tempted many homesteaders to move into the Great Plains during a few favorable years (Box 2.1). This belief was strongly promoted by the railroads, which profited from the movement of new settlers into the region.

The risk of salt accumulation in the soil caused by restricted soil drainage or the use of saline irrigation water was well recognized in the 1950s and was considered the main challenge to irrigated agriculture in drylands (USDA, 1954). Both Richards (1956) and Hayward (1956) emphasized drainage and leaching

Fig. 7.2 Severely eroded farmland during the Dust Bowl era (rill/gully erosion and deflation), the most dramatic example of soil erosion in US history. (Photo courtesy of USDA Natural Resources Conservation Service)

requirements to avoid salt accumulation in the soil. However, there was no discussion in *The Future of Arid Lands* about the disposal of drainage water from agricultural fields, and no mention of the environmental implications of attempts to manage it. Where the management of salt accumulation in irrigation schemes had failed in the past, there was general optimism about the prospects of reclaiming these salinized lands and bringing them back into production in the future.

In the face of increasing evidence of "overuse" in the USA, Luker (1956, p. 226) advocated "'using the land within its capability'... [by].... recognizing the physical limitations affecting each acre of land and being guided by those factors into the kind or kinds of use for which the land is best suited, and under which it can produce most efficiently on a sustainable basis". He failed to make explicit the assumption that, for any plot of land, there was an ideal land use that could be identified based on physical conditions alone.

7.2 The Situation Today

While the appropriate use and management of drylands is as relevant now as it was in the 1950s, several developments have changed our perspective on what "appropriate land use and management" means. First are the advances in basic research, especially in the climate and ecological sciences, which have modified our understanding of long-term sustainability. Second is a process of accelerated economic, technological, and political globalization since the 1950s which has created both challenges and opportunities for drylands, by opening up new alternatives for land use other than agriculture. Third, the last few decades have brought increased awareness of the environmental, social, and aesthetic values that shape our perspectives about what is possible and what is desirable. These changes are embodied in a growing number of multilateral environmental agreements and have affected management decisions. Finally, indigenous knowledge and traditional land use systems, which were formerly ignored or actively denigrated, have gained greater recognition as viable options among scientists as well as policymakers (Chapter 8).

As a result, a more integrated and more global perspective on land use and management has emerged, which considers multiple land use alternatives for drylands. Current research questions about these alternatives can be summarized as follows:

- How can our improved understanding of the dryland environment be translated into better management?
- What land use options are economically viable and ecologically sustainable for drylands in a global economy?
- How do management requirements differ for various dryland regions (with different economic, social, and cultural conditions) within the developing and the developed worlds?
- How can indigenous knowledge and traditional land use systems be integrated into modern sustainable land management?

7.2.1 Multiple Land Use Alternatives

While several of the authors of *The Future of Arid Lands* briefly mentioned the prospects of wind and solar energy production in drylands (e.g., Dickson, 1956; Kellogg, 1956), they did not discuss land use alternatives other than agriculture in any detail. This shortcoming did not go unnoticed. In his review of the book the year after it was published, Logan (1957, p. 282) bordered on the prophetic in his comments regarding the types of land uses that drylands could support:

> With the march of modern technology, the whole future potential of arid areas is being rapidly altered. In this symposium, the effect of the harnessing of solar radiation is discussed briefly as a factor in the desalinization of sea water, but its tremendous range of possibilities as a power source for industry in these sun-drenched climes goes unconsidered. Nor is there mention of the increasing aesthetic appreciation of the desert, with resultant tourist developments whose monetary value bids fair to outstrip that of desert agriculture, and whose inspirational and relaxational values to a harried urban civilization are quite beyond the measure. The urbanization and industrialization of some desert areas is inevitable, and will change drastically the influences of many of the factors considered in this book.

At the beginning of the twenty-first century, not only are multiple alternatives beyond agricultural land use – such as urban development, recreation and tourism, and energy production – being considered for drylands but also the perspectives on agricultural land uses themselves have evolved significantly. Moreover, for many dryland regions, different land uses are no longer seen as mutually exclusive, but as different elements in one integrated land use system (see also Section 7.2.2).

Agriculture

Contrary to the expectations expressed in *The Future of Arid Lands*, global agricultural area has expanded insignificantly since the 1950s. A process of agricultural intensification, including irrigation of previously nonirrigated lands (often drylands) has made possible a steady increase in world food production, which – contrary to Malthus' predictions – has kept up with global population growth (Fig. 7.3). Technological innovations such as center pivot and drip irrigation systems have transformed commercial dryland agriculture since the 1950s.

Writing in *Scientific American*, Splinter (1976, p. 90) asserted that center pivot irrigation was "the most significant mechanical innovation in agriculture since … the tractor". By using overhead sprinklers carried on a wheeled boom, it was possible to cultivate rolling and sandy lands previously unsuited for irrigation, such as arid and hyperarid drylands in Saudi Arabia, North Africa, and North America. Sprinklers also required far less labor than basin or furrow irrigation, were more water efficient, transportable, and allowed the application of fertilizers directly along with irrigation waters.

Drip irrigation minimizes water consumption by applying precise amounts of water directly to the root zone of individual plants through a network of pipes,

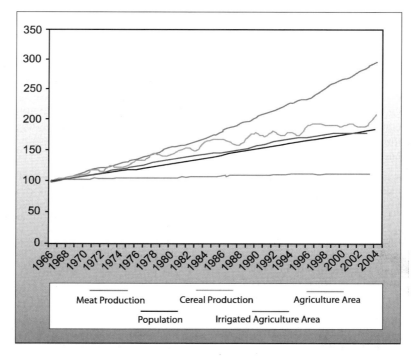

Fig. 7.3 Population, agricultural area and global food production indices (1966 = 100) (FAOSTATS)

valves, and emitters. Water engineers in Israel developed the first commercial surface drip irrigation emitters in the late 1950s (Blass, 1973). Within a decade, this successful method spread to Australia and the Americas.

Along with the development of these new technologies, international trade has risen considerably (Rosegrant et al., 2001), which eases the pressure on drylands to grow their own food. Importing "virtual water" in the form of agricultural products from water-rich countries has become a viable alternative for water-scarce dryland countries to meet market demand (Allan, 2003; Vörösmarty, 2000; Chapter 3).

Meeting market demand, however, does not necessarily assure food security (Sen, 1981). Indeed, food insecurity persists in many of the drylands of the developing world, not because of food scarcity on the market, but because of the limited purchasing power of the poor, who rely on subsistence agriculture and thus are directly affected by the boom-and-bust dynamics caused by rainfall variability (Chapter 2). Expansion of the area under cultivation has not resolved food shortage problems for them and has led to unintended environmental changes in some places, such as the Aral Sea basin (Box 3.1) or the Sahel (Glantz, 1994).

With the realization that the large-scale, top-down approach of the Green Revolution has not produced the desired results in most drylands outside southern Asia (Chapter 5), current trends in land use and management have emphasized bottom-up approaches and support for smallholders. Agrosilvopastoralism, which has emerged as a new conservation and development paradigm for drylands, is rooted – in part – in traditional management approaches built on multiple production strategies. Because of erratic rainfall patterns and wide fluctuations in yield, mixed systems combining forestry, cultivation, and livestock keeping are often the most sustainable land use option (Stroosnijder and van Reenen, 2001). At the same time, these traditional land use systems employ practices that conserve resources and maintain ecosystem processes (Brookfield et al., 2003). Forestry plays an important role in maintaining the soil and water resources necessary for cultivation. Moreover, it yields fuelwood, food products, and fodder reserves. Cultivation and pastoralism are spatially overlapping but seasonally discrete livelihood and land use which practices are traditionally governed by complex rights and regulations. In the Sahel, farmers' land may be used during the dry season by pastoralists, whose animals feed on harvest residues and at the same time fertilize the fields (Reynaut and Lavigne Delville, 1997; Fig. 7.4).

The increased support of smallholder agriculture since the 1990s has been accompanied by systematic research into farmers' traditional knowledge, which has been recognized as highly adapted to their environment (Reij and Waters-Bayer, 2001; Stroosnijder and van Reenen, 2001). Research methods focusing on the land use priorities of individual households and village communities, such as participatory rural appraisal and focus group discussions, took off in the 1980s (e.g., Richards, 1985; Chambers et al., 1989) and have since become more and more widely used in research and extension. Innovation in response to increasing resource-use pressures was found to be a common phenomenon among small-scale farmers (Reij and Waters-Bayer, 2001). Farmers in Burkina Faso, for example, invested in the rehabilitation of degraded lands by improving technologies in areas

Fig. 7.4 Mixed agriculture in Burkina Faso in 2002 (Courtesy Grey Tappan, USGS, EROS Data Center)

such as soil and water conservation, soil fertility management and agroforestry (Box 9.1, Chapter 9).

Longitudinal studies of agricultural systems over several decades have yielded increasing evidence that resources can actually be enhanced by management, rather than necessarily being degraded under human use. In keeping with Boserup's land-mark work in *The Conditions of Agricultural Growth* (1965), Tiffen et al. (1994), Mortimore et al. (2000) and Reij and Steeds (2003) have observed that agricultural intensification has been accompanied by land rehabilitation in various African dry-lands previously characterized as hotspots of land degradation. These findings contradict the prevailing conventional wisdom that population growth was a major factor in resource overuse and degradation; instead, they suggest that increasing population provided the labor necessary for agricultural intensification.

In stark contrast to the mixed agricultural systems of subsistence farmers in the drylands in the developing world, highly specialized, commercial agricultural operations have dominated in many developed drylands. What *The Future of Arid Lands* did not foresee was the expansion of controlled environment agriculture in drylands. This combination of horticultural and engineering techniques ranges from simply covering individual rows of crops with semitransparent materials for part of the growing season to building highly automated, fully environmentally controlled greenhouses. The latter exploit the high light incidence and warm temperatures of drylands in winter, while otherwise insulating crops from the natural environment by using artificial substrate, nutrient supply, ventilation and cooling, and irrigation water (MA, 2006). Because of the substantial investment required, greenhouse agriculture is only suitable for the production of high-value cash crops in capital-rich dryland countries. Thus, it is primarily used in areas such as the Negev desert in Israel (Portnov and Safriel, 2004), the southwestern USA and northwestern Mexico (e.g., Steta, 2004). Another example is the eastern Almeria region of Andalucia, Spain, where only low-water-use crops were grown up until the 1950s. Investment in irrigation since then, together with a steady expansion of area under plastic since the 1970s, have totally transformed land use in the region (Baldock et al., 2000; Figs. 7.5a, 7.5b, 7.5c, 7.6a and 7.6b). While controlled environments have been commended as a land use alternative that does not induce large-scale land degradation (MA, 2006), they can have potentially severe impacts on their immediate environment, such as pollution from high levels of chemical input. Moreover, the aesthetic aspects of a landscape under plastic are a concern.

Urbanization

Given the limited agricultural potential of drylands and the adverse environmental impacts associated with some forms of dryland agriculture, urban development presents a logical land use alternative for drylands (e.g., Portnov and Hare, 1999; Portnov and Safriel, 2004). Moreover, the localized occurrence of resources, particularly water, in drylands favors concentrated over dispersed types of land use.

Only 2% of the land area in drylands is currently classified as urban (MA, 2006); however, these urban centers concentrate a significant portion of economic and

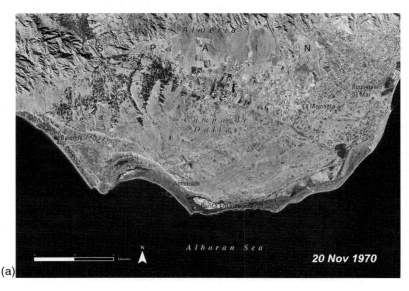

Figs. 7.5a,b, and c Greenhouses in Campo de Dalias, Almeria Province, Spain, 1970–2004. (a) 1970; (b) 1987; (c) 2004 (UNEP/GRID Sioux Falls)

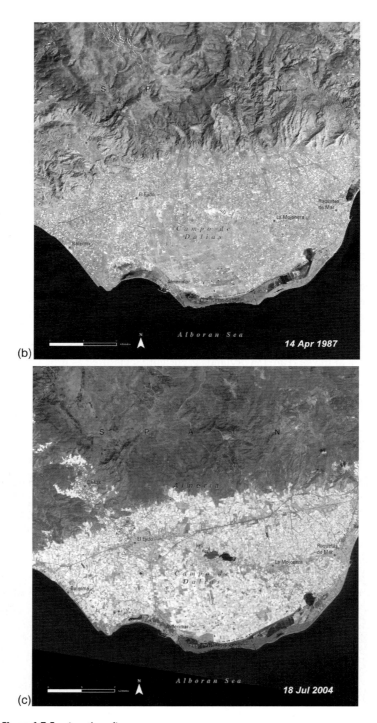

(b)

(c)

Figs. 7.5b, and 7.5c (continued)

Agricultural Land Use in Campo de Dalias, Almeria

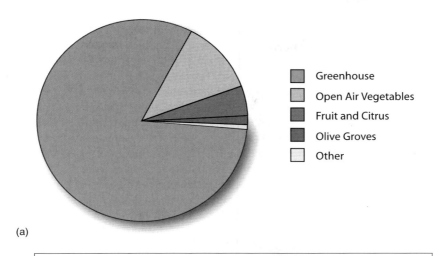

(a)

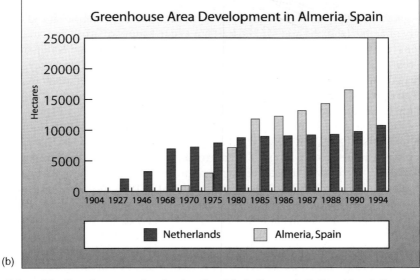

(b)

Figs. 7.6a and b Greenhouse area has developed rapidly in Campo de Dalias, Almeria Province, Spain. (a) Currently, greenhouses represent by far the major agricultural land use in the Campo de Dalias area. (b) The land area devoted to greenhouses in Almeria Province overall surpassed the greenhouse area in the Netherlands by the mid-1980s

development opportunities for the drylands population. Improvements in infra-structure and technology for groundwater extraction, unanticipated in the 1950s, have since fueled enormous urban growth in drylands. The population of Phoenix, Arizona (USA), for example, has grown six-fold in 50 years, reaching 3 million in

2000 (Baker et al., 2004). High urban growth rates have also been recorded in many African drylands (Park and Baro, 2003) and in the Middle East. The population of Riyadh, Saudi Arabia, for example, has increased more than seven-fold during the last three decades, reaching over four million inhabitants in 2005, and is expected to exceed ten million by the year 2020 (Herrmann et al., 2006).

Drylands offer two advantages for urbanization over more humid areas: lower land prices and a climate conducive to energy saving. Depending on building material, architecture and urban planning, dryland cities can be designed to maximally exploit the high insolation for solar energy generation (Faiman, 1998) and the low humidity for passive climate control (i.e., evaporative cooling), thus reducing fossil fuel consumption (MA, 2006). True, rising urban water demand can be offset only partially by water-sensitive urban design. On the other hand, higher economic value can be achieved per unit water from municipal and industrial land use than from agricultural land use. In recent years, this reasoning has been used to justify water transfers from agricultural to urban consumers in an ongoing confrontation between southern California's growing coastal cities and the agriculturally important Imperial Valley of the adjacent desert (Chapter 3). Moreover, urban areas also provide both a market for, and a constant and reliable and source of, water and organic matter – in the form of sewage – that can be treated and then used for high-value vegetable production. For example, given its high rate of urbanization and the scarcity of arable land, the arid Middle East has a long history of urban agriculture, with some of its water demand met by wastewater recycling (Nasr and Kaldjian, 1997). Urban agriculture is also an important component of household economy, particularly for the urban poor, in African cities. The continual output of urban wastewater even during droughts, when the migration from rural to urban areas is particularly high, can contribute significantly to food security (Bruins, 1997; Chapter 3).

Although dryland urbanization seems a profitable land use option from an economic perspective, if it is not carefully and appropriately planned, its ecological impacts can be severe, ranging from groundwater overdraft to urban heat island effects to increasing nitrate concentrations in soil and water. A Long-Term Ecological Research (LTER) site was established in 1997 for the Central Arizona–Phoenix (CAP) area, one of only two such urban-focused sites in the LTER network (http://www.lternet.edu/). CAP-LTER researchers study the ecological changes and environmental risks associated with urban sprawl in a dryland environment, hence preparing the ground for more rational city planning (Baker et al., 2004). Projects carried out at CAP-LTER have found that biogeochemical cycling in the urban ecosystem differs significantly from that in unaltered ecosystems, resulting from human-induced changes in hydrology (construction of impervious surfaces, import of water, drainage), atmospheric chemistry (higher concentrations of carbon, nitrogen, aerosols, metals, and ozone), climate (higher air temperatures), and nutrient sources (import of fertilizer and food) (Kaye et al., 2006).

Another underappreciated advantage of desert urbanization is that it may reduce population pressure and land use competition in more favorable agricultural areas. Portnov and Safriel (2004) considered urbanization and agricultural expansion as two alternative land use strategies for the Negev Desert and came to the conclusion that compact urban development there minimized anthropogenic impacts on the desert environment while slowing urban sprawl in central Israel. Because of its rather small extent, good infrastructural development, and centralized land use planning, the Negev might be a special case, not necessarily transferable to other drylands.

Recreation and Tourism

Warm temperatures, abundant sunshine and spectacular landscapes make some drylands a destination for tourism and recreational activities (Figs. 7.7a, 7.7b and 7.7c). The growing affluence and mobility of the middle-class population of the developed world have raised tourism to a truly global economic force.

In some cases, the management of drylands as recreational space, combined with environmental conservation (such as in the designation of national parks), can offer an alternative income to that from agriculture. Thus, ecotourism has provided additional income to Bedouins throughout North Africa and the Middle East and an incentive to preserve pristine landscapes (Chatelard, 2006).

Conventional tourism, however, can consume significant amounts of water through the maintenance of landscaping and large groomed areas such as golf courses. Therefore, great caution needs to be exercised in the planning and implementation of tourist and recreation sites in drylands (MA, 2006). Water-efficient

(a)

Figs. 7.7a, 7.7b, and 7.7c Tourism potential in drylands: (a) and (b) scenic views from the Namib and Sonoran deserts (c) camel trekking with Bedouins in the Sinai peninsula

Figs. 7.7a, 7.7b, and 7.7c (continued)

technologies and wastewater reuse, as well as education about the value of water in drylands, are crucial in dealing with the water demands of tourists.

Like urbanization, tourism is a suitable land use alternative for the more accessible drylands, particularly those in close proximity to large population centers that have relatively good infrastructure. In remote drylands, far more considerable constraints to tourism exist.

Climate Change Mitigation

Climate change mitigation offers two potential land uses for drylands, both of which are still in the future and depend on policy directions taken in the next commitment period of the Kyoto Protocol: (1) encouraging soil carbon sequestration to offset atmospheric carbon dioxide; and (2) exploiting solar energy to reduce carbon dioxide emissions from burning fossil fuels into the atmosphere.

Carbon sequestration has been promoted as a potential win–win strategy, helping reduce atmospheric carbon dioxide while at the same time reclaiming degraded dryland soils whose organic matter content has been depleted (Tschakert, 2004). Depending on land use and management, soils can act as sources or sinks of carbon dioxide. Research on the potential of carbon sequestration in dryland soils has shown that erosion and other forms of soil degradation deplete soil carbon stocks, whereas the rehabilitation of degraded soils can restore them (Lal, 1999). Land management options to restore degraded soils and increase carbon sequestration include reduced tillage, mulching, crop rotations, composting, manure application, fallowing, agroforestry, and soil salinity control (Tschakert et al., 2004). In addition to garnering financial support from the Clean Development Mechanism (CDM) proposed under article 12 of the Kyoto Protocol (Batjes, 2001; Ringius, 2002; Chapter 8), these management practices are conducive to increasing soil fertility and restoring biological productivity. A point of controversy remains whether resource-poor farmers will be reached and their livelihoods improved by carbon sequestration projects, particularly in the most arid drylands. Moreover, even in more favored drylands, some skeptics fear that national and local leaders and better-off farmers might likely be the main beneficiaries (Tschakert et al., 2004).

Sparse cloud cover and high insolation in drylands provide ideal natural conditions for solar energy generation. Moreover, only drylands offer the large and comparatively inexpensive land area necessary to collect this very dispersed form of energy (Kurokawa, 2003). The use of solar power, however, is currently hindered by the high cost of solar cells and its future economic viability depends very much on whether these prices can become competitive with fossil energy prices. Although the photovoltaic effect – the conversion of light into electricity – has been known for a long time, the first solar cells were manufactured only in the 1950s and had low conversion efficiencies (Brown, 2002). Since then, conversion efficiencies have multiplied and commercial use of solar energy has expanded accordingly (Figs. 7.8a and 7.8b). Despite this progress, solar energy's costs of production must still be reduced by using less expensive materials; increasing conversion efficiency remains a key target of solar research (Brown, 2002). Other difficulties to be resolved before solar energy can be implemented at a larger scale include the possibilities of storage and transport of its output (Scheer, 2001).

7.2.2 *Systems Approaches in Land Management*

As with the sectors of water (Chapter 3), agriculture (Chapter 5), and ecology (Chapter 6), more integrated approaches towards land management have gained ground during the last two decades. These approaches take into account all relevant biophysical and

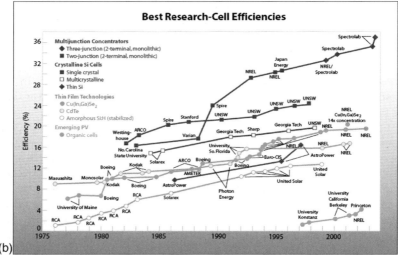

Figs. 7.8a and 7.8b Solar energy potential in drylands (a) Springerville photovoltaic power plant in Arizona (Courtesy Tucson Electric Power Company) (b) Development of photovoltaic cell efficiencies since 1975 (National Renewable Energy Laboratory)

socioeconomic processes within clearly defined geographic boundaries (Stroosnijder and van Rheenen, 2001), from the farm level to the watershed or ecoregion level. In the 1950s, land management was predominantly, if not exclusively, concerned with the land itself and the natural resources found therein. Since the 1980s, it has become more people-centered, taking stakeholders into account and considering their roles in making decisions about land use and land management.

The CGIAR's shift in the 1990s towards a more integrated systems approach based on ecoregions (CGIAR, 1992; Chapter 5), offers significant evidence that the validity of this approach, as well as the crucial role of humans as actors in systems, was beginning to be accepted in policy as well as science. Environmental sustainability, income generation, and poverty reduction, and participatory methods of research and decision-making have since been added as policy priorities (CIFOR, 1999).

The systems approach to land management has been developed and implemented at different hierarchical levels. Two examples relevant to drylands management are the *gestion de terroirs* concept at the village level and integrated watershed management at a regional level.

Gestion de Terroirs

The realization that large single-sector, technological development projects often performed poorly and failed to contribute significantly to rural poverty reduction gave rise to the *gestion de terroirs* ("[community-scale] land management") approach in francophone West Africa in the 1980s (Cleary, 2003). The *terroir* – a rural space that is managed by local communities – is the basic management unit (Mando et al., 2001). This approach acknowledged that the environmental and developmental problems of the Sahel resulted from a complex interplay of biophysical, economic, demographic, and institutional factors – such as land tenure arrangements – and therefore could not be resolved by technical projects alone.

The *gestion de terroirs* approach focuses on three interrelated systems relevant to natural resource management: (1) technical resource conservation; (2) socioeconomic factors; and (3) the legal system (Toulmin, 1994). Technical resource conservation includes long-term investments to improve the natural resource base, such as soil erosion control, reforestation, and crop–livestock integration. In addition, the approach aims at strengthening the socioeconomic base by supporting livelihood diversification in a region where more than 80% of the population relies on agriculture (Mando et al., 2001). Further components of the approach are capacity building in local institutions and empowerment of the rural population by the incorporation of their local knowledge in planning and development. Thus, *gestion de terroirs* can be seen as transferring control of natural resources management and use from government structures to local people (Toulmin, 1994). Land tenure questions play a major role in land use and management in much of dryland Africa and are often the underlying cause of resource use conflicts. Most traditional tenure systems practice collective ownership of the land: individual property rights are secondary to community land use rights. The difference is profound. Property rights are often exclusive; land use rights are often more inclusive, as for example when different groups of land users hold access rights at different times or to different categories of resources in a given area (Toulmin et al., 2002). Since colonial times, these traditional tenure systems have been competing with statutory tenure systems imposed by governments, with implications for resource use and management. In some places, traditional systems have remained largely intact and can be built upon. In other places, where traditional systems have essentially vanished, *gestion de terroirs* projects must essentially create new systems by implementing village committees to discuss the interests of different groups and make land use decisions (Meinzen-Dick et al., 2002).

Integrated Watershed Management

The concept of using watersheds as management units is not new, particularly in the drylands, where water is most critical in determining land use. Powell (1962) appreciated the significance of watersheds and came up with the revolutionary recommendation that land management should be organized around them in the arid region of the USA (Hutchinson, 2000). Throughout his career, Gilbert White advocated tirelessly for the concept of integrated watershed management; it was one of the issues that he promoted in *The Future of Arid Lands*. However, even if the concept was embraced, making the transition from a system that was tied to land ownership to one that was tied to landscape units existing separately from ownership could not be made quickly. As a consequence, most water and land management practices continued to address single, localized problems without taking into account possible impacts on the larger watershed system. It was not until the 1970s that more concerted efforts were made to begin this transition. Today there is far greater consensus that the watershed is the optimal unit for managing not only water resources but natural resources in general; however, viable strategies for implementing integrated watershed management are still evolving (Heathcote, 1998; Lal, 2000).

Integrated watershed management starts with the understanding that whatever happens in one part of a watershed – e.g., groundwater extraction, soil erosion, or land use change – affects the functioning of the system as a whole. Acknowledging these connections can minimize the likelihood that management interventions aimed at solving problems in one part will cause problems in another (NRC, 1999). Most obviously, the expansion of an irrigation project upstream can cause water shortages, deterioration of water quality, and changes in vegetation composition downstream. The term *integrated* refers not only to linkages among different components of the system (water, soil, vegetation), but also across geographic regions (upstream and downstream), political boundaries, disciplines involved in management decision-making (hydrology, ecology, economy, and social science), and the government agencies that are responsible for each of them.

The most concentrated efforts to develop integrated water management strategies currently tend to be aimed at transboundary watersheds (Box 7.2). From before the time of Herodotus, river courses have been used to demarcate political boundaries, with the result that watersheds have often been split into separate political entities. Water allocation among states sharing a watershed has caused much conflict in the past; more recently, the realization of the vital role of water has the potential to advance transboundary cooperation and the implementation of integrated watershed management programs (Heathcote, 1998; Wolf, 1998).

7.2.3   Dryland Management in The Context of Global Debates

Beginning with the United Nations Conference on the Human Environment (UNCHE) in Stockholm in 1972, debate about society–environment relationships

---

Box 7.2 Integrated River Basin Management: The Nile Basin Initiative

---

The Nile River is an important development axis for the ten African countries that share its basin (Rwanda, Burundi, Democratic Republic of Congo, Uganda, Tanzania, Eritrea, Ethiopia, Kenya, Sudan, and Egypt). Many of them are located in drylands and are thus highly dependent on Nile waters. The river basin covers about 3.1 million km^2 and is home to a fast-growing population of about 160 million people. Agriculture is the dominant economic sector.

Like many other transboundary river basins, the Nile Basin looks back on a millennia-long history of competition, tension, and conflict over water resources. Development projects often sprang up uncoordinated, and unilateral water diversions caused environmental and socioeconomic problems for the whole basin. Occasionally, there were efforts of bilateral cooperation on the development of the Nile, but most of them were short-lived.

In 1999, the ten riparian countries set up the Nile Basin Initiative (NBI), which provides a basin-wide framework for cooperation. Their shared vision is "to achieve sustainable socioeconomic development through the equitable utilization of, and benefit from, the common Nile Basin resources" (http:// www.nilebasin.org/). The initiative is helping to build a foundation of trust and confidence among its members and facilitates joint planning and management of land and water resources of the basin.

The NBI has implemented a Strategic Action Program that includes basin-wide and subbasin projects, with particular emphasis on improving technical, institutional, and human capacities. Among other things, data acquisition has been strengthened by the introduction of modern monitoring technologies throughout the basin, and a spatially referenced Nile Basin database has been established to enable data sharing and to inform planning and management. Although the initiative so far has primarily emphasized confidence building, its ultimate goal is to enable development in upstream states while ensuring sustainable water supply for downstream states. It may mean less water for some, but cooperation is the only viable alternative to the chronic insecurity that characterized development in the Nile basin in the past (Lemma, 2001).

---

has become central to the international agenda. The scope of this conference signaled that environmental and social problems like land degradation and poverty, which tend to have widely varying local impacts, were no longer seen as isolated local issues but as global concerns requiring global efforts to find a solution.

UNCHE has been followed by further global initiatives – including the Brundtland commission (convened in 1983), the United Nations Conference on Environment and Development (1992) and the World Summit on Sustainable Development (2002) – that served as platforms for discussion and helped raise global awareness about pressing environmental issues. The depletion and degradation of the natural resource base, on which all human and societal development depends, emerged as a pressing issue that land management must address. The policy documents resulting from these global environmental initiatives, while potentially strong foundations for the formulation of land use and management plans, are plagued with vague problem definitions and sweeping generalizations. This might be one reason why the implementation of their principles is, at least to date, so rare.

Two global debates important to drylands have evolved around the notions of sustainability and of desertification, with desertification often being interpreted as a major challenge to sustainability in drylands.

Sustainability and Sustainable Development

Debate over sustainability was fueled by the Brundtland Report (WCED, 1987), published by an international group of politicians and experts. The report stresses the urgency of pursuing a form of economic development that could be sustained without degrading the environment. Its importance stems less from what it says than the reaction it provoked and the broad consensus it forged from East to West and from North to South (Brooks, 1993). Sustainability has since become an official policy adopted by governmental and nongovernmental organizations, most notably the World Bank (2001, 2002) and incorporated in most development projects, despite its generally weak conceptual basis (Sneddon, 2000).

Three fundamental components, the "triple bottom line", are necessary to achieve sustainable development: environmental protection, economic growth, and social equity. These aims conflict to some extent, yet the scientific community has helped to create at least the illusion of making them simultaneously possible through scientific and technological progress (Ludwig et al., 1993). Despite general consensus on the need, thus far few examples of truly sustainable land use and management are known, particularly in the industrialized world.

The vagueness of the definition of sustainability and the lack of tangible criteria for its evaluation have hindered its practical implementation (Warren et al., 2001). Only a few coherent frameworks exist, one of them being the "five capitals" model, which defines sustainability as the maintenance or enhancement of different types of capital: (1) natural (e.g., soil and water resources); (2) economic or financial (e.g., savings, remittances); (3) human (e.g., skills, health); (4) physical or manufactured (e.g., infrastructure); and (5) social (e.g., networks and institutions) (FFF, 2005). These capitals can offer a starting point for designing sustainable land management schemes.

The question is whether and to what extent the different capitals can be substituted for one another without jeopardizing overall sustainability. With respect to this question, Serageldin (1996) identified three levels of sustainability: (1) "Strong sustainability", which dominated most early discussions, allows no substitution between capitals. (2) "Weak sustainability", in contrast, allows unfettered substitution between capitals as long as the overall capital stock is maintained. That is, a technological innovation like desalinated seawater (human or economic capital) can replace equal amounts of a depleted resource like freshwater (natural capital).

(3) "Sensible sustainability" allows substitution of capitals within critical boundaries of each type of capital. Defining a critical boundary, however, is not straightforward and depends very much on development scenarios and how different resources are valued within them. For example, a scenario in which agriculture in marginal lands was almost completely abandoned because other income opportunities were strengthened implies a different critical boundary of natural capital than a scenario of agricultural intensification (Warren et al. 2001).

The sustainable livelihoods approach (Carney, 1998; Scoones, 1998) builds on the capitals model. Rural households manage their livelihoods based on the assets available to them in each of the five capitals (Ellis, 2000). Examples of this approach in rural drylands include Twyman's (Twyman et al., 2004) assessment of smallholder farming strategies on the margins of the Kalahari and their adaptations to environmental variability and policy changes. Fratkin and Mearns (2003) examine the sustainability of pastoral livelihoods of the East Africa and Mongolia. Both groups are increasingly under pressure to diversify their asset base in order to remain sustainable: the East African Maasai because their lands have been targeted for commercial ranching and farm enterprises; the Mongolian pastoralists in order to cope with the increasing wealth differentiation among livestock keepers and competition for the highest value grazing land.

The Desertification Debate

Much debate has grown up around the concept of desertification as land degradation in arid, semiarid, and subhumid zones of the globe (UNCCD, 1994). Although this concept goes back to the time of colonial rule in West Africa (Aubréville, 1949), it drew increased attention when a series of drought years beginning in the late 1960s caused famine and environmental degradation across the Sahel. The United Nations Conference on Desertification (UNCOD), held in Nairobi in 1977 after the initial round of droughts, launched desertification as a political issue and triggered a great deal of scientific interest – and controversy. Debate has raged since then over what exactly desertification is, what its causes are, how it is manifested, and how it relates to natural processes and human activities (Herrmann and Hutchinson, 2005). Blame was alternately assigned between human factors like overpopulation and irrational land management (e.g., Le Houérou, 2002; Mainguet, 1991), and natural processes, particularly rainfall variability (e.g., Tucker and Nicholson, 1999). Skeptics claimed that there was little actual land degradation (Warren, 2002); in fact, ground data from selected locations showed no long-term declines of agricultural productivity over the previous few decades (e.g., Mortimore, 1998; Niemeijer and Mazzucato, 2002; Tiffen and Mortimore, 2002). Other critics consider desertification a 'myth', based on unsubstantiated claims, that has developed a life of its own (Thomas and Middleton, 1994). But, the term refuses to fade away, whether in science or policy, despite its obvious inadequacies.

Our understanding of desertification has evolved significantly since the 1970s, based on developments in climatology and ecology as well as on changing interpretations of socioeconomic processes (Herrmann and Hutchinson, 2005; MA, 2006): Advances in climate observation, monitoring technology, and modeling have given us a better idea of the magnitude of (natural) climate variability (Chapter 4). In ecology, the equilibrium paradigm, on which much of the desertification concept was originally founded, has been challenged (Chapter 6). And, contrary to earlier assumptions, it is now understood that most indigenous people have developed dynamic strategies that cope well with climatic uncertainty and make economic and ecological sense (Blaikie and Brookfield, 1987; Hutchinson, 1989; Mortimore, 1989). Numerous examples

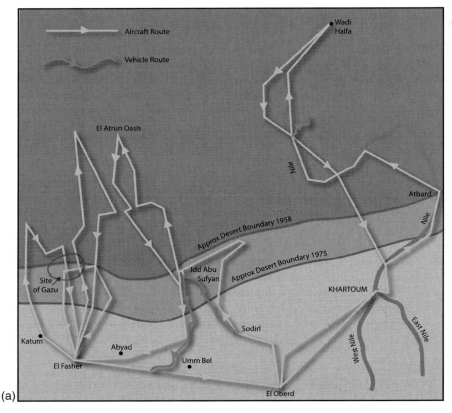

(a)

Figs. 7.9a, 7.9b, and 7.9c Early survey of the extent of desertification (Lamprey, 1988) (Fig.7.9a) contrasted with recent examples or remote sensing studies of vegetation greenness as a proxy for bioproductivity in the Sahel (Fig. 7.9b, Fig. 7.9c) (Eklundh and Olsson, 2003; Herrman et al. 2005). Remote sensing has added "observation density" in both the temporal and the spatial dimension and contributed to a change in understanding of vegetation dynamics and desertification. Eklundh and Olsson show positive and negative trends in overall vegetation greenness between 1982 and 1999. Herrmann et al. show trends in vegetation greenness from 1982 to 2003, which are not explained by changes in precipitation during the same time period but are hypothesized to express the outcome of land use and management

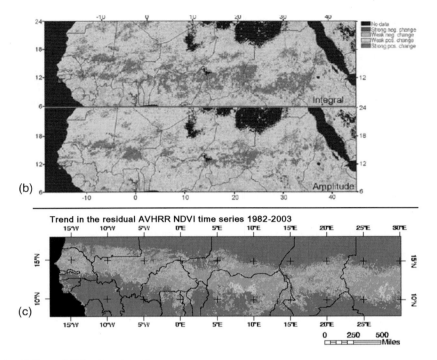

Figs. 7.9b, and 7.9c (continued)

show that dryland populations can rehabilitate degraded lands, building on long-term experience paired with innovative capacity (MA, 2006).

While these developments have affected the interpretation of the driving forces of desertification and the feedback mechanisms among them, the alleged extent of land affected by desertification has been questioned as improved methods of assessing and quantifying have evolved (MA, 2006). In particular, time series analysis of remote sensing data offers significant advantages over isolated observations extrapolated in space and time – the conventional assessment method of the 1970s (Fig. 7.9a), which was revealed as clearly inappropriate for monitoring a phenomenon as dynamic and spatially heterogeneous as desertification.

Overall, the more complex picture of land-cover change in drylands that is now emerging has made the initial notion of desertification appear overly simplistic. Depending on environment, policies and market opportunities, a wide range of different situations is possible, to which land management responses must be matched if degradation is to be avoided. Despite the scientific uncertainties surrounding it, it is virtually certain that the desertification issue will not go away any time soon. First, the fundamental problems of attempting to make maximum return from land under a highly variable climate will remain. Second, at the very least, it will persist because it has been recognized through the creation of a United Nations convention. Assuming that the desertification issue will continue to play a role in the future of drylands, identifying individual problem areas seems likely to be much more effective than raising a general alarm based on questionable scientific evidence (MA, 2006).

Chapter 8
Policy In and For Drylands

Policy establishes an institutional framework in which land use and management decisions are made. In essence, it sets the rules by which the game is played.

As such, policy guides the process of decision-making and policy implementation concerning a multitude of environmental, economic, and social issues. From the global to the local level, governmental and nongovernmental organizations make policy. Each can offer opportunities or pose constraints to the use and management of dryland resources, both directly, as in water and grazing policies, and indirectly, as in policies on subsidies, international trade, or climate-change mitigation. In an ideal world, policy is based on science, that is, on a firm understanding of the behavior of both natural and human systems. In reality, linking science and policy has proved a challenge, with policy not always reflecting the most current scientific thinking. Both in the 1950s and now, policy has been guided as much by other factors, such as political and underlying financial concerns, as by science. And, as the current debate on global warming illustrates, science too can become politicized.

8.1   The Situation in The 1950s

In his preface to *The Future of Arid Lands*, White (1956, p. vi) acknowledged the importance of policy for development problems in drylands, stating that "much of the deterioration of semiarid lands now being used at low efficiency is due to such conditions as tenure, property rights, political control, social attitudes, and taxes which impede application of new technology and techniques".

However, much of *The Future of Arid Lands* dealt mostly with scientific advances, technology development, and the improvement of predictive capabilities of the physical and biological sciences rather than tackling constraints that fell into the realm of social science, including policy questions. Limitations in data availability and understanding were the constraints on drylands development most frequently mentioned throughout the book (Chapter 1). Only one author even mentioned that progress in social science was important to drylands development (Kellogg, 1956).

C. F. Hutchinson and S. M. Herrmann, *The Future of Arid Lands – Revisited.*
© Springer 2008

The ideas in *The Future of Arid Lands* might not be entirely representative of the general understanding of policy options available at the time, other than illustrating that policy questions obviously took a back seat to technological and hard scientific issues when it came to dryland development. The 1955 meetings, however, which preceded the publication of the book, also included discussion group sessions on topics such as "administrative and legal problems of arid land development" (White and Duisberg, 1955, p. 220), which were not fully presented in *The Future of Arid Lands*.

The political map of the world looked quite different in the 1950s. India and Pakistan had recently become independent states. Most of the African drylands were still colonies. Tunisia, Morocco, and Sudan gained independence in 1956, followed by many other French and British colonies in Africa in the early 1960s, and Portuguese colonies in the 1970s. The drylands of Soviet Central Asia and China were subject to a socialist political and centrally planned economic system.

In addition to these obvious geopolitical differences, which affected policymaking in and for drylands, other factors characteristic of the policy environment of the 1950s included: (1) the prevalence of the modernization paradigm of development; (2) the unchallenged importance of national governments as political actors; and (3) the establishment of global institutions.

8.1.1   Development Through "Modernization"

The concept of modernization – a process by which each society was thought to evolve to greater levels of development by replicating the trajectory of the western industrialized nations – best describes the view on development that shaped policy goals in the 1950s (Peet and Hartwick, 1999). Modernization and stages-of-economic-development theories were developed and popularized during this period. The basic concepts of stages in economic growth were in particular outlined by Rostow (1952, 1956), although his summation of these ideas in the landmark publication *Stages of Economic Growth* did not appear until 1960.

Modernization theories were framed in Eurocentric, technocentric, and hierarchical worldviews, with the rich and powerful expected to direct global economic regulation in a top-down manner (Peet and Hartwick, 1999). According to these theories, technology development played a key role as a catalyst to enable economic takeoff for the less well-off nations and would be delivered to them by scientists and aid bureaucrats (Adger et al., 2001). Technological interventions were also expected to provide solutions to environmental problems that might occur during the process of economic growth, such as land degradation and overexploitation of water and other natural resources.

Examples of top-down efforts at modernization included the activities of the International Monetary Fund and the World Bank, which were established to provide short-term loans and longer-term investments respectively (Section 8.1.3). In the 1950s, most World Bank loans were meant to spur economic growth after

World War II. Great faith was placed in the trickle-down effect; that is, increasing the overall gross domestic product was expected to bring greater prosperity and development to the majority of the population (Kapur et al., 1997).

In concentrating on economic growth, these institutions showed little concern for the environment. The overriding objective was to increase production; rather than adapting to the constraints of dryland environments, policymaking believed that they could overcome such constraints, transforming the environment to meet human needs, particularly through irrigation (Chapter 3), or even by controlling rainfall (Chapter 4). The "intentional large-scale manipulation of the environment" (Keith, 2000, p. 247) was captured by the notion of geoengineering, which emerged in the 1950s and implies, among other things, intentional climate modification. It can also refer to other large-scale projects, such as plans for diverting Siberian rivers into arid Central Asia, which had been discussed periodically since the late 1940s (Chapter 3).

8.1.2   National Governments as Key Political Actors

As the 1950s opened, civil society and nongovernmental organizations were not yet a powerful political force; nor were international organizations. The key political actors then were national governments, and they were expected to play a major role in modernization and development. Policymaking and policy implementation were applied on the basis of political units, particularly nation-states. That political borders rarely coincided with the boundaries of ecological systems had been acknowledged much earlier (Powell, 1962), but even though White (1956) explicitly noted this challenge, it had otherwise rarely been acknowledged at that time and few institutions were then in place to tackle the problem.

Drylands were seen as marginal, unproductive environments in many countries and were often neglected in national policymaking. Problems of dryland development ranked low on national agendas because of perceived poor returns on potential investment. Moreover, outside irrigated areas, dryland inhabitants were frequently poor and were underrepresented in government and its institutions. Nomadic pastoralists in particular, who traditionally made up a large part of the population in many drylands, were seen as a regressive social formation that threatened the integrity of the state (Johnson, 1993). Most government policies were not intended to accommodate mobile livelihood systems, which were also frequently blamed for environmental degradation.

8.1.3   Global Institutions in Their Beginning

Although there was little awareness of the global scope of some of the environmental problems affecting drylands, the authors of *The Future of Arid Lands* expressed the need for international scientific cooperation (Chapter 1). The United Nations was established after World War II to promote cooperation in international law, international security, and economic development. By 1956, a number of additional specialized agencies and conferences had been convened to advance issues considered of particular global concern. Of these, the UN Educational, Scientific, and Cultural Organization (UNESCO) and the Food and Agriculture Organization (FAO) were most relevant to environment and also development issues. However, much international attention was limited to narrowly defined environmental problems, such as the conservation of specific wildlife species (e.g., the International Convention for the Regulation of Whaling, 1946) (Soroos, 2005). Furthermore, the scope for action and the effectiveness of the UN agencies was influenced by Cold War politics. However, as early as 1948, UNESCO considered the establishment of an International Institute of the Arid Zone, and it created an advisory Committee on Arid Zone Research in 1951. The initiative eventually became the Major Project on Arid Lands, launched in 1956, which coincided with the publication of *The Future of Arid Lands*.

International economic organizations like the World Bank and the International Monetary Fund (IMF) were also international players; however, their importance for dryland development was still weak in 1956. Established as lending institutions to provide capital for postwar reconstruction in Europe in the 1940s, they began to function as more global development institutions only from the end of the 1950s (Section 8.2). Many of the earlier World Bank loans had been aimed at the development of natural resources in European colonies. Loans also went to independent India and Pakistan, for example, to support large-scale water engineering projects. Agriculture and education received only modest support then (and up until the 1970s) because they did not promise significant returns. Not surprisingly, lending policies were also affected by cold war politics. The USA, which, as a major contributor, had a correspondingly large influence on World Bank policies, favored loans for those countries that were considered part of the anticommunist camp (Kapur et al., 1997).

8.2   The Situation Today

During the last 50 years, not only has our understanding of development processes and of the complexity of human–environment relationships evolved and affected policymaking; the policy framework itself has become more complex. Several new actors now influence policymaking at all levels. The world political system has undergone vast transformations, such as the dissolution of colonial empires and the Soviet Union, both of which have served to increase the number of sovereign states and thus the number of players in the policymaking arena. New institutions and multilateral environmental agreements have emerged, many of which are – directly or indirectly – relevant to drylands (Table 8.1). In addition, a multitude of civil society actors, virtually nonexistent in the 1950s, has sprung up.

Table 8.1 Summary of some international organizations, global conferences and scientific initiatives relevant to drylands since 1956

International organizations, treaties, and global conferences	International scholarly initiatives and international years and decades
	1956 UNESCO Major Project on Arid Lands
	1957–58 International Geophysical Year
1961 World Wildlife Fund established	1964–74 International Biological Programme
1965 United Nations Development Program	1965–74 International Hydrological Decade
1972 UN Conference on the Human Environment (Stockholm Conference)	1971 UNESCO's Man and the Biosphere Programme launched
1972 UN Environment Programme (UNEP) founded	1974 World Population Year
1972 UNESCO Convention Concerning the Protection of the World Cultural and Natural Heritage (World Heritage Convention)	1975 UNESCO International Hydrological Programme founded
1974 World Population Conference	
1977 UN Conference on Desertification	
1983 World Commission on Environment and Development ("Brundtland Commission") established	1987 International Geosphere Biosphere Programme started
	1988 Intergovernmental Panel on Climate Change (IPCC) established (first IPCC Assessment Report completed in 1990)
1992 UN Conference on Environment and Development (UNCED) (Earth Summit; Rio Conference)	1991 Global Environment Facility (GEF) created
1992 UN Framework Convention on Climate Change (UNFCCC)	1996 International Year for the Eradication of Poverty
1992 UN Convention on Biological Diversity (UNCBD)	1997–2006 United Nations Decade for the Eradication of Poverty
1992 Agenda 21 adopted	
1992 Commission on Sustainable Development	
1994 UN Convention to Combat Desertification	
1994 UN Conference on Population and Development	
1994 World Trade Organization (WTO)	
1996 World Water Council established (launched four "World Water Forums" since 1997)	
1997 Kyoto Protocol to the UNFCCC	
2000 Millennium Summit of the United Nations	2001 Millennium Ecosystem Assessment begins
2002 UN Millennium Project commissioned	
2002 UN World Summit on Sustainable Development (Johannesburg Summit)	2003 UN International Year of Freshwater
2005 World Summit (follow-up on the 2000 Millennium Summit): action plan for achieving the Millennium Development Goals	2005–2015 International Decade for Action, "Water for Life"
	2005–2014 UN Decade of Education for Sustainable Development
	2006 UN International Year of Deserts and Desertification
	2008 (in preparation) UN International Year of Planet Earth

Cooperation among the diverse sets of actors has increased, at least nominally. At the same time, different sectors of policymaking, such as climate and sustainable development, have become increasingly integrated owing to growing awareness of the interrelatedness of the issues they deal with. Some policy questions relevant to drylands today include:

- What incentives are needed to secure sustainable livelihoods in drylands?
- How can the intertwined problems of poverty and environmental degradation in drylands be addressed effectively?
- What actions can be taken at local, national, and international institutional levels to facilitate land tenure reform and ensure land tenure security?
- How can coherence in international efforts in dryland development be reached?
- How do policy decisions taken outside drylands affect dryland environments and what can be done about such effects, which are often unintended?

8.2.1   New Views on Development

Since the publication of *The Future of Arid Lands* in 1956, development thinking has moved beyond its narrow focus on modernization. While modernization theory has never completely lost its appeal – and some argue that the interventions it justifies are still the name of the game in many development efforts (e.g., Mortimore, 2003b) – another direction of thinking appeared in the 1960s and 1970s in response to its shortcomings.

This "new" direction derived from Marxist and neo-Marxist dependency theories (e.g., Cardoso and Faletto, 1979; Dos Santos, 1970; Prebisch, 1971) and world system theories (Wallerstein, 1974), holds that underdevelopment of some nations (named "periphery" or "satellites") is intrinsically linked to the development success of other nations (named "center", "core", or "metropolis") in that the success of the latter is based on extracting resources from the former. Indeed, the growth of the global market and the worldwide division of labor seem to have widened structural differences that were generated during colonialism. Modernization and dependency theories are two poles between which most contemporary development models can be located. These comprise neoliberal export-led growth models, which are closer to modernization; the sustainable development model postulated in the Brundtland Report (WCED, 1987), which attempts to reconcile economic growth and environmental protection; and poverty alleviation (UNMP, 2005). None of these directions, however, have come to dominate development thinking in the way modernization did in the 1950s and 1960s.

Some poststructural and postdevelopmental thinkers (e.g., Escobar, 1995, 2004) have gone so far as to denounce the term "development" altogether as a construct of the language of Western domination. Instead of any established notion of development, be it based on modernization or dependency thinking, they promote social justice, under which people are permitted to proceed along their own and very localized paths.

New perceptions of the nature of development have encouraged a rethinking of development policies applied to drylands. The prevailing view – inspired by modernization – had long been that new technologies and new knowledge must be imported from outside and promoted in opposition to the traditional knowledge of local people, who were blamed for degrading their resource base because of ignorance or poverty. However, there is little scientific evidence to support this hypothesis. On the contrary, more recent dryland studies have shown a more complex picture revealing that this degradation hypothesis rested on a great deal of misunderstanding of traditional land-use practices (e.g., Fairhead and Leach, 1996; Mortimore, 1998; Mortimore and Adams, 1999). Independent research from different locations has shown that local peoples' strategies, such as productive efficiency, resource conservation, accumulation, diversification, and mobility, are not only essential to their survival (Mortimore, 2003b; Scoones, 2001; Tiffen et al., 1994), but also generally well adapted to management of risk and marginal resources. However, these strategies are often constrained by inappropriate government policies, unfavorable terms of trade, market failures, and insecure rights over land and resources (Scherr, 1999; Way, 2006).

Given the poor record of past and present development policies, Mortimore (2003a) argued for a new paradigm for dryland development, which would build on these indigenous survival strategies, derive policy lessons from understanding "success stories" of dryland development (Box 9.1), and strengthen incentives for investment in these areas. Directly addressing poverty alleviation, this reasoning is in line with the Millennium Project on marginal lands in its call for increased investment in drylands (Way, 2006).

8.2.2 Global Environmental Governance

At the beginning of the twenty-first century, the Earth's physical and biological systems are increasingly affected by world population growth and people's efforts to enhance their living standards, which are accompanied by increasing consumption of natural resources and release of pollutants (Soroos, 2005). Many environmental problems caused by these impacts are of global scope and have potentially severe implications for the sustainability of life on our planet. Moreover, consumption or degradation of resources by one country diminishes opportunities available to humans as a whole, including future generations. This makes global environmental problems too large and too complex for national governments alone to address, and too much is at stake for humanity if they are left unaddressed (Axelrod et al., 2005).

Although scientists and conservationists recognized some of these global threats more than a century ago (e.g., Arrhenius, 1896), only in the last three decades have they been addressed on a global scale (Vig, 2005). The UN Conference on the Human Environment, held in Stockholm in 1972, was the first to bring the environment and its relationship to economic development onto the international agenda

(Caldwell, 1996). This led to the establishment of the UN Environment Programme (UNEP) as a permanent institution charged with monitoring the global environment, convening meetings, and negotiating international agreements (Vig, 2005). The Stockholm conference also coincided with a wave of public concern about the environment, mainly in the industrialized countries, which began to build during the late 1960s. This marked the beginning of global civil society interest and engagement in environmental issues (Section 8.2.4).

Two decades later, in 1992, the UN Conference on Environment and Development (UNCED) was convened in Rio de Janeiro ("Rio Summit") to mark the beginning of the new era of sustainable development called for by the Brundtland Commission in 1987 (WCED, 1987). The Rio Summit resulted in three major global environmental treaties: the UN Framework Convention on Climate Change (UNFCCC), the UN Convention on Biological Diversity (UNCBD) and the UN Convention to Combat Desertification (UNCCD), as well as a comprehensive plan of action, the *Agenda 21*. The principles laid down in the Rio Summit and the commitment to implement the *Agenda 21* were reaffirmed at the World Summit on Sustainable Development held in Johannesburg in 2002 ("Johannesburg Summit").

The system of global environmental governance resulting from such efforts consists of: (1) a network of intergovernmental organizations, including UNEP and others; (2) a framework of international environmental law and commitments; and (3) financing institutions, particularly the Global Environment Facility (GEF), aimed at helping developing countries to meet treaty commitments. A growing number of bilateral and multilateral regional treaties complements this system (Vig, 2005). Although celebrated as an achievement by some, the system is perceived as weak and ineffective by others (see Biermann and Bauer, 2004). The charges are that it is fragmented, uncoordinated, and has no built-in enforcement mechanisms. In addition, the treaties are only binding on participating states. This problem became particularly critical when the USA (the world's top polluter) and Australia withdrew their commitment to the Kyoto Protocol.

Two fields of global environmental governance particularly relevant to drylands are desertification and climate change.

Desertification

Desertification is a challenge that, by definition, uniquely affects drylands. It is considered a global issue because it affects, in similar forms, drylands throughout the world. Originally of little interest to most of the world outside drylands, desertification became an issue of international concern when a series of drought years hit the West African Sahel region beginning in the late 1960s. The UN Conference on Desertification (UNCOD) held in Nairobi in 1977 launched it into the political arena (Thomas and Middleton, 1994). The conference produced a Plan of Action to Combat Desertification that contained guidelines and recommendations for countries to develop national action plans and for international assistance to be coordinated. However, it resulted in little substantive action, partly due to a lack of resources and coordination, but also due to institutional turf battles. Moreover, formulation and policy implementation of antidesertification measures were hindered by the ongoing debate, and lack of scientific consensus, on the nature and causes of desertification (Herrmann and Hutchinson, 2005).

Despite these scientific shortcomings, a new attempt at addressing the problem was made with the UNCCD. This convention entered into force in 1996 after intense global negotiations that were an unusual example of the developing countries pushing for "their" treaty and the industrialized countries resisting it (Najam, 2006). Another novel aspect of the UNCCD is that nongovernmental organizations, the majority representing grassroots interests, were involved in negotiations for it to an unprecedented extent (Corell and Betsill, 2001).

The dual focus of the UNCCD on both environment and poverty makes it a global sustainable development convention as much as a global environmental convention (Johnson et al., 2006). This does justice to the complexity of the problem. Because past top-down efforts obviously failed, the UNCCD emphasizes action at the community level and popular participation, which is to be integrated into other national development policies. Thus, the convention provides a framework of cooperation between local land users, NGOs, governments, international organizations, funding agencies, and donor countries. Only developing countries affected by desertification qualify for assistance (Corell and Betsill, 2001), making it the first international convention ever to simultaneously target dryland problems and developing countries. It places particular emphasis on the African drylands, a large region which has not received much international attention in the past and, with the exception of one paper on Tunisia by Tixeront (1956), was not much mentioned in *The Future of Arid Lands*.

Climate Change

Climate change is arguably the most complex environmental challenge that has ever confronted world society. Its causes and effects transcend national boundaries, calling for international cooperation in response (Betsill, 2005). Drylands are considered particularly vulnerable to the adverse effects of climate change, which are expected to include more frequent droughts and a decline of water resources (Chapter 4). Global climate policy began with the First World Climate Conference in 1979, which called on the world's governments "to foresee and prevent potential man-made changes in climate that might be adverse to the well-being of humanity" (WMO, 1979, p. 709), and was reinforced with the adoption of the UNFCCC in 1992 by 154 nations. As of August 2006, more than 160 countries have ratified the Kyoto Protocol to the UNFCCC, which assigns specific obligations consistent with the convention's general principles.

International cooperation and consensus, however, have been impeded by a number of still unresolved questions, such as: How much should society pay now to reduce future risk? Who should bear responsibility for mitigating climate change? Which instruments of emission control – price-based policies or quantitative caps – are most efficient? What level of CO_2 emissions would be allowed in the long run? (Anderson, 2005; Betsill, 2005; Pizer, 2005). A special point of contention among countries and NGOs participating in international climate negotiations has been the role of flexible mechanisms in reaching emission targets. Flexible mechanisms, such as emissions trading, joint policy implementation and the Clean Development Mechanism defined in the Kyoto Protocol, allow rich countries to "meet" their emissions targets by purchasing other countries' "unused" emissions (Noble and Scholes, 2001). Not surprisingly, industrialized countries with numerous high-emission industries welcomed these mechanisms, but they may offer advantages for developing countries as well.

For drylands in developing countries, the Clean Development Mechanism in particular potentially offers an opportunity to mobilize resources for carbon sequestration projects (Chapter 7). Enhancing carbon sequestration in dryland soils through improved land use and crop management could simultaneously help achieve the goals of the UNFCCC and the UNCCD. At the same time, such projects provide a mechanism for transfer of funds from the Global Environment Facility – the UNFCCC's funding mechanism – to the UNCCD, whose own funding mechanism can only facilitate, but not itself provide, funding for projects to prevent land degradation (FAO, 2000). However, despite several years of discussion (Lal, 1999), very few such projects have actually been implemented to date.

8.2.3 Intersectoral and Interinstitutional Coordination and Cooperation

While the environmental and developmental problems of drylands were treated as isolated, seemingly unrelated issues in 1956, coordination and cooperation are now fairly well established among policy sectors, among institutions, and across scales. The rapid advances in communication technologies over the last 50 years have facilitated this development (Chapter 2).

The systems perspective adopted in science since the 1960s, which stresses interlinkages and feedback mechanisms between different physical and human phenomena, first found expression in the ecosystem concept (Chapter 6) and was soon adopted by other disciplines (e.g., climate, water, and land-use systems). This new integrative perspective has also started to affect policy, albeit more slowly. Only during the last decade or so has it been realized that, to be effective, policy must meet the needs of different sectors and must also integrate the requirements of various governance instruments, such as institutions and multilateral environmental agreements.

One example of policy integration is the growing acknowledgement of multiple links between climate change and sustainable development in each subsequent IPCC assessment (Najam et al., 2003). Today, climate change is seen as both an environmental and a development issue, affecting water resources, human health, and agriculture among other things (Watson, 2002). This perspective requires greater involvement of the social sciences and humanities in the preparation of assessment reports and design of policy instruments to mitigate climate change. The challenge is to develop policies (such as the option of carbon sequestration contained in the Clean Development Mechanism) that not only address emission reductions but also ensure that inequities between countries are not exacerbated and that mitigation strategies are aligned with the goals of sustainable development (IPCC, 2001b).

A second example of policy integration is the incorporation of poverty reduction goals into desertification control policies, as outlined in the UNCCD. In the 1970s and 1980s, for example, environmental rehabilitation had often been pursued by creating natural reserves, thereby excluding people from the very resources their livelihoods depended on (Way, 2006). At the same time, economic policies put in place to reduce poverty tended to disregard the special environmental situation of drylands and, as a result, were conducive to land degradation (Forsyth et al., 1998). Learning from the past failures, the UNCCD calls for desertification policies that simultaneously address poverty issues and are integrated into the overall development strategy of a country or region (Johnson et al., 2006).

Climate change and energy policy would also benefit immensely from a more integrated vision. The present global energy system, based as it is on fossil fuels, is the main cause of global climate change. Transforming it into a low-emissions system is a major challenge of the future, but one in which drylands could play a crucial role (Chapters 7 and 9). A transition to renewable energies – such as solar, wind, and geothermal – would simultaneously curb greenhouse gas emissions and provide sustainable energy for a growing population. Moreover, in the poor drylands, it would help reduce people's use of fuelwood for energy, thus helping to mitigate land degradation and biodiversity reduction caused by deforestation, particularly in the vicinity of settlements. Different models for the diffusion of renewable energy exist, such as employing disincentives for greenhouse gas emissions and incentives for innovation and adoption of renewable energy technologies (Fischer and Newell, 2005). Yet, there seems to be insufficient political will or interest to turn these models into binding policies at present (Axelrod et al., 2005). Energy is a cornerstone of all modern economies, and the resistance to change is high, particularly among the biggest energy consumers. In the absence of an international energy authority, numerous actors must get involved and alliances of early adopters must be formed if further progress towards a sustainable energy system is to be made (Fritsche and Matthes, 2003).

One more example of intersectoral policy coordination is found in the economic and environmental arenas. Until the 1990s, economic development and environmental protection were pursued separately. Thus, the World Bank and the IMF adopted a purely economic perspective in designing policies to promote economic growth, generate income, and pay off debt. The principal instrument for development would be the free markets rather than development agencies. This led to World Bank's encouraging privatization, trade liberalization, and export orientation. The negative environmental implications of these so-called structural adjustment policies were explored and revealed for the first time in a study conducted by the Worldwide Fund for Nature (Reed, 1992). Subsequently, the World Bank

(1992, p. 2) acknowledged the need to integrate environmental considerations into policymaking: "Without adequate environmental protection, development is undermined; without development, resources will be inadequate for needed investments, and environmental protection will fail." In dryland ecosystems, the emphasis on exports and structural adjustment policies put pressure on natural resources, particularly in the less productive drylands, and encouraged soil degradation and loss of plant diversity (Oriang, 1994). Livestock is one of the few sectors in which drylands could offer some comparative advantage (i.e., low land value) (Chapters 5 and 7), but an increase in herd size can lead to degraded rangelands, particularly in peri-urban systems or large commercial operations.

8.2.4   Civil Society, Participation and Empowerment

The sharp increase in the number of global institutions and agreements in the past decades, while diminishing the authority of the nation state, has not led to a centralized, supranational form of "world government". Rather, the growing influence of global institutions on policymaking has been paralleled by a powerful counterforce: the increasingly important role of local participation and empowerment (O'Byrne, 2005). Global and local policymaking are not seen as separate, but as constantly interacting with and feeding into one another, as illustrated in the example of the UNCCD (Section 8.2.2).

Community-based organizations and NGOs, in their totality referred to as "civil society", have gradually evolved since the 1950s. However, it was only in the 1990s that they began to seriously influence public policy. NGO participation reached a then unprecedented level in the Rio Summit of 1992 (UNCED), where NGO representatives sought to engage directly in intergovernmental negotiations and influence their outcomes (Hill, 2004). This gave impetus for the adoption of a new UN resolution granting UN consultative status to NGOs in 1996 (UN ECOSOC, 1996), which formally recognized the growing importance of NGOs as players in development and aimed at facilitating their participation in UN meetings through improved dissemination of information and documentation and more transparent and simpler procedures for attendance.

An example of an international NGO relevant to dryland development is the International Institute for Sustainable Development (http://www.iisd.org), which disseminates knowledge and advances policy recommendations on economic policy, climate change and adaptation, trade and investment, and community sustainability. Examples of local NGOs operating in drylands include (1) ACFED/SAHEL in Burkina Faso (Appui conseil femmes environnement développement au Sahel), which conducts research on women and desertification, and holds national workshops on the role of women in the national action plan to combat desertification; and (2) the Pastoralist Development Network of Kenya, a forum for pastoralist communities in which they can articulate and advance their development priorities and social needs and communicate them to the government.

The Millennium Development campaign further cemented the role of civil society by engaging NGO expertise and perspectives in support of the Millennium Development goals (UNMP, 2005). A shift in focus from large-scale structural adjustment to poverty reduction at the community level has also become apparent in the policies of the World Bank in recent years (Bebbington, 2006). Its World Development Report 2000 is devoted to "Attacking Poverty" and recognizes both empowerment of poor people and mobilization of their skills and knowledge as key to reducing poverty. Today, 70% of loans and credits approved by the World Bank involve civil society organizations (World Bank, 2006).

Although there is broad consensus today on the validity of the concepts of empowerment and participation in development, their practical policy implementation is only beginning and is often hampered by infrastructural and political constraints. Empowerment can come from local or global actions. Locally, access to market opportunities and public sector services, decentralization, and community development can empower people. Globally, greater participation by poor people and countries in national and global forums can ensure that international agreements consider their needs and respect their interests (World Bank, 2000). One pertinent example is the International Treaty on Plant Genetic Resources for Food and Agriculture, which recognizes local farmers' legal rights to their own traditional knowledge of plant use (Chapter 5). Finally, the form in which international aid is delivered in emergencies, such as drought events, can empower rather than patronize poor people if, instead of prescribing a single solution (e.g., food aid), it increases the number of options among which the beneficiaries can choose based on their own particular situation (Box 8.1).

Recognition of the value of traditional knowledge could be viewed as another dimension of empowerment. In drylands, many introduced technologies and policies failed in the past because they were too inflexible to manage marginal environments and focused more on the resource base than on the knowledge, skills, and innovative capacity of local people (Anderson et al., 2004). For example, until the 1980s, governments policies in many dryland countries – supported by international donors – promoted policies developed in more humid regions (e.g., privatization of rangeland, commercial ranching with controlled stocking rates in fenced pastures, and sedentarization of nomads) (Fratkin, 1997). However, this well-meant transfer displayed a grave lack of understanding of the effectiveness of pastoralist strategies for exploiting risky environments based on herd flexibility, diversity, and mobility (Scoones, 1994). The imported policies that were intended to "improve" these pastoralist strategies were ineffective at best, if not downright damaging to environment and people.

8.2.5 The Evolution of The Dialogue Between Science and Policy

Although White (1956, pp. v–vi) emphasized "the importance of translating scientific findings into action at the level of operating farmers, herders, and land

Box 8.1 Cash Aid Distribution in Tanout, Niger

Niger, a landlocked West African country located partly in the semiarid Sahel and partly in the arid Sahara, frequently makes headlines for drought and subsequent food crises, the most recent one in early 2005. The donor community typically responds with emergency food aid programs (Fig. 8.1). However, what Niger typically experiences is less a sudden catastrophe than a chronic environmental challenge, coupled with poverty and chronic malnutrition, which makes people vulnerable to rises in food prices. The effectiveness of food aid in this situation has increasingly been questioned, as it drives down food prices for local farmers, undermines self-reliance, and increases dependency. One way to make aid more effective, which has been gaining acceptance rapidly in recent years, is to distribute cash instead of food to vulnerable households. While skeptics fear that the cash might be misused, lead to corruption or fuel conflicts, the advantages of cash aid lie in its cost-effective and timely delivery and its potentially positive effects on local economic activity. Moreover, cash aid allows recipients greater self-determination and dignity (Harvey, 2005).

In October 2005 the British Red Cross, in conjunction with the Niger Red Cross and the International Federation of the Red Cross and Red Crescent, undertook a large-scale cash aid distribution in Niger's Tanout province, which had been hit particularly hard by the drought. More than 5,700 households in 87 villages received a one-time cash distribution of 120,000 CFA

Fig. 8.1 Conventional food aid: grain supply in a Red Cross storage and distribution center.

Box 8.1 (continued)

francs (about US$240) each, which corresponds to the subsistence rate needed to feed a family of seven for 40 days. This amount enabled them not only to cover immediate consumption needs but also to make small investments. An evaluation study that accompanied the project has suggested an overall improvement in the socioeconomic conditions of the target population following the cash infusion, and noticeable differences in comparison with the control group. While much of the money went to purchase grains cover immediate consumption needs but also to make small investments and restock lost herds, households also bought clothing and pooled some of the cash for joint projects, including the construction and stocking of cereal banks, repair of local mosques, and purchase of donkeys and carts for water transport and to serve as ambulances (Fig. 8.2). Most of the villages involved experienced a decrease in out-migration (BARA, 2006). While a variety of challenges and needs remain, the cash assistance helped to reduce some of the difficulties that the poorer households faced during the drought crisis. The preliminary results of the project add to the growing body of evidence that cash aid can contribute to poverty reduction (Farrington et al., 2005).

Fig. 8.2 Villager in Wala Kanta with a new donkey cart, purchased from cash assistance received from the Red Cross.

most of the authors of *The Future of Arid Lands*. They implicitly assumed that good dryland science would either automatically translate into good dryland policies or would have to be made to influence policy specifically, in a one-way process. The transition from science to policy, or research to operations, has evolved considerably since then, even though it is still undervalued. Major challenges remain, because scientists and policymaking speak fundamentally different languages, have different priorities, and operate on different timescales (Nutley, 2003). Thus, researchers often cannot understand policymaking' resistance to change despite clear and convincing evidence, while policymaking complain about the inability of scientists to present their knowledge and ideas in short and simple ways (Court et al., 2004). For example, scientists often communicate uncertainty – such as variability of rainfall in drylands – by using cumulative probability distributions; but many policymaking and practitioners alike have difficulty understanding and applying probability-based information and are more likely to grasp climatic uncertainty and risk when presented as frequencies (for example, two years in ten) or time-series graphs (Huda and Packham, 2004).

While this is an easy-to-solve example, bridging the gap between science and policy can be so difficult that it has even been referred to as "crossing the valley of death" (NRC, 2000), The challenge is twofold: On the one hand, it is about "harnessing science to society" (UNESCO, 2002); that is, promoting applied research that is relevant to solving societal problems. On the other hand, it is about science-guided policymaking; that is, "putting the best available evidence from research at the heart of policy development and policy implementation" (Philip Davies, quoted in Sutcliffe and Court, 2006, p. 1).

Outreach and extension services have formed an important link between science, policy, and land management at least since the early twentieth century. However, the extension paradigm has gradually changed from a top-down linear approach in which knowledge is transmitted from the extension agent to the land user, to a bottom-up collaborative approach, in which problems and solutions are discussed and priorities defined among extension agents, government officials and land users alike in a participatory way (Huda et al., 2004) (Box 8.2). In this approach, land users are seen not as passive recipients of knowledge but as experts whose knowledge and opinions are crucial to appropriate solution development. In some contexts, farmer-to-farmer extension has been effective. In the semiarid areas of Kenya, for example, a government-initiated forestry project has been started, in which farmers are trained in tree planting and communication skills and expected to act as extension agents to other farmers (Muok et al., 2001). It is likely that better practices in the participatory approach will continue to spread in the near future.

Based on inspiring research findings on farmer investment and resource management from 1960 to 2000 in four dryland countries – Kenya, Senegal, Niger, and Nigeria –Mortimore and Tiffen (2003, 2004) have advocated a stronger research–policy interaction at different levels of development policymaking. Their research has not only confirmed that rural population growth, improved farm productivity, and sustainable resource management are not incompatible (Tiffen and Mortimore, 1992), but has also identified policies that provide an enabling environment for

Box 8.2 A New "International Center for Desert Affairs" in Western China

In the last two decades, China has seen rapid development, particularly in its eastern coastal regions, along with widening economic disparities and social inequity between its eastern and western regions. Western China is composed of drylands and is thus affected by environmental constraints such as wind erosion, infertile soils, uncertain precipitation, and vulnerability to global climate change. It is also home to most of the minority cultures in China (Fig. 8.3). In 2000, the Chinese government launched the ambitious Western Region Development Strategy (*Xibu Da Kaifa*) to improve infrastructure and promote development in this marginal region. Unlike earlier large-scale government programs, this program explicitly listed environmental sustainability and support of ethnic minorities among its goals.

Nevertheless, observers from both inside and outside China are concerned about the potential impacts of extensive infrastructure projects on the environment and on minority cultures. The Chinese bureaucracy, traditionally a command-and-control decision-making structure, has had little experience in conducting scientifically based environmental impact assessments.

To address these concerns, Xinjiang University, supported by the local government, in collaboration with the (US) National Center for Atmospheric Research (NCAR) established an "International Center for Desert Affairs" in

Fig. 8.3 Diversity: Uighur men, the largest ethnic minority in Xinjiang (The Oriental Caravan, http://www.theorientalcaravan.com/)

(continued)

Box 8.1 (continued)

Urumqi in 2002. This interdisciplinary research, education, and training institution has a regional focus on Western China and the Greater Central Asia region (Ye et al., 2003). Its philosophy builds on the "affairs" notion, which incorporates multidisciplinary aspects of environmental phenomena within their human and societal context, merging science, policy and ethics (Glantz, 2003). The center's program concentrates on the "4 Ds": drought, desertification, development (Fig. 8.4), and diversity. Courses taught at the center cover a range of desert-related topics, including desert science; human impacts on desert environments; policies, law and politics of the development of drylands; costs and benefits of dryland development; and ethical and equity issues related to dryland development. Interdisciplinary workshops are convened regularly to share information and technologies for regional development (Ye and Gao, 2006). Bringing together scientists from around the globe, the center allows them to share experiences and learn from past successes and failures in analogous development efforts in fragile environments, as Chinese leaders embark on a rapid economic development path.

Fig. 8.4 Development: new silk road under construction (The Oriental Caravan, http://www.theorientalcaravan.com/)

local populations to improve their resource management. Particularly, incentives to investment, such as secure access to land and resources and favorable macroeconomic policies, as well as improved access to markets, encouraged agricultural intensification and improved natural resource management in their four case studies. To disseminate these research findings, workshops involving villagers, researchers, and government officials were held at national and subnational levels in the respective countries. Workshops, web sites, and publications are expected eventually to present these findings in the international policy debate, which is moving towards more people-centered development strategies.

Over the course of five decades, policy has been shaped successively by four distinct perspectives. The first was that national governments were the most effective actors to initiate and achieve useful change. The second was spawned by the realization that many of the problems confronting the world extended far beyond national boundaries and thus required international cooperation to address. The third was initiated by the reality that the marketplace was a more powerful and often more efficient means by which to effect change than government, and that the marketplace had come to be a truly global force. The fourth, which has emerged over the last two decades, is that individuals and communities have interests that rarely coincide with those of governments or businesses. Civil society organizations have emerged as a countervailing force that seeks to represent individuals and communities and offset the power of governments and business. We have now arrived at a point where all of these actors – governments (national and international), markets, and NGOs – are acknowledged as having crucial roles to play, but the balance among them is still in flux.

Chapter 9
The Future of Arid Lands – Revisited

In this final chapter, we revisit some of the themes that have emerged in the preceding chapters with an eye toward deciding what has been learned over the last 50 years and what still remains unresolved. From this, we speculate on where things might go in the future.

9.1 What We Have Learned

There are a number of lessons that we might take away from this exercise. It is hard to find a rationale in the evolution of science and technology over the last 50 years that might be applicable to the next half century. However, as we have tried to capture, it is possible to describe the differences in terms of science and the issues that were addressed then and now. From these two points, we can make educated guesses about the general trajectory of progress and what the future might hold.

More than two generations ago, *The Future of Arid Lands* showed a fair amount of arrogance – perhaps naïveté – about the possibility of controlling nature with science and technology. Given the dramatic advances that had occurred prior to 1956 (such as nuclear energy) this faith is not so surprising. Similar faith may still exist in some quarters, but most of us are more cautious.

Optimism about the future was reflected in all themes of *The Future of Arid Lands*, whether the search for new sources of water (e.g., desalination), controlling the weather (as by cloud seeding), or finding new crops that could feed the world. Weather modification is a case in point. As described in Chapter 4, there was great interest in guiding the weather – making it rain where and when it was desired – to benefit ourselves or our friends and punish our enemies. It is ironic that this optimism has been replaced by the grim realization that we have been inadvertently changing our global climate in ways we did not want and may well be unable to reverse, at least in the next 50 years. As shown in Chapter 5, the deliberate introduction of plant species into new environments in order to increase economic production released a host of unforeseen negative impacts – local, regional, and global – which often offset or negated the putative lasting benefits. The search for more water-efficient crops from among existing dryland plant species, in order to replace thirsty crops from humid

C. F. Hutchinson and S. M. Herrmann, *The Future of Arid Lands – Revisited.*
© Springer 2008

regions, turned out to be fruitless for the most part. Even the gains of the Green Revolution were found to have little effect on the plight of the drylands, which, lacking irrigation water and finance to invest in seed and fertilizers, were often discovered to be "suboptimal" environments for revolution. With time, it became apparent that magic bullets were the exception rather than the rule, and that the few that did emerge were of limited value and rarely, if ever, panaceas. This is the most important lesson learned in the last 50 years, although it is a lesson too often forgotten.

The lessons – learned or unlearned – are now much more likely to be applied with tempered expectations than with the conviction that they will resolve all difficulties. Rather than continuing to search for new sources of water (through desalination or weather modification), there emerged an appreciation of what might be achieved through more deliberate evolutionary means. The general acknowledgement that there is essentially no "new" water has opened other doors of inquiry: given a finite amount of fresh water, we need prudent management. In fact, these ideas were nascent in what Gilbert White was writing even in the 1950s. His persistent message had been the need for integrated watershed management, particularly within the drylands, and the message was there in *The Future of Arid Lands*. Yet, his vision of water-related constraints on development and the need to balance competing interests took some time to take hold.

Along with the acceptance of constraints and the need to acknowledge and accommodate competing demands for resources came the rise of "systems thinking". The application of these ideas – cybernetics – to climate, economic, and ecological systems was also beginning by 1956. The combined lesson about constraints and intelligent management is that we live with and attempt to manage dynamic systems, both natural and human. This realization has two benefits. First, if we can describe these systems – such as climate – we can predict their behavior and adapt our behavior accordingly. Second, in attempting to improve the performance of a system – such as agriculture or water supply – relatively small changes in the performance of various individual system components can result in large changes in overall system performance. Management should be able to hasten desirable changes, like the range of benefits that accrue to farmers by keeping the soils of their fields in place, and to limit undesirable changes, like the loss of valuable local plant species and the reduction in biodiversity that often accompany the introduction of exotic plants into a new environment.

We have also learned that most natural systems are very complex. The example of climate modeling in Chapter 4 demonstrates how complexity has emerged through painstaking research. The first global climate models were straightforward descriptions of how the atmosphere circulated, but then grew increasingly complex as interactions of the atmosphere with land and sea surfaces and the composition of the atmosphere itself were added. Similarly, as discussed in Chapter 7, the concept of sustainability grew from a simple ecological notion about limits, to one that encompassed economic, political, and social considerations – all those factors that ultimately define what is possible and acceptable.

Along with the appreciation of the complexity of systems has come the understanding that they are not necessarily self-regulating, nor do they necessarily seek a single equilibrium state. As related in Chapter 6, the concept of the equilibrium model has been difficult to dispel, largely because at first sight systems appear to behave that way. The basic argument in equilibrium thinking was that if a system was perturbed, it would return to its initial state if the perturbation ceased. For example, if a pasture was heavily grazed there might be a reduction in plant cover and a change in species composition, but if grazing were to be suspended, the pasture would return to its prior ungrazed state. It turned out that rangeland grazing systems did not always behave this way. We have learned over time that changes in plant cover and species composition may cause other fundamental changes – such as a redistribution of water resources and a loss of soil fertility – that preclude a return to an earlier state, no matter what management strategies are used. Moreover, systems may more often be in transition among any number of equilibrium states. As was explored in Chapter 6, understanding that disequilibrium tends to prevail is a lesson that can be applied not only in natural resource management, but also in human social, political, and economic systems. However, as pointed out in Chapter 8, this understanding does not lead immediately to better decisions. Developing "adaptive" land management policies that can accommodate these types of change is a challenge that is difficult to meet because systems are almost always in flux.

Appreciation for the systems perspective, and a better understanding of the often chaotic nature of climate and ecosystems, also brought attempts to better understand traditional livelihood systems that had persisted, mostly in the developing world. In 1956, the value of traditional animal breeds adapted to local conditions, and of the past use of some plants such as guayule, received only passing note. The whole-livelihood systems that sustained families in drylands were largely overlooked or, at times, denigrated as "backward." As noted in Chapter 5, when it became apparent that the Green Revolution had largely bypassed the drylands, attention eventually moved from individual crops to complete "farming systems" in which the family or household was the functioning unit. From this perspective, as noted in Chapter 7, the behaviors of traditional pastoralists that some in 1956 had considered random and often pointless were now seen as highly adapted to climate variations in time and space. The strategies that traditional societies developed to deal with the peculiar opportunities and constraints offered by the drylands they occupied have come to be understood and valued in themselves. More important, as we were reminded in Chapter 8, it is far more practical to develop an understanding of the existing local system, and make incremental improvements within this framework, than to replace it wholesale with something developed in other economic, environmental, or cultural settings.

Another radical shift in perspective has been brought about by globalization. Gilbert White himself raised the need to search for solutions from the local to the regional, but it would have been very difficult in 1956 to envision the global environment and global economy that exist today. Several lessons emerge from an appreciation of this change. First, in Chapter 4 we pointed to some of the environmental problems that plague the world's drylands that may be local or regional in occurrence but perhaps global in their potential impact. For example, the dust that emanates from Saharo–Sahelian region of Africa (Fig. 4.5) may have climate and human health effects that threaten other regions of the globe and will require international attention if they are to be abated. Given the size of the areas involved and the limited number of options for their development, solving problems like this is a physically and financially daunting task. However, the second global phenomenon – the global economy – might provide help. As noted in Chapter 7, in 1956 the only land use envisioned for the drylands was agriculture. Since then, the global economy has opened far more opportunities for the drylands. These opportunities enhance the adaptive capacity of farmers and pastoralists in the developing drylands by offering them a broader range of income-generating opportunities than agriculture alone. Without providing income alternatives, poor dryland households are at the whim of climate variability. Left with no alternatives during bad times, farmers and pastoralists must further exploit an overtaxed environment through overgrazing and woodcutting in the short term, and the extension of agriculture and grazing into increasingly marginal lands over the long term. Thus, as has repeatedly been noted, the problems of poverty and environment are linked and by addressing the former, you go a long way towards solving the latter (Box 9.1).

Box 9.1   Trends for The Future in African Drylands?

The 1970s and 1980s were bleak for the African Sahel. Droughts brought production declines, eroded fields, dry wells, scarce firewood, and migration of the rural population (Kaboré and Reij, 2004). Prospects for recovery were poor. Yet, in this scene of desolation were the seeds of hope. In the Yatenga region of Burkina Faso around 1980, a desperate farmer began to experiment with a traditional form of cultivation, small planting pits or *zaï*. He made them larger (30 cm wide by 20 cm deep) than usual and put manure in them, thus concentrating both water and nutrients around his crops of millet and sorghum. His results were so promising that his neighbors began to adopt the technique. This development was quickly noted by nongovernmental organizations (NGOs) operating in the region; they introduced it to neighboring villages with the addition of stone bunds built on contours, which reduced erosion and protected the *zaï*. Significantly, stone bunds had previously been rejected by farmers because they had not been integrated into their field management scheme (Kaboré and Reij, 2004). While this demonstrates the potential of local ingenuity, official policies promoting such strategies must be implemented if more smallholders are to succeed.

Based on similar "success stories" in African drylands, Mortimore (2005) suggested five policy conditions for success. First is access to markets, which can be facilitated by eliminating unfair competition from imports and by stabilizing prices. Second is physical infrastructure, especially roads and electronic communications that enhance the movement of goods and services. Third is institutional infrastructure (government or nongovernment), to provide services (e.g., extension), manage resources (e.g., forests), or facilitate interactions (e.g., trade). Fourth is knowledge management or valuing and building on local practices, like the *zaï*. Finally is diversification, or opportunities to generate income from off-farm work, typically urban. Restrictions on the movement of people and commodities are obstacles to diversification.

(continued)

Box 9.1   (continued)

Zaï in Burkina Faso (Chris Reij)

The agents that might be recruited to address poverty and, as a result, environmental concerns have changed. In 1956, the problem of making full productive use of the drylands was seen as a global issue that would require international cooperation to undertake the research necessary to achieve that goal. Moreover, as argued in Chapter 8, it was assumed that both the research and implementation of research results would be carried out – or at least facilitated – with support from public institutions at international, national, and local levels. With respect to international cooperation in research – especially in the developing world – this model largely has played out as witnessed by the achievements of the CGIAR. However, over time, two things became apparent. First was that many governments in the developing world were unable to effect substantive change even with extensive outside assistance. Second, it was recognized that market forces at local, national, and international levels might provide another engine for change in many of the world's drylands. Thus, over the last two decades, parallel efforts have been directed toward making markets function more effectively at all levels; this has hastened globalization.

But we now know that governments at all levels tend to pursue "top-down" development strategies that may primarily benefit the wealthy and powerful. We also know that market forces are indifferent to the limited abilities of some groups and regions to participate effectively in local, regional, and global economies. To counter these tendencies, nongovernmental organizations (NGOs) emerged as a force to take up the interests of specific groups and regions, a development that was unforeseen in 1956. Thus, the number of actors in drylands development has diversified over the last 50 years: each has a role to play, with the scope and relative importance of their respective roles changing in response to the specific situation (Box 9.1).

9.2   Where We May Be Going

Concern about how a burgeoning population might be accommodated in a world with finite resources was a driving force behind *The Future of Arid Lands* in 1956. Global population has doubled since then, but food production has trebled. By 2050, though, the world's population is projected to increase by another 50%, to something over 9 billion people. While Malthus' bleak view of the future has been held at bay over the last 50 years, there still remain the challenges he saw 200 years ago of feeding the world's population and meeting their other needs while not degrading our planet's productive capacity.

Over the next 50 years, it is hard to imagine that the drylands will not assume a role in a world economy that is larger and surely even more integrated than it is now. As pointed out in Chapter 7, the drylands may also benefit from the global economy's development of new markets and products based on more intangible values (e.g., land for recreation, or for the provision of environmental services). For example, from a global perspective, the value of conserving wetlands in dry regions to support migratory birds now outweighs the potential value of such areas to support local agriculture. Similarly, the aesthetic value of many drylands makes them more attractive for urban development and for tourism than for agriculture.

Water – from sources other than received rainfall – will continue to be the issue that defines and prescribes the future of drylands. However, in keeping with the concept of the finite nature of this resource, increased attention will likely be paid to improving water-use efficiency and conservation, and to increasing the reclamation and reuse of wastewaters, rather than to searching for new water resources.

Some recent developments hold out hope for the future of drylands in developing countries. As pointed out in Chapter 7, in the more remote developing drylands, there have been promising results from local soil and water conservation efforts using simple technology at the farm level (Box 9.1). These improvements may be attributed in large part to the ingenuity and persistence of farmers in these regions, but may also be attributed in part to more favorable weather conditions prevailing in the last decade. It must not be forgotten that local efforts, however ingenious, need to be encouraged and protected by well-crafted policies if they are to be successful in the long run. But the boom-and-bust character of the dryland climate (Box 2.1) will always be a major challenge that requires special attention.

In the developed drylands and near urban centers in all drylands, agriculture's share of water probably will continue to decline as competing urban demands grow, as argued in Chapter 3. Some of this tendency may be offset by improved technologies (e.g., controlled environment agriculture, drip irrigation), as well as by the use of treated but nonpotable urban effluent for irrigation. It may also be that dryland agricultural production will continue to evolve toward incorporating more livestock and higher-value crops

---

Box 9.2   Drylands Meet The Terawatt Challenge?

By 2050, the world's population is expected to reach more than 9 billion. In addition, global energy demand per capita will rise with economic development, as the cases of China and India already show. Currently, we consume 10 terawatts (TW) of energy in various forms – of which the USA alone consumes 3 TW. Future global energy demand is projected to more than triple. The Earth intercepts about 125,000 TW of sunlight, making solar a very attractive and probably inevitable option for satisfying much of our energy budget (Hoffert et al., 2002; Zweibel, 2005). Given current performance and requirements of solar photovoltaic technology (direct conversion of sunlight into electricity), about 1.4% of the Earth's land surface would be required to collect 20 TW of solar energy. The most conservative estimates suggest this need for space could be met by six areas each measuring 160 km on a side, scattered around the world (Smalley, 2005; Zweibel, 2005). Part of the energy generated would be consumed directly as electricity; some would be used to separate water into its component oxygen and hydrogen, with the latter being used as a fuel for transportation. Humanity's other energy needs would be met by "traditional" sources. Ultimately, less land area would be required to generate this much power, as the technology becomes more efficient and more easily incorporated into new and existing buildings. To be effective, this system would require a more highly – though still not totally – integrated global power grid, because the sun illuminates only half the world at any one moment (Hoffert et al., 2002). Much of the sun's radiation falls in drylands. Thus, drylands have an energy advantage as well as land availability and price advantages. It has been noted, ironically, that many areas with large existing petroleum reserves are also "vast empty desert areas with large amounts of consistent sun" (Bradford, 2006, p. 165).

(e.g., fruits and vegetables) to meet growing demands of a population that is increasingly more affluent and urban. Overall, as suggested in Chapter 5, there may be greater willingness to invest in dryland agriculture in the future, if the return on investment is higher than in more humid regions, as it may become.

As we argue in Chapter 7, whether it is realized or not, drylands may hold a competitive advantage for land uses that have lower water demands than other uses, but require large tracts of inexpensive land. A distinct opportunity is the development of solar energy, particularly photovoltaics (Box 9.2). The physical, climatic, and economic advantages that the world's drylands possess for solar energy production are undeniable, and its development is consistent with the need to develop "greener" energy sources as more concrete actions are taken to address global warming. This option has received renewed attention recently, and will doubtlessly be pursued more consistently as petroleum reserves decline and prices rise (Turner 1999). Nevertheless, despite the seemingly obvious advantages of these options, we should not overlook one of the main findings of this book, which is the disappointment that has followed so many of the magic bullets of the past.

As found in Chapter 3, though, there is at least one troubling aspect of water in the future. Groundwater was not considered a major option in 1956, but it turned out to be one of the major resources that fueled the Green Revolution and brought new drylands into production. Yet, despite this central role in dryland development during the last 50 years, groundwater has rarely been sustainably managed or even adequately measured. Only one global assessment has been made of how much of it there might be, but it is clear that much of the groundwater resource in drylands is finite and being rapidly depleted. With the certainty of population growth the overallocation of existing surface waters and the likelihood that these will be seriously affected by global warming, the possibility of having to manage the drylands without groundwater resources one day is truly ominous.

The findings of Chapters 7 and 8 assert that developing management policies that can adapt both to highly variable climate and to ecosystems in a persistent state of disequilibrium is a challenge that will persist. In Chapter 8 and Box 9.1, we argue that the goal is to provide inhabitants of drylands with a broader range of livelihood options, some of which are decoupled from agriculture or local climate variability. Dryland inhabitants themselves implicitly favor such goals, as witnessed by the movement of the increasing numbers of people to urban centers in both the developing and the developed drylands – a trend that is projected to continue. Thus, policy now and in the future must recognize and accommodate efforts to increase the adaptive capacities of dryland inhabitants by allowing them more opportunities, something that is totally consistent both with notions of globalization and with sensibilities about equity and social justice.

The drylands will undoubtedly play a greater future role in meeting the needs of the world than they have in the past. First, as pointed out in Chapter 7, the increasingly global economy has freed us from the notion that all regions should strive to be agriculturally self-sufficient, so it may be that drylands will increasingly provide a home for more of the world's growing population. This general idea was put forward by Shantz (1956, p. 21) who suggested that "unproductive occupancy" of land (e.g., cities, highways, landing fields, reservoirs, recreational areas, factories) be shifted to drylands so as to free up "productive" land (i.e., more humid regions) for agriculture. With very few exceptions (e.g., China), that such a wholesale readjustment toward more "rational" land use could be achieved through any government action is highly unlikely. Such a readjustment might, though, be driven by changing land values, making drylands more attractive, and, indeed, precisely this kind of shift is already being seen in the development of dryland cities and resorts.

It may well be that the need to address issues surrounding global warming will define the future of drylands. It is certain that the world's energy demands will continue to grow at rates that may substantially outpace actual population growth (Box 9.2). It is equally true that the decline in petroleum reserves will drive energy prices higher and spur the search for alternative sources of energy. The option of removing large amounts of CO_2 from the atmosphere through sequestration programs can serve as only a bridge to some newer "clean" energy technology over the long term. However, given the critical need to reduce emissions of greenhouse gases into the atmosphere, other energy options are limited. The prevailing argument about solar technology becoming a major energy is not a matter of "if", but "when".

The two cases portrayed here (Boxes 9.1 and 9.2) serve as optimistic bookends to frame the range of futures that might unfold for the world's drylands over the first half of the twenty-first century. In the case of the *zaï*, there is a sense that one path to the future is found at the local level, built on local initiative and ingenuity, driven by linkages to markets – local, regional, and national – but nurtured and sustained by policies and institutions that protect that initiative, facilitate interactions both near and far, and provide opportunity. In the case of the terawatt challenge, the path to the future is built around global efforts to provide the energy that the world's population will demand and expect, while attempting to reverse the greenhouse gas emissions that drive global warming. Development of solar energy resources exploits the particular advantages of the drylands – sunlight and inexpensive land – and connects them to both the global economy and the global environment.

In the case exemplified by the *zaï*, we see what is happening now, and will likely continue to happen if we provide institutional and economic frameworks in which local ingenuity might thrive. In the case of the terawatt challenge, we are speculating about something that is quite distant from where we are now and that may turn out to be another chimeric magic bullet. Regardless, in both these examples, drylands continue to become increasingly connected to the rest of the world. As a consequence, the historic isolation of many of the world's drylands will continue to diminish under the onslaughts of population growth and the twin globalizations of economy and environment. People who, perhaps romantically, enjoy drylands as they currently are will view their incorporation into the broader world as a tragic loss. The more pragmatic will see drylands as stepping up to the global role for which they have long been destined.

References

Adger, W. N., Benjaminsen, T. A., Brown, K. and Svarstad, H. 2001. Advancing a political ecology of global environmental discourses. *Development and Change*, Vol. 32, pp. 681–715.

Agrawala, S., Moehner, A., Hemp, A., van Aalst, M., Hitz, S., Smith, J., Meena, H., Mwakifwamba, S., Hyera, T. and Mwaipopo, O. 2003. *Development and Climate Change in Tanzania: Focus on Mount Kilimanjaro*, Paris: Organisation for Economic Co-operation and Development. (COM/ENV/EPOC/DCD/DAC(2003)5/FINAL.) http://www.oecd.org/dataoecd/47/0/21058838. pdf (Accessed 29 September 2006.)

Al-Fenadi, Y. 2003. Cloud seeding in Libya. *Eighth World Meteorological Organization Scientific Conference on Weather Modification*, Casablanca, Morocco, 7–12 April 2003, Geneva: World Meteorological Organization.

Alghariani, S. A. 2003. *Water Transfer Versus Desalination In North Africa: Sustainability And Cost Comparison*, London: School of Oriental and African Studies, University of London. Occasional Paper No. 49.

Allan, J. A. 1997. *"Virtual Water": A Long Term Solution for Water in Middle Eastern Economies?* London: School of Oriental and African Studies, University of London. http://www.soas.ac. uk/waterissues/occasionalpapers/OCC03.PDF (Accessed 24 June 2006.)

Allan, J. A. 2003. Virtual water – the water, food and trade nexus: useful concept or misleading metaphor? *Water International*, Vol. 28, pp. 4–11.

Allison, H. E. and Hobbs, R. J. 2004. Resilience, adaptive capacity, and the "Lock-in Trap" of the Western Australian Agricultural Region. *Ecology and Society*, Vol. 9, No. 1, p. 3.

Alward, R., Detling, J. K. and Milchunas, D. G. 1999. Grassland vegetation changes and nocturnal global warming. *Science*, Vol. 283, No. 5399, pp. 229–231.

American Meteorological Society Council (AMSC). 1998. Scientific Background for the AMS Policy Statement on Planned and Inadvertent Weather Modification. *Bulletin of the American Meteorological Society*, Vol. 79, No. 12, pp. 2773–2778.

Anderson, D. and Willebrand, J. 1992. Recent advances in modelling the ocean circulation and its effects on climate. *Reports on Progress in Physics*, Vol. 55, pp. 1–37.

Anderson, J., Bryceson, D., Campbell, B., Chitundu, D., Clarke, J., Drinkwater, M., Fakir, S., Frost, P. G. H., Gambiza, J., Grundy, I., Hagmann, J., Jones, B., Jones, G. W., Kowero, G., Luckert, M., Mortimore, M., Phiri, A. D. K., Potgieter, P., Shackleton, S. and Williams, T. 2004. Chance, change and choice in Africa's drylands. A new perspective on policy priorities. Jakarta, Center for International Forestry (CIFOR). http://www.cifor.cgiar.org/publications/ pdf_files/research/livelihood/Dryland.pdf (Accessed 28 October 2006.)

Anderson, J. W. 2005. *How Climate Change Policy Developed: A Short History*. Resources for the Future (RFF), Washington, DC. (RFF Backgrounder.) http://www.rff.org/rff/Documents/RFF-BCK-ClimateChangePolicy.pdf (Accessed 28 October 2006.)

Andreoli, R. and Kayano, M. 2005. ENSO-related rainfall anomalies in South America and associated circulation features during warm and cold Pacific Decadal Oscillation Regimes. *International Journal of Climatology*, Vol. 25, pp. 2017–2030.

Angelakis, A., Koutsoyiannis, D. and Tchobanoglous, G. 2005. Urban wastewater and stormwater technologies in ancient Greece. *Water Research*, Vol. 39, pp. 210–220.

Anyamba, A., Tucker, C. and Mahoney, R. 2002. From El Niño to La Niña: Vegetation response patterns over East and southern Africa during the 1997–2000 period. *Journal of Climate*, Vol. 15, pp. 3096–3103.

Arnell, N. W. 1999. Climate change and global water resources. *Global Environmental Change*, Vol. 9, pp. 831–849.

Arnon, I. 1992. *Agriculture in Drylands: Principles and Practice*, Amsterdam: Elsevier. (Developments in Agriculture and Managed Forest Ecology, 26.)

Aronson, J. 1985. Economic halophytes: a global review. In: Wickens, G. E., Goodin, J. R. and Field, D. V. (eds), *Plants for Arid Lands*, Boston, MA: George Allen & Unwin, pp. 177–188.

Arrhenius, S. 1896. On the influence of carbonic acid in the air upon the temperature of the ground, London, Edinburgh, and Dublin. *Philosophical Magazine and Journal of Science (fifth series)*, Vol. 41, pp. 237–275.

Arriaga, L., Castellanos, A. E., Moreno, E. and Alarcón, J. 2004. Potential ecological distribution of alien invasive species and risk assessment: a case study of buffel grass in arid regions of Mexico. *Conservation Biology*, Vol. 18, No. 5, pp. 1504–1514.

Asano, T. and Levine, A. D. 1995. Wastewater reclamation, recycling and reuse: past, present and future. *Second International Symposium on Wastewater Reclamation and Reuse*, Iraklio, Greece, 17–20 October 1995.

Ashby, W. 1956. *An Introduction to Cyberkinetics*, London: Chapman & Hall.

Ashley, R., Russell, D. and Swallow, B. 2006. The policy terrain in protected area landscapes: challenges for agroforestry in integrated landscape conservation. *Biodiversity and Conservation*, Vol. 15, pp. 663–689.

Asner, G., Elmore, A., Olander, L., Martin, R. and Harris, A. 2004. Grazing systems, ecosystem responses, and global change. *Annual Review of Environmental Resources*, Vol. 29, pp. 261–299.

Aubréville, A. 1949. *Climats, Forêts Et Désertification De l'Afrique Tropicale* [Climates, Forests and Desertification in Tropical Africa], Paris, Société d'Éditions Géographiques, Maritimes et Coloniales.

Axelrod, R. S., Downie, D. L. and Vig, N. J. 2005. *The Global Environment: Institutions, Laws and Policy*, 2nd edn, Washington, DC: CQ Press.

Ba, M. B., Nicholson, S. E. and Frouin, R. 2001. Satellite-derived surface radiation budget over the African continent. Part II: climatologies of the various components. *Journal of Climate*, Vol. 14, pp. 60–76.

Bailey, K. 2005. Fifty years of systems science: further reflections. *Systems Research and Behavioral Science*, Vol. 22, pp. 355–361.

Bailey, R. W. 1956. Summary Statement. In: White, G. (ed), *The Future of Arid Lands: Papers and Recommendations from the International Arid Lands Meetings*, Washington, DC: American Association for the Advancement of Science, pp. 172–5. (Publication No. 43 of the AAAS.)

Baker, L. A., Brazel, A. T. and Westerhoff, P. 2004. Environmental consequences of rapid urbanization in warm, arid lands: case study of Phoenix, Arizona (USA). In *Sustainable Cities*, Sienna, Italy.

Baldock, D., Caraveli, H., Dwyer, J., Einschütz, S., Petersen, J. E., Sumpsi-Vinas, J. and Varela-Ortega, C. 2000. *The Environmental Impacts of Irrigation in the European Union: A Report to the Environment Directorate of the European Union*, London: Institute for European Environmental Policy. http://ec.europa.eu/environment/agriculture/pdf/irrigation.pdf (Accessed 29 September 2006.)

Barnett, T., Pierce, D., Latif, M., Dommenget, D. and R. Saravana 1999. Interdecadal interactions between the tropics and midlatitudes in the Pacific basin. *Geophysical Research Letters* 26(5):615–618.

Barnett, T. P., Adam, J. C. and Lettenmaier, D. P. 2005. Potential impacts of a warming climate on water availability in snow-dominated regions. *Nature*, Vol. 438, No. 7066, pp. 303–309.

Bashyal, B. P., Wijeratne, E. M. K., Faeth, S. H. and Gunatilaka, A. A. L. 2005. Globosumones A-C, cytotoxic orsellinic acid esters from the Sonoran Desert endophytic fungus *Chaetomium globosum*. *Journal of Natural Products*, Vol. 68, pp. 724–728.

Batisse, M. 2005. *The UNESCO Water Adventure From Desert To Water, 1948–1974: From the Arid Zone Programme to the International Hydrological Decade* [Du désert jusqu'a l'eau 1948–1974. La question de l'eau et l'UNESCO: de la Zone aride a la Décennie hydrologique], Paris: UNESCO.

Batjes, N. H. 2001. Options for increasing carbon sequestration in West African soils: an exploratory study with special focus on Senegal. *Land Degradation and Development*, Vol. 12, pp. 131–142.

Battrick, B. 2005. *Global Earth Observing System of Systems: 10-Year Implementation Plan*, Noordwijk, The Netherlands: European Space Agency.

Bebbington, A. (ed). 2006. *The Search for Empowerment: Social Capital as Idea and Practice at the World Bank*, Bloomfield, CT: Kumarian Press.

Belnap, J. 2003. The world at your feet: desert biological soil crusts. *Frontiers in Ecology and the Environment*, Vol. 1, No. 5, pp. 181–189.

Beniston, M. 2003. Climatic change in mountain regions: a review of possible impacts. *Climate Change*, Vol. 59, pp. 5–31.

Berger, A. 1988. Milankovitch theory and climate. *Reviews of Geophysics*, Vol. 26, pp. 624–657.

Berkes, F., Kislalioglu, M., Folke, C. and Gadgil, M. 1998. Exploring the basic ecological unit: ecosystem-like concepts in traditional societies. *Ecosystems*, Vol. 1, pp. 409–415.

Bertram, R. B. 1993. New crops and the international agricultural research centers. In: Janick, J. and Simon, J. E. (eds), *New Crops: Exploration, Research and Commercialization*, New York: Wiley, pp. 11–22.

Bestelmeyer, B. T., Herrick, J. E., Brown, J. R., Trujillo, D. A. and Havstad, K. M. 2004. Land management in the American Southwest: a state-and-transition approach to ecosystem complexity. *Environmental Management*, Vol. 34, pp. 38–51.

Betsill, M. M. 2005. Global climate change policy: making progress or spinning wheels? In: Axelrod, R. S., Downie, D. L. and Vig, N. J. (eds), *The Global Environment: Institutions, Law, and Policy*, Washington, DC: CQ Press, pp. 103–124.

Bhagwati, J. N. and Srinivasan, T. N. 2002. Trade and poverty in the poor countries. *American Economic Review*, Vol. 92, No. 2, pp. 180–183.

Biermann, F. and Bauer, S. 2004. Assessing the effectiveness of intergovernmental organisations in international environmental politics. *Global Environmental Change*, Vol. 14, No. 2, pp. 189–193.

Billings, W. D. 1958. Two symposia on desert ecology. *Ecology*, Vol. 39, No. 3, pp. 563–564.

Bjerknes, J. 1969. Atmospheric teleconnections from the equatorial Pacific. *Monthly Weather Review*, Vol. 97, No. 3, pp. 163–172.

Bjornlund, H. 2003. Efficient water market mechanisms to cope with water scarcity. *International Journal of Water Resources Development*, Vol. 19, No. 4, pp. 553–567.

Blaikie, P. and Brookfield, H. 1987. *Land Degradation and Society*, London/New York: Methuen.

Blanchard, D. 1996. Blanchard, D. 1996 Serendipity, scientific discovery, and Project Cirrus. *Bulletin of the American Meteorological Society*, Vol. 77, No. 6, pp. 1279–1286.

Blass, S. 1973. *Me Merivah U-maas* [Water in Strife and Action], Ramat-Gan, Israel, Masadah.

Bonner, J. 1991. The history of rubber. In: Whitworth, J. W. and Whitehead, E. E. (eds), *Guayule Natural Rubber*, Tucson, AZ: Office of Arid Lands Studies, University of Arizona, pp. 1–6.

Borchert, J. R. 1957. The Future of Arid Lands (Book Review). *The Journal of Geography*, Vol. 56, No. 8, pp. 391–392.

Borlaug, N. 1972. Nobel lecture (1970). In: Haberman, F. W. (ed), *Nobel Lectures, Peace 1951–1970*, Amsterdam: Elsevier.

Boserup, E. 1965. *The Conditions of Agricultural Growth: The Economics of Agrarian Change Under Population Pressure*, London: George Allen & Unwin.

Bouwer, H. 2000. Integrated water management: emerging issues and challenges. *Agricultural Water Management*, Vol. 45, No. 3, pp. 217–228.

Bowen, E. 1956. Induced Precipitation. In: White, G. (ed), *The Future of Arid Lands: Papers and Recommendations from the International Arid Lands Meetings*, Washington, DC: American Association for the Advancement of Science, pp. 291–299. (Publication No. 43 of the AAAS.)

Bowers, J. E. 1988. *A Sense of Place: The Life and Work of Forrest Shreve*, Tucson, AZ: University of Arizona Press.

Bradford, T. 2006. *Solar Revolution: The Economic Transformation of the Global Energy Industry*, Cambridge, MA: MIT Press.

Briske, D. D., Fuhlendorf, S. D. and Smeins, F. E. 2003. Vegetation dynamics on rangelands: a critique of the current paradigms. *Journal of Applied Ecology*, Vol. 40, pp. 601–614.

Brönnimann, S. 2002. Picturing climate change. *Climate Research*, Vol. 22, pp. 87–95.

Brookfield, H., Parsons, H. and Brookfield, M. (eds). 2003. *Agrodiversity: Learning from Farmers across the World*, Tokyo: United Nations University Press.

Brooks, D. 1993. Beyond catch phrases: what does sustainable development really mean? *Arid Lands Newsletter*, Vol. 33, pp. 2–5.

Brown, C. E. 2002. *World Energy Resources*, New York: Springer.

Bruins, H. 1997. Drought mitigation policy and food provision for urban Africa: potential use of treated wastewater and solar energy. *Arid Lands Newsletter*, No. 42. http://ag.arizona.edu/OALS/ALN/aln42/bruins.html (Accessed 20 December 2006.)

Bureau of Applied Research in Anthropology (BARA). 2006. *2005 Tanout Cash Transfer Project Final Monitoring Report*, Tucson, AZ: BARA, The University of Arizona.

Burgess, T. L., Bowers, J. and Turner, R. 1991. Exotic plants at the Desert Laboratory, Tucson, Arizona. *Madroño*, Vol. 38, pp. 96–114.

Burke, J., Moench, M. and Sauveplane, C. 1999. Groundwater and society: problems in variability and points of engagement. *Groundwater: Legal and Policy Perspectives*, Washington, DC: World Bank. http://www-wds.worldbank.org/servlet/WDSContentServer/WDSP/IB/1999/12/30/000094946_99122006354976/Rendered/PDF/multi_page.pdf (Accessed 29 September 2006.)

Caldwell, L. K. 1996. *International Environmental Policy*, 3rd edn, Durham, NC: Duke University Press.

Canfield, R. 1942. *Sampling Ranges by the Line Intercept Method: Plant Cover, Composition, Density, and Degree of Forage Use*, Tucson, AZ: US Department of Agriculture, Forest Service. (Research Report 4.)

Cardoso, F. H. and Faletto, E. 1979. *Dependency and Development in Latin America*, Berkeley: University of California Press.

Carney, D. (ed). 1998. *Sustainable Rural Livelihoods: What Contribution Can We Make?* London: Department for International Development.

Carson, R. 1962. *Silent Spring*, London: Houghton Mifflin.

Caughley, G. 1976. The elephant problem: an alternative hypothesis. *East African Wildlife Journal*, Vol. 14, pp. 265–283.

Caveney, S., Charlet, D. A., Freitag, H., Maier-Stolte, M. and Starratt, A. N. 2001. New observations on the secondary chemistry of world Ephedra (Ephedraceae). *American Journal of Botany*, Vol. 88, No. 7, pp. 1199–1208.

Center for International Forestry Research (CIFOR). 1999. *Progress in the Ecoregional Initiative: Emerging Issues and Future Directions*. http://www.inrm.cgiar.org/documents/CDC/cdc_ecoregional_init.htm (Accessed 14 November 2006.)

CGIAR. Technical Advisory Committee. 1992. *Review of Priorities and Strategies*. (FAO/TAC Secretariat Report AGR/TAC:IAR/92/18.1.) http://www.fao.org/Wairdocs/TAC/X5756E/X5756E00.htm (Accessed 1 December 2006.)

Chambers, R., Pacey, A. and Thrupp, L. A. (eds). 1989. *Farmer First: Farmer Innovation and Agricultural Research*, London: Intermediate Technology Development Group (ITDG).

Charney, J., Stone, P. H. and Quirk, W. J. 1975. Drought in the Sahara: a biogeophysical feedback mechanism. *Science*, Vol. 187, No. 4175, pp. 434–435.

Chatelard, G. 2006. Desert tourism as a substitute for pastoralism? Tuareg in Algeria and Bedouin in Jordan. In: Chatty, D. (ed), *Nomadic Societies in the Middle East and North Africa: Entering the 21st Century*, Leiden: Brill, pp. 710–736.

Chen, Z., Meng, X. and Jin, X. 2003. The overview of recent scientific research on weather modification in China. *Eighth World Meteorological Organization Scientific Conference on Weather Modification*, Casablanca, Morocco, 7–12 April 2003, Geneva: World Meteorological Organization.

Chiew, F., Piechota, T., Dracup, J. and McMohon, T. 1998. El Niño/Southern Oscillation and Australian rainfall, streamflow and drought: links and potential for forecasting. *Journal of Hydrology* 204:138–149

City of Tucson Water Department. 2004. *Water Plan: 2000–2005*. Tucson: Tucson Water. http://www.ci.tucson.az.us/water/docs/waterplan.pdf (Accessed 29 September 2006.)

Clarke, P. J., Latz, P. K. and Albrecht, D. E. 2005. Long-term changes in semi-arid vegetation: invasion of an exotic perennial grass has larger effects than rainfall variability. *Journal of Vegetation Science*, Vol. 16, pp. 237–248.

Cleary, D. 2003. *People-centred Approaches: A Brief Literature Review and Comparison of Types*, Rome: FAO. (Livelihood Support Program, 5.)

Clements, F. 1936. The origin of the desert climax and climate. In: Goodspeed, T. H. (ed), *Essays in Geobotany in Honor of William Albert Setchell*, Berkeley: University of California Press, pp. 87–140.

Clements, F. E. 1916. *Plant Succession; An Analysis of the Development of Vegetation*, Washington, DC: Carnegie Institution.

Cohen, M. J., Morrison, J. I. and Glenn, E. P. 1999. *Haven or Hazard: The Ecology and Future of the Salton Sea*, Oakland, CA: Pacific Institute for Studies in Development, Environment, and Security.

Collier, P. and Dollar, D. 2001. *Globalization, Growth, and Poverty: Building an Inclusive World Economy*, Washington, DC/Oxford: World Bank/Oxford University Press.

Cook, R. and Calvin, L. 2005. *Greenhouse Tomatoes Change the Dynamics of the North American Fresh Tomato Industry*, Washington, DC: US Department of Agriculture. (Economic Research Report 2.)

Corell, E. and Betsill, M. M. 2001. A comparative look at NGO influence in international environmental negotiation: desertification and climate change. *Global Environmental Politics*, Vol. 1, No. 4, pp. 86–107.

Cotton, W. and Pielke, R. 1995. *Human Impacts on Weather and Climate*, New York: Cambridge University Press.

Court, J., Hovland, I. and Young, J. 2004. *Bridging Research and Policy in International Development: Evidence and the Change Process*, Rugby: Intermediate Technology Development Group (ITDG).

Darcy, H. 1856. *Les fontaines publiques de la ville de Dijon* [The public fountains of the city of Dijon], Paris: Dalmont.

de Rosnay, J. 1997. *Analytic vs. Systemic Approaches*, Brussels: Principia Cybernetica. (Principia Cybernetica Web http://pespmc1.vub.ac.be/ANALSYST.html (Accessed 18 December 2006.)

Delgado, C., Rosegrant, M., Steinfeld, H., Ehui, S. and Courbois, C. 1999. *Livestock to 2020: The Next Food Revolution. Food*, Washington, DC: International Food Policy Research Institute. (Agriculture and the Environment Discussion Paper 28.)

Delgado, C. L., Rosegrant, M. W. and Miejer, S. 2001. Livestock to 2020: the revolution continues. *Annual meetings of the International Agricultural Trade Research Consortium (IATRC)*, Auckland, New Zealand, 18–19 January 2001.

Delmer, D. P. 2005. Agriculture in the developing world: connecting innovations in plant research to downstream applications. *Proceedings of the National Academy of Sciences of the United States of America*, Vol. 102, No. 44, pp. 15739–15746.

Dessai, S., Lu, X. and Risbey, J. S. 2005. On the role of climate scenarios for adaptation planning. *Global Environmental Change*, Vol. 15, pp. 87–97.

Dice, L. 1955. What is ecology? *The Scientific Monthly*, Vol. 80, No. 6, pp. 346–351.

Dickson, B. 1956. The challenge of arid lands research and development for the benefit of mankind. In: White, G. F. (ed), *The Future of Arid Lands: Papers and Recommendations from the International Arid Lands Meetings*, Washington, DC: American Association for the Advancement of Science, pp. 47–66. (Publication No. 43 of the AAAS.)

Dilley, M. 2003. Regional Responses to Climate Variability in Southern Africa. In: Vogel, C. and O'Brien, K. (eds), *Coping with Climate Variability: The Use of Seasonal Climate Forecasts in Southern Africa*, Burlington: Ashgate, p. 220.

Dilley, M. and Heyman, B. 1995. ENSO and disaster: droughts, floods and El Niño/southern oscillation warm events. *Disasters*, Vol. 19, pp. 181–193.

Dixey, F. 1956. Variability and predictability of water supply. In: White, G. F. (ed), *The Future of Arid Lands: Papers and Recommendations from the International Arid Lands Meetings*, Washington, DC: American Association for the Advancement of Science, pp. 121–140. (Publication No. 43 of the AAAS.)

Dixon, I. R., Dixon, K. W. and Barrett, M. 2002. Eradication of buffel grass (*Cenchrus ciliaris*) on Airlie Island, Pilbara Coast, Western Australia. In: Veitch, C. R. and Clout, M. N. (eds), *Turning the Tide: The Eradication of Invasive Species*, Gland, Switzerland: IUCN, pp. 92–101.

Dollar, D. and Kraay, A. 2001. *Trade, Growth, and Poverty*, Washington, DC: World Bank. (World Bank Development Research Group Working Paper 2615.) http://econ.worldbank.org/files/24986_wps2615.pdf (Accessed 29 September 2006.)

Dorroh, J. H. Jr 1956. Beneficial use of water in arid lands. In: White, G. (ed), *The Future of Arid Lands: Papers and Recommendations from the International Arid Lands Meetings*, Washington, DC: American Association for the Advancement of Science, pp. 156–160. (Publication No. 43 of the AAAS.)

Dos Santos, T. 1970. The structure of dependence. *The American Economic Review*, Vol. 60, pp. 231–236.

Draz, O. 1956. Adaptation of plants and animals. In: White, G. F. (ed), *The Future of Arid Lands: Papers and Recommendations from the International Arid Lands Meetings*, Washington, DC: American Association for the Advancement of Science, pp. 331–342. (Publication No. 43 of the AAAS.)

Draz, O. 1978. Revival of the hema system of range reserves as a basis for the Syrian range development program. In: Hyder, D. N. (ed), *Proceedings of the First International Rangeland Congress*, Denver, CO: Society for Range Management, pp. 100–103.

Dregne, H. E. (ed). 1970. *Arid Lands in Transition*, Washington, DC: American Association for the Advancement of Science. (Publication No. 90.)

Droppelmann, K. J., Lehmann, J., Ephrat, J. E. and Berliner, P. R.. 2000. Water use efficiency and uptake patterns in a runoff agroforestry system in an arid environment. *Agroforestry Systems*, Vol. 49, pp. 223–243.

Durgin, F. A. 1962. The virgin land programme 1954–1960. *Soviet Studies*, Vol. 13, No. 3, pp. 255–280.

Dutt, G. R., Hutchinson, C. F. and Anaya-Garduno, M. (eds). 1981. *Rainfall Collection For Agriculture In Arid And Semiarid Regions*, Slough: Commonwealth Agricultural Bureaux.

Dyksterhuis, E. 1949. Condition and management of range land based on quantitative ecology. *Journal of Range Management*, Vol. 2, pp. 104–115.

Edens, T. C. and Koenig, H. E. 1980. Agorecosystem management in a resource-limited world. *BioScience*, Vol. 30, No. 10, pp. 697–701.

Eklundh, L. and Olsson, L. 2003. Vegetation index trends for the African Sahel 1982–1999. *Geophysical Research Letters*, Vol. 30, No. 8, p. 1430.

Ellis, F. 2000. *Rural Livelihoods and Diversity in Developing Countries*, Oxford: Oxford University Press.

Ellis, J. E. and Swift, D. M. 1988. Stability of African pastoral ecosystems: alternate paradigms and implications for development. *Journal of Range Management*, Vol. 41, pp. 450–459.

Escobar, A. 1995. *Encountering Development: The Making and Unmaking of the Third World*, Princeton, NJ: Princeton University Press.

Escobar, A. 2004. Beyond the Third World: imperial globality, global coloniality and anti-globalisation social movements. *Third World Quarterly*, Vol. 25, pp. 207–230.

Ettouney, H. M., El-Dessouky, H. T., Faibish, R. S. and Gowin, P. J. 2002. Evaluating the economics of desalination. *Chemical Engineering Progress*, Vol. 98, No. 12, pp. 32–40.

Evenari, M. 1987. *Und Die Wueste Trage Frucht. Ein Lebensbericht*, Gerlingen: Bleicher Verlag.

Evenari, M. and Koller, D. 1956. Desert agriculture: problems and results in Israel. In: White, G. F. (ed), *The Future of Arid Lands: Papers and Recommendations from the International Arid*

Lands Meetings, Washington, DC: American Association for the Advancement of Science, pp. 390–413. (Publication No. 43 of the AAAS.)

Evenari, M., Shanan, L. and Tadmor, N. 1982. *The Negev: The Challenge of a Desert*, Cambridge, MA: Harvard University Press.

Evenson, R. E. and Gollin, D. 2003a. Assessing the impact of the Green Revolution 1960–2000. *Science*, Vol. 300, pp. 758–762.

Evenson, R. E. and Gollin, D. 2003b. *Crop Variety Improvement and Its Effect on Productivity: The Impact of International Agricultural Research*, Wallingford: CAB International.

Evenson, R. E. and Rosegrant, M. W. 2003. Economic consequences of crop genetic improvement programmes. In: Evenson, R. E. and Gollin, D. (eds), *Crop Variety Improvement and Its Effect on Productivity: The Impact of International Agricultural Research*, Wallingford: CAB International, pp. 473–498.

Faiman, D. 1998. Solar energy in arid frontiers: designing a photoboltaic power plant for Kibbutz Samar, Israel. In: Bruins, H. and Lithwick, H. (eds), *The Arid Frontier*, Dordrecht, The Netherlands: Kluwer, pp. 321–336.

Fairhead, J. and Leach, M. 1996. *Misreading the African Landscape: Society and Ecology in a Forest-Savanna Mosaic*, Cambridge: Cambridge University Press. (African Studies Series 90.)

Falcon, W. P. and Fowler, C. 2002. Carving up the commons: emergence of a new international regime for germplasm development and transfer. *Food Policy*, Vol. 27, pp. 197–222.

FAO. 2000. *Carbon Sequestration Options under the Clean Development Mechanism to Address Land Degradation*, Rome: FAO. (World Soil Resources Report 92.) http://www.fao.org/clim/docs/998_carb%20seq%2011.pdf (Accessed 29 September 2006.)

FAO Committee of Agriculture. 2005. *Water Desalination for Agricultural Applications*. http://www.fao.org/docrep/meeting/009/j4238e.htm

Farrington, J., Harvey, P. and Slater, L. 2005. *Cash Transfers: Just Giving Them the Money?* (ODI Opinions 55.) http://www.odi.org.uk/publications/opinions/55_cash_transfers_sept05.pdf (Accessed 17 December 2006.)

Fischer, C. and Newell, R. G. 2005. *Environmental and Technology Policies for Climate Change and Renewable Energy*, Washington, DC: Resources for the Future (RFF). (Report RFF DP 04–05 rev.)

Florida, R. 2002. *The Rise of the Creative Class*, New York: Basic Books.

Folland, C. K., Parker, D. E., Colman, A. W. and Washington, R. 1999. Large scale modes of ocean surface temperature since the late nineteenth century. In: Navarra, A. (ed), *Beyond El Niño: Decadal and Interdecadal Climate Variability*, Berlin, Springer, pp. 73–100.

Forsyth, T., Leach, M. and Scoones, I. 1998. *Poverty and Environment: Priorities for Research and Policy: An Overview Study*, Falmer: Institute of Development Studies (IDS). http://www.eldis.org/static/DOC6628.htm (Accessed 28 November 2006.)

Forum for the Future (FFF). 2005. *Models of Sustainable Development: The Five Capitals Model*. http://www.forumforthefuture.org.uk/aboutus/sdtools_page398.aspx#FCM (Accessed 2 November 2006.)

Foster, M. A. and Coffelt, T. A. 2005. Guayule agronomics: establishment, irrigated production, and weed control. *Industrial Crops and Products*, Vol. 22, pp. 27–40.

Franklin, K. A., Lyons, K., Nagler, P. L., Lampkin, D., Glenn, E. P., Molina-Freaner, F., Markowa, T. and Huete, A. R. 2006. Buffelgrass (*Pennisetum ciliare*) land conversion and productivity in the plains of Sonora, Mexico. *Biological Conservation*, Vol. 127, pp. 62–71.

Fraser, E. D. G. 2006. Examining past famines to identify food systems vulnerable to global environmental change. *Organisational Meeting for GECAFS Vulnerability of Food Systems Research Network*, Oxford, UK, 17–18 May 2006. Global Environmental Change and Food Systems (GECAF).

Fratkin, E. 1997. Pastoralism: governance and development issues. *Annual Review of Anthropology*, Vol. 26, pp. 235–261.

Fratkin, E. and Mearns, R. 2003. Sustainability and pastoral livelihoods: lessons from East African Maasai and Mongolia. *Human Organization*, Vol. 62, pp. 112–122.

Freeman, D. B. 1992. Prickly pear menace in eastern Australia 1880–1940. *The Geographical Journal*, Vol. 82, No. 4, pp. 413–429.

Friedler, E. 1999. The Jeezrael Valley Project for wastewater reclamation and reuse, Israel. *Water Science and Technology*, Vol. 40, No. 4–5, pp. 347–354.

Friedman, T. L. 2005. *The World Is Flat: A Brief History of the Twenty-First Century*, New York: Farrar, Straus and Giroux.

Fritsche, U. R. and Matthes, F. C. 2003. *Changing Course: A Contribution to a Global Energy Strategy*, Berlin: Heinrich Böll Foundation. (World Summit Papers of the Heinrich Böll Foundation World Summit Paper #22.)

Gaffney, J. S. and Marley, N. A. 1998. New directions: uncertainties of aerosol effects in global climate models. *Atmospheric Environment*, Vol. 16, pp. 2873–2874.

Gates Foundation. 2006. *Bill & Melinda Gates, Rockefeller Foundations Form Alliance to Help Spur "Green Revolution" in Africa*. http://www.gatesfoundation.org/GlobalDevelopment/Agriculture/Announcements/announce-060912.htm (Accessed 2 November 2006.)

Giannini, A., Saravanan, R. and Chang, P. 2004. The preconditioning role of tropical Atlantic variability in the development of the ENSO teleconnection: implications for the prediction of Nordeste rainfall. *Climate Dynamics*, Vol. 22, pp. 839–855.

Gijsbers, P. J. A. and Loucks, D. P. 1999. Libya's choices: desalination or the Great Man Made River Project. *Physics and Chemistry of the Earth, Part B: Hydrology, Oceans and Atmosphere*, Vol. 24, No. 4, pp. 385–389.

Gillson, L. 2004. Testing non-equilibrium theories in savannas: 1400 years of vegetation change in Tsavo National Park, Kenya. *Ecological Complexity*, Vol. 1, pp. 281–298.

Gillson, L. and Lindsay, K. 2002. *Ecological Reality Questions The Need To Cull*. Kingsfold: Care for the Wild International. (Briefing Document prepared for the 12th CITES Conference of the Parties, Santiago, Chile). http://www.careforthewild.com/files/CITES02document.pdf (Accessed 29 September 2006.)

Gillson, L., Sheridan, M. and Brockington, D. 2003. Representing environments in flux: case studies from East Africa. *Area*, Vol. 35, No. 4, pp. 371–389.

Glantz, M., Betsill, M. and Crandall, K. 1997. *Food Security in Southern Africa: Assessing the Use and Value of ENSO Information*, Boulder: National Center for Atmospheric Research.

Glantz, M. H. (ed). 1994. *Drought Follows The Plow: Cultivating Marginal Areas*, Cambridge: Cambridge University Press.

Glantz, M. H. (ed). 1999. *Creeping Environmental Problems and Sustainable Development in the Aral Sea Basin*, Cambridge: Cambridge University Press.

Glantz, M. H. (ed). 2001. *Currents of Change. Impacts of El Nino and La Nina on Climate and Society*, Cambridge: Cambridge University Press.

Glantz, M. H. (ed). 2003. *Climate Affairs. A Primer*, Washington, DC: Island Press.

Gleick, P. H. 2001. Making every drop count, *Scientific American*, Vol. 284, pp. 40–46.

Gold, A. G. 1999. From wild pigs to foreign trees: oral histories of environmental change in Rajasthan. In: Madsen, S. T. (ed), *State, Society and the Environment in South Asia*, Richmond: Curzon Press, pp. 20–58.

Goodall, D. W. and Perry, R. A. (eds). 1981. *Arid-Land Ecosystems: Structure, Functioning and Management*, Cambridge: Cambridge University Press.

Goodrich, D. C., Faures, J.-M., Woolhiser, D. A., Lane, L. J., and Sorooshian, S. 1995. Measurement and analysis of small-scale convective storm rainfall variability. *Journal of Hydrology*, Vol. 173, pp. 283–308.

Gorham, E. 1991. Biogeochemistry: its origins and development. *Biogeochemistry*, Vol. 13, No. 3, pp. 199–239.

Graef, F. and Haegis, J. 2001. Spatial and temporal rainfall variability in the Sahel and its effects on farmers' management strategies. *Journal of Arid Environments*, Vol. 48, pp. 221–231.

Grey, D. and Sadoff, C. 2006. Water for growth and development. *Thematic Documents of the IV World Water Forum*, Mexico City: Comisión Nacional del Agua.

Grubb, M. and Depledge, J. 2001. Viewpoint: the seven myths of Kyoto. *Climate Policy*, Vol. 1, No. 2, pp. 269–272.

Grubb, M., Hession, M., Jackson, T., Dowlatabadi, H., Gupta, S., Michaelowa, A., La Rovere, E. and Yamagata, Y. 2001. Welcome to Climate Policy (editorial). *Climate Policy*, Vol. 1, pp. 1–2.

Gunderson, L. H. and Holling, C. S. (eds). 2002. *Panarchy: Understanding Transformation in Human and Natural Systems*, Washington, DC: Island Press.

Haarhoff, J. and Van der Merwe, B. 1996. Twenty-five years of wastewater reclamation in Windhoek, Namibia. *Water Science and Technology*, Vol. 33, No. 10–11, pp. 25–35.

Haarsma, R. J., Selten, F. M., Weber, S. L. and Kliphuis, M. 2005. Sahel rainfall variability and response to greenhouse warming. *Geophysical Research Letters*, Vol. 32.

Hall, D. C., Ehui, S. and Delgado, C. 2004. The livestock revolution, food safety, and small-scale farmers: why they matter to us all. *Journal of Agricultural and Environmental Ethics*, Vol. 17, pp. 425–444.

Hamoda, M. F. 2001. Desalination and water resource management in Kuwait. *Desalination*, Vol. 138, No. (1–3), pp. 385–393.

Hardin, G. 1968. The tragedy of the commons. *Science*, Vol. 162, No. 3859, pp. 1243–1248.

Harper, K. and Marble, J. 1988. A role for nonvascular plants inmanagement of arid and semiarid rangeland. In: Tueller, P. (ed), *Vegetation Science Applications for Rangeland Analysis and Management*, Dordrecht, The Netherlands: Kluwer, pp. 135–169.

Harries, J. 1990. *Earthwatch: The Climate from Space*, New York: Ellis Horwood.

Hartje, V., Klaphake, A. and Schliep, R. 2003. *The International Debate on the Ecosystem Approach*, Bonn: Federal Ministry of Environment, Nature Conservation, and Nuclear Safety. (Working Paper on Management in Environmental Planning 006/2003.) http://www.land-schaftsoekonomie.tu-berlin.de/fileadmin/a0731/uploads/publikationen/workingpapers/wp00603.pdf (Accessed 29 September 2006.)

Harvey, P. 2005. *Cash and Vouchers in Emergencies*, London: Overseas Development Institute (ODI). (Humanitarian Policy Group Discussion Paper.)

Hatt, B. E., Deletic, A. and Fletcher, T. D. 2006. Integrated treatment and recycling of storm water: a review of Australian practice. *Journal of Environmental Management*, Vol. 79, No. 1, pp. 102–113.

Hayward, H. E. 1956. The salinity factor in the reuse of waste waters. In: White, G. (ed), *The Future of Arid Lands: Papers and Recommendations from the International Arid Lands Meetings*, Washington, DC: American Association for the Advancement of Science, pp. 279–290. (Publication No. 43 of the AAAS.)

Heathcote, I. W. 1998. *Integrated Watershed Management: Principles and Practice*, New York: Wiley.

Heggen, R. J. 2000. Rainwater catchment and the challenge of sustainable development. *Water Science and Technology*, Vol. 42, No. 1, pp. 141–145.

Held, I. M., Delworth, T. L., Lu, J., Findell, K. L. and Knutson, T. R. 2005. Simulation of Sahel drought in the 20th and 21st centuries. *Proceedings of the National Academy of Sciences of the United States of America*, Vol. 102, No. 50, pp. 17891–17896.

Helms, D. 1990. The Soil Conservation Service in the Great Plains. *Agricultural History*, Vol. 64, pp. 58–73.

Henson, S. J. and Loader, R. J. 2001. Barriers to agricultural exports from developing countries: the role of sanitary and phytosanitary requirements. *World Development*, Vol. 29, pp. 85–102.

Herrmann, S. M. and Hutchinson, C. F. 2005. The changing contexts of the desertification debate. *Journal of Arid Environments*, Vol. 63, pp. 538–555.

Herrmann, S. M. and Hutchinson, C. F. 2006. The scientific basis: Links between land degradation, drought and desertification. In: Johnson, P. M., Mayrand, K. and Paquin, M. (eds), *Governing Global Desertification: Linking Environmental Degradation, Poverty and Participation*, Aldershot: Ashgate.

Herrmann, S. M., Anyamba, A. and Tucker, C. J. 2005. Recent trends in vegetation dynamics in the African Sahel and their relationship to climate. *Global Environmental Change*, Vol. 15, pp. 394–404.

Herrmann, S. M., Hutchinson, C. F., Nellemann, C., Nagatani, K., Warren, A., Dent, D., Morrison, S., Abdukadir, A., Ahlenius, H., Alkemade, R., Bakkenes, M., ten Brink, B., Ezcurra, E.,

Stoen, O.-G., Kaltenborn, B., Miles, L., Tekelenburg, T., Seely, M. and Vistnes, I. 2006. Desert outlook and options for action. In: Ezcurra, E. (ed), *Global Deserts Outlook*, Nairobi: UNEP, pp. 111–140.

Herrmann, T. and Schmida, U. 1999. Rainwater utilisation in Germany: efficiency, dimensioning, hydraulic and environmental aspects. *Urban Water*, Vol. 1, pp. 307–316.

Heylighen, F. and Josyln, C. 1999. Complex systems. In: Audi, R. (ed), *Cambridge Dictionary of Philosophy*, Cambridge: Cambridge University Press.

Hill, T. 2004. *Three Generations of UN-Civil Society Relations: A Quick Sketch*. New York: UN Non-Governmental Liaison Service. http://www.globalpolicy.org/ngos/ngo-un/gen/2004/ 0404generation.htm (Accessed 15 September 2006.)

Hinman, C. W. 1984. New crops for arid lands. *Science*, Vol. 225, No. 4669, pp. 1445–1448.

Hoagland, A. S. 2003. History of magnetic disk storage based on perpendicular magnetic recording. *IEEE Transactions on Magnetics*, Vol. 39, No. 4, pp. 1871–1875.

Hoffert, M. I., Caldeira, K., Benford, G., Criswell, D. R., Green, C., Herzog, H., Jain, A. K., Kheshgi, H. S., Lackner, K. S., Lewis, J. S., Lightfoot, H. D., Manheimer, W., Mankins, J. C., Mauel, M. E., Perkins, L. J., Schlesinger, M. E., Volk, T. and Wigley, T. M. L. 2002. Advanced technology paths to global climate stability: energy for a greenhouse planet. *Science*, Vol. 298, pp. 981–987.

Holling, C. 2001. Understanding the complexity of economic ecological and social systems. *Ecosystems*, Vol. 4, pp. 390–405.

Holling, C. S. 1973. Resilience and stability of ecological systems. *Annual Review of Ecology and Systematics*, Vol. 4, pp. 1–23.

Holling, C. S. and Gunderson, L. H. 2002. Resilience and adaptive cycles. In: Gunderson, L. H. and Holling, C. (eds), *Panarchy: Understanding Transformations in Human and Natural Systems*, Washington. DC: Island Press, pp. 25–62.

Holmgren, M., Stapp, P., Dickman, C., Gracia, C., Graham, S., Guitierrez, J., Hice, C., Jaksic, F., Kelt, D., Letnic, M., Lima, M., Lopez, B., Meserve, P., Milstead, W., Polis, G., Previtali, M., Ricter, M., Sabate, S. and Squeo, F. 2006. Extreme climactic events shape arid and semiarid ecosystems. *Frontiers in Ecology and the Environment*, Vol. 4, No. 2, pp. 87–95.

House, T., Near, J. Jr Shields, W., Celentano, R., Husband, D., Mercer, A. and Pugh, J. 1996. *Weather as a Force Multiplier: Owning the Weather in 2025*, US Air Force.

Huber-Sannwald, E., Maestre, F. T., Herrick, J. E. and Reynolds, J. F. 2006. Ecohydrological feedbacks and linkages associated with land degradation: a case study from Mexico. *Hydrological Processes*, Vol. 20, No. 15, pp. 3395–3411.

Huda, A. K. S. and Packham, R. G. (eds). 2004. *Using Seasonal Climate Forecasting In Agriculture: A Participatory Decision-Making Approach*, Canberra: Australian Centre for International Agricultural Research.

Huda, A. K. S., Packham, R. G., Clewett, J. F. and George, D. A. 2004. Introduction and Overview. *Using Seasonal Climate Forecasting in Agriculture: A Participatory Decision-making Approach*, Canberra: Australian Centre for International Agricultural Research, pp. 7–14.

Hull, R. B., Robertson, D. P., Richert, D., Seekamp, E. and Buhyoff, G. J. 2002. Assumptions about Ecological Scale and Nature Knowing Best Hiding in Environmental Decisions. *Conservation Ecology*, Vol. 6, No. 2. http://www.consecol.org/vol6/iss2/art12 (Accessed 15 September 2006.)

Hulme, M. 1996. Recent climatic change in the world's drylands. *Geophysical Research Letters*, Vol. 23, No. 1, pp. 61–64.

Hulme, M. 2001. Climatic perspectives on Sahelian desiccation: 1973–1998. *Global Environmental Change*, Vol. 11, pp. 19–29.

Hulme, M., Doherty, R., Ngara, T., New, M. and Lister, D. 2001. African climate change: 1900–2100. *Climate Research*, Vol. 17, pp. 145–168.

Huq, S. and Grubb, M. 2003. *Scientific Assessment of the Inter-Relationships of Mitigation and Adaptation*. http://www.ipcc.ch/activity/cct2a.pdf (Accessed 11 December 2006.)

Hurt, D. R. 1994. *American Agriculture: A Brief History*, Ames, IA: Iowa State University Press.

Hutchinson, C. F. 1989. Will climate change complicate African famine? *Resources*, Vol. 95, pp. 5–7.

Hutchinson, C. F. 2000. John Wesley Powell and the New West. *COSMOS*, Vol. 10.

Illius, A. W. and O'Connor, T. G. 1999. On the relevance of nonequilibrium concepts to arid and semiarid grazing systems. *Ecological Applications*, Vol. 9, pp. 798–816.

Intergovernmental Panel on Climate Change (IPCC). 2000. *Special Report on Emissions Scenarios*. http://www.grida.no/climate/ipcc/emissions/index.htm

Intergovernmental Panel on Climate Change (IPCC). 2001a. *Climate Change 2001: Impacts, Adaptation and Vulnerability. Contribution of Working Group II to the Third Assessment Report of the Intergovernmental Panel on Climate Change*, Cambridge: Cambridge University Press.

Intergovernmental Panel on Climate Change (IPCC). 2001b. *Climate Change 2001: Mitigation. Contribution of Working Group II to the Third Assessment Report of the Intergovernmental Panel on Climate Change*, Cambridge: Cambridge University Press.

Intergovernmental Panel on Climate Change (IPCC). 2001c. *Climate Change 2001: The Scientific Basis. Contribution of Working Group I to the Third Assessment Report of the Intergovernmental Panel on Climate Change*, Cambridge: Cambridge University Press.

IUCN. 2004. *Invasive Species Specialist Group web site*. http://www.issg.org/ (Accessed 20 December 2006.)

Jelinski, D. 2005. There is no Mother Nature – there is no balance of nature: culture, ecology, and conservation. *Human Ecology*, Vol. 33, No. 2, pp. 271–288.

Jenkins, R. 2004. Globalization, production, employment and poverty: debates and evidence. *Journal of International Development*, Vol. 16, pp. 1–12.

Jickells, T., An, Z., Anderson, K., Baker, A., Bergametti, G., Brooks, N., Cao, J., Boyd, P., Duce, R., Hunter, K., Kawahata, H., Kubilay, N., laRoche, J., Liss, P., Mahowald, N., Prospero, J., Ridgewell, A., Tegen, L. and Torres, R. 2005. Global iron connections between desert dust, ocean biogeochemistry, and climate. *Science*, Vol. 308, pp. 67–71.

Johnson, D. L. 1993. Pastoral nomadism and the sustainable use of arid lands. *Arid Lands Newsletter*, Vol. 33, No. Spring/Summer, pp. 26–34.

Johnson, P. M., Mayrand, K. and Paquin, M. 2006. The United Nations Convention to combat desertification in global sustainable development governance. In: Johnson, P. M., Mayrand, K. and Paquin, M. (eds), *Governing Global Desertification: Linking Environmental Degradation, Poverty and Participation*, Aldershot: Ashgate, pp. 1–10.

Joyce, L. 1993. The life cycle of the range condition concept. *Journal of Range Management*, Vol. 46, No. 2, pp. 132–138.

Kaboré, D. and Reij, C. 2004. *The Emergence and Spreading of an Improved Traditional Soil and Water Conservation Practice in Burkina Faso*, Washington, DC: International Food Policy Research Institute. (Discussion Paper 114.)

Kadar, Y. 1956. Water and soil from the desert: some agricultural achievements in the central Negev. *Geographical Journal*, Vol. 123, No. 2, pp. 179–187.

Kaiser, J. 1999. Salton Sea: battle over a dying sea. *Science*, Vol. 284, No. 5411, pp. 28–30.

Kapur, D., Lewis, J. P. and Webb, R. 1997. *The World Bank: Its First Half Century. Volume 1: History*, Washington, DC: Brookings Institution Press.

Kaser, G., et al. 2004. Modern glacier retreat on Kilimanjaro as evidence of climate change: observations and facts. *International Journal of Climatology*, Vol. 24, pp. 329–339.

Kayano, M., Rao, V. and Andreoli, R. 2005. A review of short-term climate variability mechanisms. *Advances in Space Research*, Vol. 35, pp. 843–851.

Kaye, J. P., Groffman, P. M., Grimm, N. B., Baker, L. A. and Pouyat, R. 2006. A distinct urban biogeochemistry? *Trends in Ecology and Evolution*, Vol. 21, pp. 192–199.

Keeling, C., Whorf, T., Wahlen, M. and van der Plicht, J. 1995. Interannual extremes in the rate of rise of atmospheric carbon dioxide since 1980. *Nature*, Vol. 375, pp. 666–670.

Keeling, C. D. 1960. The concentration and isotopic abundance of carbon dioxide in the atmosphere. *Tellus*, Vol. 12, pp. 200–203.

Keith, D. 2000. Geoengineering the climate: history and prospect. *Annual Review of Energy and the Environment*, Vol. 25, pp. 245–284.

Kellogg, C. E. 1956. The role of science in man's struggle on arid lands. In: White, G. F. (ed), *The Future of Arid Lands: Papers and Recommendations from the International Arid Lands*

Meetings, Washington, DC: American Association for the Advancement of Science, pp. 26–46. (Publication No. 43 of the AAAS.)

Kobori, I. and Glantz, M. H. 1998. *Central Eurasian Water Crisis: Caspian, Aral, and Dead Seas*, Tokyo: United Nations University Press.

Koenig, L. 1956. The economics of water resources. In: White, G. F. (ed), *The Future of Arid Lands: Papers and Recommendations from the International Arid Lands Meetings*, Washington, DC: American Association for the Advancement of Science, pp. 320–330. (Publication No. 43 of the AAAS.)

Kovda, V. A. 1961. Land use development in the arid regions of the Russian plain, the Caucasus and central Asia. In: Stamp, L. (ed), *A History Of Land Use In Arid Regions*, Paris: UNESCO, pp. 175–218.

Kraus, E. B. and Squires, P. 1947. Experiments on the stimulation of clouds to produce rain. *Nature*, Vol. 159, No. 4041, pp. 489–491.

Krause, U. 2004. Diseases in tropical agroforestry landscapes: the role of biodiversity. In: Schroth, G., da Fonseca, A. B., Harvey, C. A., Gascon, C., Vasconcelos, H. L. and Izac, A. N. (eds), *Agroforestry and Biodiversity Conservation in Tropical Landscapes*, Washington, DC: Island Press, pp. 397–412.

Kuhn, T. S. 1962. *The Structure of Scientific Revolutions*, Chicago: Chicago University Press.

Kurokawa, K. (ed). 2003. *Energy from the Desert: Feasibility of Very Large Scale Photovoltaic Power Generating Systems*, London: James & James.

Kwa, C. 2001. The rise and fall of weather modification: changes in American attitudes toward technology, nature, and society. In: Miller, C. and Edwards, P. (eds), *Changing the Atmosphere: Expert Knowledge and Environmental Governance*, Cambridge: MIT Press, 135–165.

Lal, R. 1999. Soil management and restoration for C sequestration to mitigate the accelerated greenhouse effect. *Progress in Environmental Science*, Vol. 1, pp. 307–326.

Lal, R. (ed). 2000. *Integrated Watershed Management In The Global Ecosystem*, Boca Raton, FL: CRC Press.

Lamprey, H. F. 1988. Report on the desert encroachment reconnaissance in northern Sudan. *Desertification Control Bulletin*, Vol. 17, pp. 1–7.

Lauenroth, W. and Laycock, W. (eds). 1989. *Secondary Succession and the Evaluation of Rangeland Condition*, Boulder: Westview Press.

Le Houérou, H. N. 2002. Man-made deserts: desertization processes and threats. *Arid Land Research and Management*, Vol. 16, pp. 1–36.

Lemma, S. 2001. Cooperating on the Nile: not a zero-sum game. *United Nations Chronicle Online Edition*. http://www.un.org/Pubs/chronicle/2001/issue3/0103p65.html (Accessed 20 December 2006.)

Leopold, L. B. 1956. Data and understanding. In: White, G. F. (ed), *The Future of Arid Lands: Papers and Recommendations from the International Arid Lands Meetings*, Washington, DC: American Association for the Advancement of Science, pp. 114–120. (Publication No. 43 of the AAAS.)

List, R. 2003. WMO weather modification activities: a fifty year history and outlook. *Eighth World Meteorological Organization Scientific Conference on Weather Modification*, Casablanca, Morocco, 7–12 April 2003. World Meteorological Organization.

Logan, R. F. 1957. The Future of Arid Lands (Book Review). *Economic Geography*, Vol. 33, No. 3, pp. 281–282.

Ludwig, D., Hilborn, R. and Walters, C. 1993. Uncertainty, resource exploitation, and conservation: lessons from history. *Ecological Applications*, Vol. 3, No. 4, pp. 547–549.

Luker, C. 1956. Consequences of using arid lands beyond their capabilities. In: White, G. F. (ed), *The Future of Arid Lands: Papers and Recommendations from the International Arid Lands Meetings*, Washington, DC: American Association for the Advancement of Science, pp. 226–232. (Publication No. 43 of the AAAS.)

Mack, R. N. and Lonsdale, W. M. 2001. Humans as global plant dispersers: getting more than we bargained ror. *BioScience*, Vol. 51, No. 2, pp. 95–102.

Mainguet, M. 1991. *Desertification: Natural Background and Human Mismanagement*, Berlin: Springer.

Mainguet, M. 1999. *Aridity: Droughts and Human Development*, Berlin: Springer.

Malthus, T. 1798. *An Essay on the Principle of Population, as it Affects the Future Improvement of Society with Remarks on the Speculations of Mr. Godwin, M. Condorcet, and Other Writers*, London: J. Johnson, St. Paul's Church-yard.

Mando, A., van Rheenen, T., Stroosnijder, L. and Nikiema, R. 2001. Village land use in Burkina Faso: "Gestion Terroir". In: Stroosnijder, L. and van Rheenen, T. (eds), *Agro-Silvo-Pastoral Land Use In Sahelian Villages*, Reiskirchen, Germany: Catena Verlag, pp. 17–22.

Mann, M., Bradley, R. and Hughes, M. 1999. Northern hemisphere temperatures during the past millennium: inferences, uncertainties, and limitations. *Geophysical Research Letters*, Vol. 26, No. 6, pp. 759–762.

Marsh, G. P. 1864. *Man and Nature; or, Physical Geography as Modified by Human Action*, London: S. Low, Son and Marston.

Marshall, J., Kushnir, Y., Battisti, D., Chang, P., Czaja, A., Dickson, R., Hurrell, J., McCartney, M., Saravanan, R. and Visbeck, M. 2001. North Atlantic climate variability: phenomena, impacts, and mechanisms. *International Journal of Climatology*, Vol. 21, pp. 1863–1898.

Martijn, E. J. and Redwood, M. 2005. Wastewater irrigation in developing countries: limitations for farmers to adopt appropriate practices. *Irrigation and Drainage*, Vol. 54, No. S1, pp. S63–S70.

Martin, M., Cox, J. and Ibarra, F. 1995. Climatic effects on buffelgrass productivity in the Sonoran Desert. *Journal of Range Management*, Vol. 48, pp. 60–63.

McClaran, M. 2003. A century of vegetation change on the Santa Rita Experimental Range. *Santa Rita Experimental Range Centennial Conference 2003*, Tucson, AZ: Santa Rita Experimental Range.

McClaran, M. P. and Van Devender, T. R. (eds). 1995. *The Desert Grassland*, Tucson, AZ: University of Arizona Press.

McClellan, L. N. 1956. Water resources. In: White, G. (ed), *The Future of Arid Lands: Papers and Recommendations from the International Arid Lands Meetings*, Washington, DC: American Association for the Advancement of Science, pp. 189–99. (Publication No. 43 of the AAAS.)

McCollum, J. R., Gruber, A. and Ba, M. B. 2000. Discrepancy between gauges and satellite estimates of rainfall in equatorial Africa. *Journal of Applied Meteorology*, Vol. 39, pp. 666–678.

McIntosh, R. 1985. *The Background of Ecology: Concept and Theory*, Cambridge: Cambridge University Press.

McIntosh, R. 1987. Pluralism in ecology. *Annual Review of Ecology and Systematics*, Vol. 18, pp. 321–341.

McLaughlin, S. P. 1985. Economic prospects for new crops in the southwestern United States. *Economic Botany*, Vol. 39, No. 4, pp. 473–481.

McNaughton, S. 1985. Ecology of a grazing ecosystem: the Serengeti. *Ecological Monographs*, Vol. 55, No. 3, pp. 259–294.

McNeill, J. R. 2000. *Something New Under The Sun: An Environmental History Of The Twentieth-Century World*, New York: W.W. Norton.

Medina, A. 1996. *The Santa Rita Experimental Range: Annotated Bibliography (1903–1988)*, Ft. Collins, CO: US Department of Agriculture Forest Service. (General Technical Report RM-GTR-276.)

Meinzen-Dick, R., Knox, A., Place, F. and Swallow, B. (eds). 2002. *Innovation in Natural Resource Management: The Role of Property Rights and Collective Action in Developing Countries*, Baltimore, MD: Johns Hopkins University Press.

Mekouar, M. A. 2001. Treaty agreed on agrobiodiversity: the International Treaty on Plant Genetic Resources for Food and Agriculture. *Environmental Policy and Law*, Vol. 32, No. 1, pp. 20–22.

Melillo, J. M. 1999. Warm, warm on the range. *Science*, Vol. 283, pp. 183–184.

Merton, R. K. 1936. The unanticipated consequences of purposive social action. *American Sociological Review*, Vol. 1, No. 6, pp. 894–904.

Micklin, P. P. 2000. *Managing Water in Central Asia*, London: Royal Institute of International Affairs.

Middleton, N., Thomas, D. and United Nations Environmental Programme. 1997. *World Atlas of Desertification*, 2nd edn, London: Arnold.

Millennium Assessment (MA). 2006. Current states and trends, chapter 22: dryland ecosystems. *Ecosystems and Human Well-Being*, Millennium Ecosystem Assessment, pp. 623–662.

Minarcek, A. 2003. Mount Kilimanjaro's glacier is crumbling. *National Geographic Adventure*. http://news.nationalgeographic.com/news/2003/09/0923_030923_kilimanjaroglaciers.html (Accessed 15 August 2006.)

Mokssit, A. and Grana, L. 2003. Programme Al-Ghalt: Modification artificielle du temps [Al-Ghalt Progamme: artifical modification of weather]. *Eighth World Meteorological Organization Scientific Conference on Weather Modification*, Casablanca, Morocco, 7–12 April 2003, Geneva: World Meteorological Organization.

Mönch, M. 2004. Groundwater: the challenge of monitoring and management. In: Gleick, P. H. (ed), *The World's Water: 2004–2005*, Washington, DC: Island Press, pp. 79–100.

Moorehead, R. 1989. Changes taking place in common-property resource management in the Inland Niger Delta of Mali. In: Berkes, F. (ed), *Common Property Resources: Ecology And Community-Based Sustainable Development*, London: Belhaven, pp. 256–272.

Mortimore, M. 1989. *Adapting To Drought. Farmers, Famine and Desertification in West Africa*, Cambridge: Cambridge University Press.

Mortimore, M. 1998. *Roots in the African Dust. Sustaining the Sub-Saharan Drylands*, Cambridge: Cambridge University Press.

Mortimore, M. 2003a. Is there a new paradigm of dryland development? *Annals of Arid Zone*, Vol. 42, No. 3–4, pp. 459–481.

Mortimore, M. 2003b. Long-term change in African drylands: can recent history point towards development pathways? *Oxford Development Studies*, Vol. 31, No. 4, pp. 503–518.

Mortimore, M. 2005. Dryland development: success stories from West Africa. *Environment*, Vol. 47, No. 1, pp. 8–21.

Mortimore, M. and Adams, W. M. 1999. *Working the Sahel: Environment and Society in Northern Nigeria*, London: Routledge.

Mortimore, M. and Tiffen, M. 2003. *Promoting Research-Policy Dialogues: Lessons from Four Studies of Dryland Development in Sub-Saharan Africa*, Crewkerne, UK, Drylands Research. (Drylands Research Working Paper 41.)

Mortimore, M. and Tiffen, M. 2004. Introducing research into policy: lessons from district studies of dryland development in sub-Saharan Africa. *Development Policy Review*, Vol. 22, No. 3, pp. 259–285.

Mortimore, M., Adams, B. and Harris, F. 2000. *Poverty and Systems Research in the Drylands*, London: IIED.

Moulin, C. and Chiapello, I. 2006. Impact of human-induced desertification on the intensification of Sahel dust emission and export over the last decades. *Geophysical Research Letters*, Vol. 33, pp. L18808, doi:10.1029/2006GL025923.

Muok, B., Kimondo, J. and Atsushi, I. 2001. Farmer to farmer extension: experience in drylands Kenya. *International Union of Forestry Research Organizations Extension Working Party (S6.06–03) Symposium 2001*. http://www.regional.org.au/au/iufro/2001/muok.htm (Accessed 15 September 2006.)

Najam, A. 2006. Negotiating desertification. In: Johnson, P. M., Mayrand, K. and Paquin, M. (eds), *Governing Global Desertification: Linking Environmental Degradation, Poverty and Participation*, Aldershot: Ashgate, pp. 59–72.

Najam, A., Rahman, A., Huq, S. and Sokona, Y. 2003. Integrating sustainable development into the Fourth Assessment Report of the Intergovernmental Panel on Climate Change. *Climate Policy*, Vol. 3, Suppl. 1, pp. S9–S17.

Nakayama, F. S. 2005. Guayule future development. *Industrial Crops and Products*, Vol. 22, pp. 3–13.

Nasr, J. and Kaldjian, P. 1997. Agriculture in Middle Eastern cities: commonalities and contrasts. *Arid Lands Newsletter*, No. 42, Fall/Winter 1997. http://ag.arizona.edu/OALS/ALN/aln42/nasr.html (Accessed 20 December 2006.)

National Archives of Australia. no date. *Water Dreaming*. http://www.naa.gov.au/education/activities/jaw/waterdreaming/waterdreaming.html (Accessed 20 August 2006.)

National Research Council (NRC). 1975. *Unexploited Tropical Plants with Promising Economic Value*, Washington, DC: National Academy of Sciences.

National Research Council (NRC). 1999. *New Strategies For America's Watersheds*, Washington, DC: National Academy Press.

Scoones, I. (ed). 1994. *Living with Uncertainty: New Directions in Pastoral Development in Africa*, London: Intermediate Technology Development Group (ITDG).

Scoones, I. 1998. *Sustainable Rural Livelihoods: A Framework for Analysis*, Brighton: Institute of Development Studies (IDS). (IDS Working Paper 72.) http://www.ids.ac.uk/ids/bookshop/classics/working_paper72.pdf (Accessed 20 December 2006.)

Scoones, I. 1999. New ecology and the social sciences: what prospects for a fruitful engagement? *Annual Review of Anthropology*, Vol. 28, pp. 479–507.

Scoones, I (ed). 2001. *Dynamics and Diversity: Soil Fertility and Farming Livelihoods in Africa*, London: Earthscan.

Scott, C. A., Faruqui, N. I. and Raschid-Sally, L. (eds). 2004. *Wastewater Use in Irrigated Agriculture: Confronting the Livelihood and Environmental Realities*, Wallingford: CAB International in association with IWMI and IDRC.

Sears, P. B. 1957. The Future of Arid Lands. Papers and recommendations from the International Arid Lands Meetings (Book Review). *American Antiquity*, Vol. 23, No. 1, pp. 89–90.

Sen, A. 1981. *Poverty and Famines. An Essay on Entitlement and Deprivation*, Oxford: Clarendon Press.

Serageldin, I. 1996. *Sustainability and the Wealth of Nations: First Steps in an Ongoing Journey*, Washington, DC: World Bank. (Environment and Sustainable Development Studies Monograph series 5.)

Serageldin, I. 1999. Biotechnology and food security in the 21st century. *Science*, Vol. 285, pp. 387–389.

Sere, C. and Steinfeld, H. 1995. *World Livestock Production Systems: Current Status, Issues and Trends*, Rome: FAO. (FAO Animal Production and Health Paper.)

Service, R. F. 2004. As the west goes dry. *Science*, Vol. 303, pp. 1124–1127.

Shantz, H. L. 1956. History and problems of arid lands development. In: White, G. F. (ed), *The Future of Arid Lands: Papers and Recommendations from the International Arid Lands Meetings*, Washington, DC: American Association for the Advancement of Science, pp. 3–25. (Publication No. 43 of the AAAS.)

Sheddon, C. S. 2000. "Sustainability" in ecological economics, ecology and livelihoods: A review. *Progress in Human Geography*, Vol. 24, pp. 521–549.

Sheldrick, D. 1999a. *The Elephant Debate*. Nairobi: David Sheldrick Wildlife Trust. http://www.sheldrickwildlifetrust.org/html/debate.html (Accessed 14 October 2006.)

Sheldrick, D. 1999b. *Impact in Tsavo*. Nairobi: David Sheldrick Wildlife Trust. http://www.sheldrickwildlifetrust.org/html/impact.html (Accessed 15 October 2006.)

Sheppard, P. R., Comrie, A. C., Packin, G. D., Angersbach, K. and Hughes, M. K. 2002. The climate of the US Southwest. *Climate Research*, Vol. 21, pp. 219–238.

Shiklomanov, I. 1993. World fresh water resources. In: Gleick, P. H. (ed), *Water in Crisis: A Guide to the World's Fresh Water Resources*, New York: Oxford University Press, pp. 13–24.

Shinn, E., Smith, G., Prospero, J., Betzer, P., Hayes, M., Garrison, V. and Barber, R. 2000. African dust and the demise of Caribbean coral reefs. *Geophysical Research Letters*, Vol. 27, No. 19, pp. 3029–3032.

Shippey, K., Görgens, A., Terblanche, D. and Luger, M. 2004. Environmental challenges to operationalisation of South African rainfall enhancement. *2004 Water Institute of South Africa Biennial Conference*, Cape Town, South Africa, 2–6 May 2004.

Shreve, F. 1951. *Vegetation of the Sonoran Desert*, Washington, DC: Carnegie Institution of Washington.

Shukman, D. 2006. Sharp rise in CO_2 levels recorded. *BBC News*. http://news.bbc.co.uk/2/hi/science/nature/4803460.stm (Accessed 15 August 2006.)

Sicot, A. M. 1991. Exemple de dispersion spatial des pluies au Sahel. In: Sivakumar, M. V. K., Wallace, J. S., Renard, C. and Giroux, C. (eds). *Soil Water Balance in the Sudano-Sahelian Zone* (*Proceedings of the International Workshop, Niamey, Niger, February 1991*). Wallingford: IAHS, pp. 75–84. (Institute of Hydrology publication no. 199.)

Simmonds, N. W. 1985. *Farming Systems Research: A Review*. Washington, DC: World Bank. (World Bank Technical Paper 43.)

Slingo, J. 1999. The Indian summer monsoon and its variability. In: Navarra, A. (ed), *Beyond El Niño: Decadal and Interdecadal Climate Variability*, Berlin: Springer, pp. 103–116.

Smalley, R. E. 2005. Future global energy prosperity: the terawatt challenge. *MRS Bulletin*, Vol. 30, pp. 412–417.

Smiley, T. 1956. Geochronology as an aid to study of arid lands. In: White, G. (ed), *The Future of Arid Lands: Papers and Recommendations from the International Arid Lands Meetings*, Washington, DC: American Association for the Advancement of Science, pp. 161–171. (Publication No. 43 of the AAAS.)

Smith, S. 2006. Camel dairy creams the profits. BBC News International. http://news.bbc.co.uk/2/hi/africa/5272430.stm (Accessed 20 December 2006.)

Sneddon, C. S. 2000. 'Sustainability' in ecological economics, ecology and livelihoods: a review. *Progress in Human Geography*, Vol. 24, No. 4, pp. 521–549.

Soroos, M. S. 2005. Global institutions and the environment: an evolutionary perspective. In: Axelrod, R. S., Downie, D. L. and Vig, N. J. (eds), *The Global Environment. Institutions, Law, and Policy*, 2nd edn, Washington, DC: CQ Press, pp. 21–42.

Splinter, W. E. (1976). "Center pivot irrigation." Scientific American 234(90): 93–96, 99.

Standler, R. 2002. *History and Problems in Weather Modification*. http://www.rbs.2.com/w2.htm (Accessed 20 December 2006.)

Steta, M. 2004. Mexico as the new major player in the vegetable greenhouse industry. *VII International Symposium on Protected Cultivation in Mild Winter Climates: Production, Pest Management and Global Competition*, Kissimee, FL: International Society for Horticultural Science.

Streeten, P. 1998. *Globalisation: Threat or Salvation*, London: Macmillan.

Stroosnijder, L. and van Rheenen, T. (eds). 2001. *Agro-Silvo-Pastoral Land Use in Sahelian Villages*, Reiskirchen, Germany: Catena Verlag.

Sultan, M., Sturchio, N., Hassan, F. A., Hamdan, M. A. R., Mahmood, A. M., Alfy, Z. E. and Stein, T. 1997. Precipitation source inferred from stable isotopic composition of Pleistocene groundwater and carbonate deposits in the Western Desert of Egypt. *Quarternary Research*, Vol. 48, No. 1, pp. 29–37.

Sutcliffe, S. and Court, J. 2006. *A Toolkit for Progressive Policymakers in Developing Countries*, London: Overseas Development Institute (ODI). (Research and Policy in Development Programme.) http://www.odi.org.uk/Rapid/Publications/Documents/EBP_toolkit_web.pdf (Accessed 29 September 2006.)

Tabor, J. A. 1995. Improving crop yields in the Sahel through water-harvesting? *Journal of Arid Environments*, Vol. 30, pp. 83–106.

Tansley, A. G. 1935. The use and abuse of vegetational concepts and terms. *Ecology*, Vol. 16, No. 3, pp. 284–307.

Tegen, I., Werner, M., Harrison, S. P. and Kohfeld, K. E. 2004. Relative importance of climate and land use in determining present and future global soil dust emission. *Geophysical Research Letters*, Vol. 31, No. 5, pp. L0515, doi:10.1029/2003GL019216.

Terblanche, D. 2005. Report on Mixed-Phase Cloud Precipitation Enhancement. Organization, WMO (ed), *Report of the Twenty First Session of the CAS Working Group on Physics and the Chemistry of Clouds and Weather Modification Research*, Geneva: World Meteorological Organization, pp. 21–22.

Thomas, D. S. G. and Middleton, N. J. 1994. *Desertification: Exploding the Myth*, Chichester: Wiley.

Thomas, G. W. and Box, T. W. 1969. Social and ecological implications of water importation into arid lands. In: McGinnies, W. G. and Goldman, B. J. (eds), *Arid Lands in Perspective*, Tucson: University of Arizona Press, pp. 363–e74.

Thomas, R. J., El Mourid, M., Ngaido, T., Halila, H., Bailey, E., Shideed, K., Malki, M., Nefzaoui, A., Chriyaa, A., Awawdeh, F., Hassan, S. H., Sweidean, Y. and Sbeita, A. 2003. The development of integrated crop-livestock production systems in the low rainfall areas of Mashreq and Maghreb. In: Harwood, R. R. and Kassam, A. H. (eds), *Research Towards Integrated Natural Resources Management: Examples of Research Problems, approaches and Partnerships in Action in the CGIAR*, Rome: CGIAR, FAO, pp. 97–110.

Thomas, W. L. J. (ed). 1956. *Man's Role in Changing the Face of the Earth*, Chicago, IL: University of Chicago Press.

Thompson, A. E. 1990. Arid-land industrial crops. In: Janick, J. and Simon, J. E. (eds), *Advances in New Crops*, Portland, OR: Timber Press, pp. 232–241.

Thompson, L., Mosley-Thompson, E., Davis, M., Henderson, K., Brecher, H., Zagorodnov, V., Mashiotta, T., Lin, P., Mikhalenko, V., Hardy, D. and Beer, J. 2002. Kilimanjaro ice core records: evidence of Holocene climate change in tropical Africa. *Science*, Vol. 298, pp. 589–593.

Thornthwaite, C. W. 1956. Climatology in arid zone research. In: White, G. (ed), *The Future of Arid Lands: Papers and Recommendations from the International Arid Lands Meetings*, Washington, DC: American Association for the Advancement of Science, pp. 67–84. (Publication No. 43 of the AAAS.)

Tiffen, M. and Mortimore, M. 1992. Environment, population growth and productivity. A case study of Machakos District. *Development Policy Review*, Vol. 10, pp. 359–387.

Tiffen, M. and Mortimore, M. 2002. Questioning desertification in dryland sub-Saharan Africa. *Natural Resources Forum*, Vol. 26, pp. 218–233.

Tiffen, M., Mortimore, M. and Gichuki, F. 1994. *More People, Less Erosion: Environmental Recovery in Kenya*, Chichester: Wiley.

Tilman, D., Cassman, K. G., Matson, P. A., Naylor, R. and Polasky, S. 2002. Agricultural sustainability and intensive production practices. *Nature*, Vol. 418, pp. 671–677.

Timberlake, L. 1985. The Sahel: drought, desertification and famine. *Draper Fund Report*, Vol. 14, pp. 17–19.

Tixeront, J. 1956. Water resources in arid regions. In: White, G. (ed), *The Future of Arid Lands: Papers and Recommendations from the International Arid Lands Meetings*, Washington, DC: American Association for the Advancement of Science, pp. 85–113. (Publication No. 43 of the AAAS.)

Toulmin, C. 1994. *Gestion de terroirs: Le concept et son développement* [Gestion de Terroirs: Concept and Development]. New York: UN Sudano-Sahelian Office (UNSO).

Toulmin, C., Lavigne-Delville, P. and Traoré, S. (eds). 2002. *The Dynamics of Resource Tenure in West Africa*, Oxford: James Currey.

Traoré, A. and Ouattara, F. 2003. Analyse des différentes campagnes d'ensemencement des nuages menées au Burkina Faso de 1967 à 2002 en vue de l'augmentation des précipitations [Analysis of different programs of cloud seeding carried out in Burkina Faso from 1967 to 2002 in order to augment precipitation.] *Eighth World Meteorological Organization Scientific Conference on Weather Modification*, Casablanca, Morocco, 7–12 April 2003, Geneva: World Meteorological Organization.

Trewavas, A. 2002. Malthus foiled again and again. *Nature*, Vol. 418, pp. 668–670.

Tschakert, P., Khouma, M. and Sene, M. 2004. Biophysical potential for soil carbon sequestration in agricultural systems of the Old Peanut Basin of Senegal. *Journal of Arid Environments, Special Issue on the SOCSOM Project in Senegal*, Vol. 59, pp. 511–533.

Tschakert, P. 2004. Carbon for farmers: assessing the potential for soil carbon sequestration in the old peanut basin of Senegal. *Climatic Change*, Vol. 67, pp. 273–290.

Tschakert, P. 2006. Wetter or drier? Climate change perceptions, risks, and vulnerabilities in the Sahel. *Annual Meeting of the Association of American Geographers*, Chicago, 7–11 March 2006.

Tucker, C. J., Dregne, H. E. and Newcomb, W. W. 1991. Expansion and contraction of the Sahara Desert from 1980 to 1990. *Science*, Vol. 253, No. 5017, pp. 299–301.

Tucker, C. J. and Nicholson, S. E. 1999. Variations in the size of the Sahara Desert from 1980 to 1997. *Ambio*, Vol. 28, No. 7, pp. 587–591.

Turner, B. L., Kasperson, R. E., Matson, P. A., McCarthy, J. J., Corell, R. W., Christensen, L., Eckley, N., Kasperson, J. X., Luers, A., Martello, M. L., Polsky, C., Pulsipher, A. and Schiller, A. 2003. A framework for vulnerability analysis in sustainability science. *Proceedings of the National Academy of Sciences of the United States of America*, Vol. 100, pp. 8074–8079.

Turner, J. A. 1999. A realizable renewable energy future. *Science*, Vol. 285, pp. 687–689.

Turner, M. G. and Dale, V. H. 1998. Comparing large, infrequent disturbances: what have we learned? *Ecosystems*, Vol. 1, pp. 493–396.

Twyman, C., Sporton, D. and Thomas, D. S. G. 2004. "Where is the life in farming?": the viability of smallholder farming on the margins of the Kalahari, Southern Africa. *Geoforum*, Vol. 35, pp. 69–85.

US Department of Agriculture (USDA). 1954. *Diagnosis and Improvement of Saline and Alkali Soils*, Riverside, CA: US Salinity Laboratory. (Agricultural Handbook 60.)

Umpleby, S. and Dent, E. 1999. The origins and purposes of several traditions in systems theory and cybernetics. *Cybernetics and Systems: An International Journal*, Vol. 30, pp. 79–103.

UN Convention to Combat Desertification (UNCCD). 1994. *Text of the UNCCD, Part I: Introduction, Article I: Terms*, UNCCD Secretariat, Bonn, Germany.

UN Millennium Project (UNMP). 2005. *Investing in Development: A Practical Plan to Achieve the Millennium Development Goals*. New York: UN Development Programme. http://www. unmillenniumproject.org/reports/index_overview.htm (Accessed 13 December 2006.)

UN. Economic and Social Council (ECOSOC). 1996. *Resolution 1996/31*. http://www.un.org/ documents/ecosoc/res/1996/eres1996-31.htm (Accessed 1 December 2006.)

UNESCO. 2002. *Harnessing Science to Society: Analytical Report to Governments and International Partners on the Follow-up to the World Conference on Science*, Paris: UNESCO.

United Nations Framework Convention on Climate Change (UNFCCC). 1992. *UNFCCC: Full text of the convention*. United Nations. http://unfccc.int/essential_background/convention/ background/items/1349.php (Accessed 6 June 2006.)

Utah Division of Water Resources (UDWR). 2005. *Cloud Seeding*. http://water.utah.gov/cloud-seeding/ (Accessed 18 December 2006.)

van Boxel, J. 2004. Uncertainties in modelling climate change. In: Dietz, T., Ruben, R. and Verhagen, A. (ed), *The Impact of Climate Change on Drylands: With a Focus on West Africa*, Boston, MA: Kluwer.

van der Hoek, W., ul Hassan, M., Ensink, J. H. J., Feenstra, S., Raschid-Sally, L., Munir, S., Islam, R., Hussain, R. and Matsuno, Y. 2002. *Urban Wastewater: A Valuable Resource for Agriculture: A Case Study from Haroonabad, Pakistan*, Colombo: IWMI.

Varady, R. and Iles-Shih, M. 2007. Global water initiatives: what do the experts think? Report on a survey of leading figures in the "world of water". In: Biswas, A. K. (ed), *Impacts of Mega-Conferences on Global Water Development and Management*, Berlin: Springer, pp. 15–68 (in press).

Verhulst, P. F. 1838. Notice sur la loi que la population pursuit dans son accroissement. *Correspondance mathémathique et physique*, Vol. 10, pp. 113–121.

Vietmeyer, N. D. 1986. Lesser known plants of potential use in agriculture and forestry. *Science*, Vol. 232, No. 4756, pp. 1379–1384.

Vig, N. J. 2005. Introduction: governing the international environment. In: Axelrod, R. S., Downie, D. L. and Vig, N. J. (ed), *The Global Environment. Institutions, Law, and Policy*, 2nd edn, Washington, DC: CQ Press, pp. 1–20.

Vogel, C. and O'Brien, K. 2003. Climate forecasts in southern Africa. In: O'Brien, K. and Vogel, C. (eds), *Coping with Climate Variability: The Use of Seasonal Climate Forecasts in Southern Africa*, Burlington: Ashgate.

von Bertalanffy, L. 1968. *General System Theory*, New York: George Braziller.

Vörösmarty, C. J., Green, P., Salisbury, J. and Lammers, R. B. 2000. Global water resources: vulnerability from climate change and population growth. *Science*, Vol. 289, pp. 284–288.

Walker, B. 2005. A resilience approach to integrated assessment. *The Integrated Assessment Journal*, Vol. 5, pp. 77–97.

Walker, B., Carpenter, S., Anderies, J., Abel, N., Cumming, G., Janssen, M., Lebel, L., Norberg, J., Peterson, G. D. and Pritchard, R. 2002. Resilience management in social-ecological systems: a working hypothesis for a participatory approach. *Conservation Ecology*, Vol. 6, No. 1, p. 14.

Walker, B. H., Ludwig, D., Holling, C. S. and Peterman, R. M. 1981. Stability of semi-arid savanna grazing systems. *Journal of Ecology*, Vol. 69, pp. 473–498.

Walker, K. F., Puckridge, J. T. and Blanch, S. J. 1997. Irrigation development on Cooper Creek, central Australia: prospects for a regulated economy in a boom-and-bust ecology. *Aquatic Conservation: Marine and Freshwater Ecosystems*, Vol. 7, pp. 63–73.

Wallerstein, I. 1974. *The Modern World System*, New York: Academic Press.

Walter, H. 1958. The future of arid lands (book review). *The Journal of Ecology*, Vol. 46, No. 3, pp. 777–778.

Warren, A. 2002. Land degradation is contextual. *Land Degradation and Development*, Vol. 13, pp. 449–459.

Warren, A., Batterbury, S. and Osbahr, H. 2001. Sustainability and Sahelian soils: evidence from Niger. *The Geographical Journal*, Vol. 167, No. 4, pp. 324–331.

Waser, K. 1999. Water in cities: an artificial divide. *Arid Lands Newsletter*, Vol. 45, Spring-Summer 1999. http://ag.arizona.edu/OALS/ALN/aln45/ednote45.html (Accessed 20 December 2006.)

Watson, R. T. 2002. The future of the intergovernmental panel on climate change. *Climate Policy*, Vol. 2, pp. 269–271.

Watson, R. T., Zinyowera, M. C. and Moss, R. H. 1998. *The Regional Impacts of Climate Change*, Cambridge: Cambridge University Press.

Watt, A. 1947. Pattern and process in the plant community. *The Journal of Ecology*, Vol. 35, No. 1–2, pp. 1–22.

Way, S. 2006. Examining the links between poverty and land degradation: from blaming the poor toward recognising the rights of the poor. In: Johnson, P. M., Mayrand, K. and Paquin, M. (eds), *Governing Global Desertification: Linking Environmental Degradation, Poverty and Participation*, London: Ashgate, pp. 27–42.

Weart, S. 2006a. *The Carbon Dioxide Greenhouse Effect*. http://aip.org/history/climate/pdf/co2.pdf (Accessed 15 June 2006.)

Weart, S. 2006b. *General Circulation Models of the Atmosphere*. http://aip.org/history/climate/pdf/gcm.pdf (Accessed 6 June 2006.)

West, N. 1990. Structure and function of microphytic soil crusts in wildland ecosystems of arid to semi-arid regions. *Advances in Ecological Research*, Vol. 20, pp. 179–223.

Westoby, M., Walker, B. and Noy-Meir, I. 1989. Opportunistic management for rangelands not at equilibrium. *Journal of Range Management*, Vol. 42, No. 4, pp. 268–274.

Wexler, H. 1958. Modifying weather on a large scale. *Science*, Vol. 128, No. 3331, pp. 1059–1063.

Whaley, W. G. 1952. Arid lands and plant research. *The Scientific Monthly*, Vol. 75, pp. 228–233.

White, G. F. (ed). 1956. *The Future of Arid Lands: Papers and Recommendations from the International Arid Lands Meetings*, Washington, DC: American Association for the Advancement of Science. (Publication No. 43 of the AAAS.)

White, G. F. (ed). 1960. *Science and the Future of Arid Lands*, Paris: UNESCO.

White, G. F. (ed). 1980. Environment. *Science*, Vol. 209, No. 4452, pp. 183–190.

White, G. F. and Duisberg, P. C. 1955. International Arid Lands Meetings in New Mexico. *Science*, Vol. 121, No. 3137, pp. 218–220.

Whitford, W. G. 2002. *Ecology of Desert Systems*, San Diego, CA: Academic Press.

Whitman, C. E. and Meyer, R. E. 1990. Strategies for increasing the productivity and stability of dry-land farming systems. In: Singh, R. P., Parr, J. F. and Stewart, B. A. (eds), *Dryland Agriculture: Strategies for Sustainability Advances in Agriculture*, Berlin: Springer, pp. 347–358.

Whyte, R. O. 1956. Grazing Resources. In: White, G. F. (ed), *The Future of Arid Lands: Papers and Recommendations from the International Arid Lands Meetings*, Washington, DC: American Association for the Advancement of Science, pp. 179–188. (Publication No. 43 of the AAAS.)

Wickens, G. E., Goodin, J. R. and Field, D. V. (eds). 1985. *Plants for Arid Lands*, Boston, MA: George Allen & Unwin.

Wijeratne, E. M. K., Turbyville, T. J., Zhang, Z., Bigelow, D., Pierson, I., L. S., VanEtten, H. D., Whitesell, L., Canfield, L. M. and Gunatilaka, A. A. L. 2003. Cytotoxic constituents of *Aspergillus terreus* from the rhizosphere of Opuntia Versicolor of the Sonoran Desert. *Journal of Natural Products*, Vol. 66, pp. 1567–1573.

Williams, J. 1994. *Microbiotic Crusts: A Review (Final Draft)*, Interior Columbia Basin Ecosystem Management Project. http://www.icbemp.gov/science/williams.pdf (Accessed 20 December 2006.)

Williams, M. A. J. and Balling, R. C. 1996. *Interactions of Desertification and Climate*, London: Arnold.

Wittfogel, K. A. 1957. *Oriental Despotism: A Comparitive Study of Total Power*, New Haven, CT, Yale University Press.

Wolf, A. T. 1998. Conflict and cooperation along international waterways. *Water Policy*, Vol. 1, No. 2, pp. 251–265.

Woodbury, A. M. 1955. Science, population, and arid lands. *Science, New Series*, Vol. 122, No. 3161, pp. 200–201.

World Bank. 1992. *World Development Report 1992: Development and the Environment*, Washington, DC: World Bank. (Report 10517.) http://www-wds.worldbank.org/external/default/WDSContentServer/WDSP/IB/2000/12/13/000178830_9810191106175/Rendered/PDF/multi_page.pdf (Accessed 29 September 2006.)

World Bank. 2000. *World Development Report 2000/2001: Attacking Poverty*, Oxford: Oxford University Press.

World Bank. 2001. *Making Sustainable Commitments: An Environment Strategy for the World Bank*, Washington, DC: World Bank.

World Bank. 2002. *World Development Report 2003: Sustainable Development in a Dynamic World: Transforming Institutions, Growth, and Quality of Life*, Washington, DC: World Bank.

World Bank. 2006. *World Bank – Civil Society Engagement: Review of Fiscal Years 2005–2006*, Washington, DC: World Bank.

World Commission on Dams (WCOD). 2000. *Dams and Development: A New Framework for Decision-making*, London: Earthscan Publications.

World Commission on Environment and Development (WCED). 1987. *Our Common Future: Report of the World Commission on Environment and Development*, Oxford: Oxford University Press.

World Meteorological Organization. 1979. *Proceedings of the First World Climate Conference – A Conference of Experts on Climate and Mankind*, Geneva, 12–23 February 1979.

World Meteorological Organization. 2005. Report of the Twenty First Session of the CAS Working Group on Physics and the Chemistry of Clouds and Weather Modification Research. WMO (ed), *Programme on Physics and Chemistry of Clouds and Weather Modification Research*, Geneva, Switzerland: World Meteorological Organization, p. 138.

World Wildlife Fund (WWF). 2005. *Going, Going, Gone! Climate Change and Global Glacier Decline.* http://www.wwf.fi/wwf/www/uploads/pdf/glaciersraportti.pdf. (Accessed 19 October 2006.)

Worster, D. 1977. *Nature's Economy: A History of Ecological Ideas*, 2nd edn, Cambridge: Cambridge University Press.

Worthington, E. B. (ed). 1975. *The Evolution of IBP*, Cambridge: Cambridge University Press.

Wright, J. G. 1954. Two-year food shortage heightens tensions in the USSR: the farm crisis in the Soviet Union. *Fourth International*, Vol. 15, No. 4, pp. 118–121.

Ye, Q. and Gao, W. 2006. *Current Status and Progress Report on the International Center for Desert Affairs*, Chinese Association for Sciences and Technology.

Ye, Q., Glantz, M. H., Pan, X., Gao, W. and Ma, Y. 2003. Desert Affairs Program: an initiative on integrating research, education and application for sustainable development in arid and semi-arid lands. In: Pan, X., Gao, W., Glantz, M. and Honda, Y. (eds), *Ecosystems Dynamics, Ecosystem-Society Interactions, and Remote Sensing Applications for Semi-Arid and Arid Land. Proceedings of the SPIE, Volume 4890*, The International Society for Optical Engineering, pp. 230–236.

Yin, Y., Levin, Z., Reisin, T. and Tzivion, S. 2000. The effects of giant cloud condensation nuclei on the development of precipitation in convective clouds: a numerical study. *Atmospheric Research*, Vol. 53, pp. 91–116.

Young, C. 1998. Defining the range: the development of carrying capacity in management practice. *Journal of the History of Biology*, Vol. 31, pp. 61–83.

Zaady, E. 2005. Seasonal change and nitrogen cycling in a patchy Negev Desert: a rview. *Arid Land Research and Management*, Vol. 19, pp. 111–124.

Zaady, E., Offer, Z. and Shachak, M. 2001. The content and contributions of deposited aeolian organic matter in a dry land ecosystem of the Negev Desert, Israel. *Atmospheric Environment*, Vol. 35, pp. 769–776.

Zaffos, J. 2006. Snow Job. in *iNews*. http://csindy.com/csindy/2006-02-16/cover.html

Zonn, I., Glantz, M. and Rubenstein, A. 1994. The virgin lands scheme in the former Soviet Union. In: Glantz, M. (ed), *Drought Follows the Plow: Cultivating Marginal Areas*, Cambridge: Cambridge University Press, pp. 135–150.

Zweibel, K. 2005. *The Terawatt Challenge for Thin-film PV*, Golden, CO: National Renewable Energy Laboratory. (NREL/TP-520-38350.) http://www.osti.gov/servlets/purl/15020000-0M4FOM/ (Accessed 29 September 2006.)

Appendix 1

Table of Contents Reproduced from *The Future of Arid Lands* (1956)

BETTER USE OF PRESENT RESOURCES

PROSPECTS FOR ADDITIONAL WATER SOURCES

BETTER ADAPTATION OF PLANTS AND ANIMALS TO ARID CONDITIONS

Appendix 2

Brief Biographies of Authors Cited from *The Future of Arid Lands*

Collected here are brief biographies to provide the reader with some background on the authors whose chapters in *The Future of Arid Lands* are cited in *The Future of Arid Lands – Revisited*. Even in the age of the Internet, researching the authors' lives proved to be a challenge. For many of them, a great deal of information is available. For others, after the passage of 50 years, information was sparse. In the following list, a name followed by no information indicates a cited author from the previous book for whom no biographical information could be located.

Gilbert F. White, editor, *The Future of Arid Lands*. Department of Geography, University of Chicago, Illinois, USA

Gilbert White was a towering figure in the emergence of environmental sciences in the twentieth century. In the latter part of his career, he served as a spokesman for science, but that role was preceded by his long and productive career as a geographer. His work focused on the often contentious intersections of human activity and the environment and how we attempt to resolve them through policy. He was a major figure in studies of flood plain management, water, drylands, and the environment in general.

White served a special role in the development of UNESCO's Major Project on Arid Lands in the 1950s, a project that eventually evolved into the International Hydrology Program. Not only was he editor of *The Future of Arid Lands* (1956), providing the general tenor of the volume; he later produced *Science and the Future of Arid Lands* (1960) for the UNESCO Symposium on the Problems of the Arid Zone, as an assessment of what science and international cooperation had achieved in the world's drylands. He played an active and influential role in UN affairs throughout his long and very productive career (Batisse, 2005).

Dr. White received his undergraduate and graduate degrees from the University of Chicago. He served from 1934 to 1940 in the New Deal administration of Franklin D. Roosevelt as the secretary to the Mississippi Valley Committee,

National Resources Committee, and National Resources Planning Board. From 1946 to 1955, he was President of Haverford College; after that, he returned to the University of Chicago as Chair of the Department of Geography. From 1970 to 1978, he was Professor of Geography and Director of the Institute of Behavioral Science at the University of Colorado; from 1980 until his death, he was the Gustavson Distinguished Professor Emeritus of Geography there. He was also the founder and Director of the University's Natural Hazards Research and Applications Information Center from 1976 to 1984 and again from 1992 to 1994.

White's contributions to science and policy were well recognized. He won the Association of American Geographers' Lifetime Achievement Award in 2002 and in 2000 received both the highest US scientific honor, the National Medal of Science, and the National Academy of Sciences' highest honor, the Public Welfare Medal. Other awards and honors included the 2006 UNESCO GARD leadership award in disaster reduction, the 1995 Volvo Environmental prize, the 1987 Tyler Prize for Environmental Achievement, and eight honorary degrees. He was member of the National Academy of Sciences, the American Academy of Arts and Sciences, the American Philosophical Society, the Russian Academy of Sciences, and the Cosmos Club. A biography of Dr. White was recently published,[1] and his full resume is available at (http://www.colorado.edu/hazards/gfw/). Gilbert White died on October 5, 2006.

Reed W. Bailey (Summary Statement on Variability and Predictability of Water Supply) – Intermountain Forest and Range Experiment Station, US Department of Agriculture, Ogden, Utah, USA

By the early 1930s, Bailey had started working in various capacities for the US Department of Agriculture, and by 1950, he had become Director of the Intermountain Forest and Range Experiment Station. In that same year, the US Secretary of Agriculture presented him with a Superior Service Award for creative thinking and dynamic leadership in research in watershed management, especially in the fields of rangeland rehabilitation and flood and erosion control. In 1954, the Northern Rocky Mountain was merged with the Intermountain Forest and Range Experiment Station; Dr. Bailey continued as director of the station after the consolidation.

Edward G. Bowen (Induced Precipitation) – Division of Radiophysics, Commonwealth Scientific and Industrial Research Organization, Sydney, Australia

Edward Bowen was a prominent wartime British physicist. Born in Wales in 1911, he was educated at Swansea University College and King's College in London. He made his mark in the development of ground and airborne radar in Britain. In 1940,

---

[1] Hinshaw, R.E. 2006. *Living with Nature's Extremes. The Life of Gilbert Fowler White*. Boulder, Johnson Books.

Bowen helped the USA to develop microwave radar as fighting weapon. After the war, Bowen joined the Radiophysics Laboratory at CSIRO (Commonwealth Scientific and Industrial Research Organisation) in Australia, becoming Chief of the Division of Radiophysics in 1946. Bowen and his colleagues worked in the fields of radioastronomy and cloud and rain physics, and played a major role in the construction of the 210 ft radiotelescope at Parkes, New South Wales. Bowen took up research on cloud and rain physics in Australia in 1946, following initial research in the USA that reported on the possibility of inducing rain by cloud seeding with dry ice. Bowen recognized the potential importance of cloud seeding for arid areas and aimed at improving rainfall in arid Australia. His early successes in cloud seeding led in 1947 to a systematic cloud-seeding program that continued for the next 24 years. His contributions to cloud studies included spraying water into the warm clouds that are responsible for much of the rainfall in the warmer parts of Australia. Bowen also saw great potential for seeding large areas from the air using silver iodide burners mounted on aircraft. He died in 1991.

Bertram T. Dickson (Challenge of Arid Lands Research and Development for Benefit of Mankind) – Member, UNESCO Advisory Committee on Arid Zone Research, Canberra, Australia

Bertram Dickson was a botanist and plant pathologist, born in England in 1886 and educated in Canada. He moved to Australia in 1927, where he was chief of the Division of Plant Industry in CSIR (Council of Scientific and Industrial Research; later CSIRO) until his retirement in 1951. He was also appointed to the Council of Canberra University College in 1937 and was its chairman from 1953 to 1960. Dickson prepared the report on the feasibility and site selection of the Botanic Gardens in Canberra, emphasizing the scientific role of botanical gardens and promoting the use of native plants. Dickson also played a prominent role in the Major Project on Arid Lands, by leading the effort to prepare one of its first documents, *Guide Book to Research Data for Arid Zone Development* (1957). Dickson died in 1982.

Frank Dixey (Variability and Predictability of Water Supply) – Colonial Geological Surveys, London, UK

Frank Dixey was born in 1892 in Bristol, UK and educated at the University of Wales. He was a geomorphologist and hydrogeologist and served as geological advisor to British colonial governments, mainly in sub-Saharan Africa. Dixey was involved in geological surveying throughout this region. Later his focus shifted towards the provision of improved groundwater supplies in the African territories. In 1948, he became the first director of the Directorate of Colonial Geological Surveys in London. After 1959, Dixey worked actively with UNESCO as a hydrologist. Within this context, he became deeply interested in the challenges in drylands. Dixey was chairman of the scientific advisory committee on arid zone research for 1959–1961 and published several UNESCO works of international scope on water resources development. He was also a cofounder and editor of the Journal of Hydrology, first published in 1965. Moreover, Dixey recognized the potentials of remote sensing (then called photogeology) in the 1940s. Dixey died in 1982.

John H. Dorroh, Jr. (Beneficial Use of Water in Arid Lands) – Soil Conservation Service, USDA, Albuquerque, New Mexico

John Dorroh was a hydrologist and worked for the Soil Conservation Service in Albuquerque, New Mexico. He was known for his work on hydrology in the US Southwest.

Omar Draz (Adaptation of Plants and Animals) – Desert Range Development Project, Desert Institute, Mataria, Egypt

Omar Draz was the director of the Desert Range Development Project of the Desert Institute, Mataria. He was the senior range and pasture officer of FAO for the WANA (West Asia and North Africa) region and worked on understanding access to grazing lands. Draz conducted research on the tribal *hema* range management system in Saudi Arabia and on collective ownership. In 1967, he was appointed chief advisor to the Syrian government on rangeland issues, following the failure of the Asrya Project. This project, implemented by the Syrian Government with FAO assistance in 1963, had aimed to revitalize the pastoral sector by introducing supplementary feeding systems and controlling grazing areas. It largely failed in its attempt to control access to and utilization of rangelands and to establish a central-ized system of rangeland management. Draz had convinced FAO of the importance of considering human factors, proposing a return to a system of communal owner-ship by local tribal groups with traditional land and grazing rights and collective management systems to improve the pastoral economy. Draz's recommendations acknowledged the need to work in collaboration with Bedouin society and sug-gested that control over range management be returned to them. His recommenda-tions were implemented well into the 1990s. In addition, Draz initiated programs to test the use of nonindigenous species, e.g., *Atriplex*, for steppe rehabilitation in the WANA region.

Michael Evenari (Desert Agriculture: Problems and Results in Israel [coauthor]) – The Hebrew University of Jerusalem, Israel

Michael Evenari, born as Walter Schwarz in Alsace-Lorraine in 1904, was a pio-neer of research in plant ecophysiology. He received his Ph.D. in botany from Frankfurt's Johann Wolfgang Goethe University in 1926 and worked in the depart-ment of plant physiology of the German University in Prague. Following that, he joined the botany department of the Technical University in Darmstadt, Germany, until the rise of the National Socialists to power in 1933 precipitated his emigration to Palestine. In 1934, he became a lecturer in the plant physiology and anatomy section of the botany department of Hebrew University. In 1935 he became a citizen of Palestine, officially adopting the name Michael Evenari. Following World War II, during which he served in the British Army, he rejoined the botany department, becoming its head for 20 years. He also served as vice president of Hebrew

University from 1953 to 1959. It was during this period that he first visited the remains of desert agriculture near the ruins of the Nabatean city of Avdat. This began his 20-year period of collaboration with Naftali Tadmor and Leslie Shanan to investigate the ancient runoff agriculture of the Negev highlands. The work involved rebuilding a series of ancient farms, first near Shivta, then near Avdat, and later in Wadi Mashash; the farm at Avdat has since developed into an ecological experiment station. Dr. Evenari retired in 1971, at the age of 67, but continued his investigations of the biology and ecology of the Negev for many years thereafter. In 1988, he was awarded the prestigious Balzan Prize in Applied Botany by the Balzan Foundation, which focuses on promoting humanity, peace, and brotherhood among all peoples. He died in 1989.

H. E. Hayward (Salinity Factor in Reuse of Wastewaters) – US Salinity Laboratory, Riverside, California

Hayward was director of the US Salinity Laboratory in Riverside, California. His research career focused on soil salinity, salinity problems in irrigated agriculture and its control, salinity tolerance of agricultural crops, effects of salinity on plant growth and development, and salt accumulation in soils. He also worked with the UNESCO Major Project on Arid Lands, focusing on plant growth under saline conditions and the potential of saline water use for irrigation.

Charles E. Kellogg (Role of Science in Man's Struggle on Arid Lands) – Soil Conservation Service, US Department of Agriculture, Washington DC, USA

Charles Kellogg was a major figure in soil science both in the USA and around the world. Educated as a soil scientist at Michigan State College, he became a professor of soil science at North Dakota State University in 1929. In 1934, Kellogg was appointed chief of the Soil Survey Division of the USDA Soil Conservation Service, a position he held until his retirement in 1971. Under his leadership the Soil Survey Division grew to an organization with more than 1,400 soil scientists. In his career, Kellogg focused on tools to improve soil surveys and promoted the development of a new soil classification system that made greater use of laboratory analyses. He worked to make the soil survey more useful for land managers by including interpretations that assessed the suitability of soils for particular land uses. His 1937 *Soil Survey Manual* standardized terms and procedures and has been widely adopted around the world. Kellogg died in 1980.

Louis Koenig (The Economics of Water Sources) – Southwest Research Institute, San Antonio, Texas, USA

Louis Koenig came to the Southwest Research Institute in 1951 from the Stanford Research Institute. SwRI is a nonprofit applied research organization in San Antonio, Texas (USA). On his appointment, he took responsibility for chemistry, minerals, metals, and applied biology. He became vice president of the institute in 1955 and resigned in 1956.

Dov Koller (Desert Agriculture: Problems and Results in Israel [coauthor]) – Hebrew University of Jerusalem, Israel

Dov Keller was a Ph.D. student of Michael Evenari's during Evenari's tenure as vice president of Hebrew University. He received his Ph.D. from Hebrew University in 1954 and became a full professor there in 1969. Throughout his career, his research interests have included photobiology and photomorphogenesis in plants, light-driven leaf movements, and plant movements. Since 1994, following his retirement, he has held the title of Jack Futterman Professor Emeritus of Agricultural Botany at Hebrew University.

Luna B. Leopold (Data and Understanding) – US Geological Survey, Department of the Interior, Washington DC, USA

Luna Leopold was a major figure in American science, particularly in hydrology. He was born in New Mexico in 1915. Son of the famous wildlife ecologist and conservationist Aldo Leopold, he was educated at University of Wisconsin, University of California–Los Angeles and Harvard University in civil engineering, geomorphology, and hydrology. Leopold joined the USGS in 1950 and stayed with the agency for 22 years, eventually becoming chief hydrologist of the Water Resources Division. Under Leopold, the division grew to a well-respected research organization. Leopold significantly contributed to the study of rivers and streams, particularly through quantitative explanations for the natural forms of rivers. He was considered a leading expert on how rivers shape the landscape. In 1972, Leopold became joint professor of Earth and Planetary Science and of Landscape Architecture at the University of California, Berkeley, where he stayed until his retirement in 1986. He was known both for his integration of engineering, science, and policy, and for his work as a well-known conservationist who significantly influenced the way we think about environmental problems and the broader relationship between people and nature. He was a member of the National Academy of Sciences and received numerous honors, including the National Medal of Science in 1991, the Penrose Medal of the Geological Society of America, the Warren Prize of the National Academy of Sciences, and the Busk Medal of the Royal Geographical Society. Leopold died in 2006.

Cyril Luker (Consequences of Using Arid Lands Beyond Their Capabilities) – Soil Conservation Service, US Department of Agriculture, Washington DC, USA

Cyril Luker was a soil conservation expert and worked for the Soil Conservation Service in Texas and New Mexico, in charge of soil erosion control practices. In 1956, he was appointed chair of the Great Plains Inter-agency Group. This group was composed of USDA agencies and was formed as part of the Great Plains Conservation Program created in response to the Dust Bowl and to drought experiences in the Great Plains in the 1950s. It was responsible for formulating guidelines to promote conservation in the Great Plains while at the same time helping farmers to develop economically stable farm and ranch units.

Leslie N. McClellan (Water Resources) – Bureau of Reclamation, US Department of the Interior, Denver, Colorado, USA

Leslie McClellan was a chief electrical engineer with the Bureau of Reclamation.

Sheppard T. Powell (Demineralization of Saline Waters) – Consulting Engineer, Baltimore, Maryland, USA

Sheppard Powell was a chemical engineer and worked as a consultant. He established Sheppard T. Powell Associates in Baltimore in 1921; the company still specializes in treatment of boiler water, industrial water, makeup water, and recovery boiler water.

Raymond Price (Possibilities of Increasing and Maintaining Production from Grass and Forest Lands Without Accelerating Erosion) – Rocky Mountain Forest and Range Experiment Station, USDA, Fort Collins, Colorado, USA

Raymond Price was the director of the Southwestern Forest and Range Experiment Station (Tucson, Arizona) from 1942 to 1953. He then served as director of the Rocky Mountain Forest and Range Experiment Station (Fort Collins) until 1971.

L.M. Pultz (Problems in the Development and Utilization of Arid Land Plants). Agricultural Research Service, US Department of Agriculture, Beltsville, Maryland, USA

Lorenzo A. Richards (Agricultural Use of Water Under Saline Conditions) – US Salinity Laboratory, Riverside, California, USA

Lorenzo Richards was educated in physics at Utah State University and Cornell University. He spent most of his career working as a soil physicist at the US Salinity Laboratory in Riverside, California. Richards is considered one of the most influential scientists in the field of soil physics. His Ph.D. thesis from Cornell made critical progress in the development of Darcy's law to describe water movement in unsaturated soils (known as Richard's equation). His key interest was in the energy status and transport of water in the soil; he was instrumental in developing the principles, construction, and operation of the tensiometer and soil capillary potential measurements. His work on soil–water–plant relations helped to standardize characteristic soil–water properties and define accepted moisture potential values for plant growth, i.e., field capacity and permanent wilting point. Richards died in 1993.

Kanwar Sain (Better Use of Present Resources: Concluding Remarks) – General Water and Power Commission, Ministry of Irrigation and Power, New Delhi, India.

Dr. Kanwar Sain, one of India's most renowned water resources engineers, was born in 1899. After graduating from Thompson Engineering College of Roorkee in 1922, he worked in the water sector for almost four decades, eventually becoming Chairman of the Central Water and Power Commission. He was elected as President of Central Board of Irrigation and Power in 1953, Vice President of International Commission on Irrigation and Drainage 1954, and President of the Institute of Engineers of India in 1956. He is particularly remembered for his work in planning the Rajasthan Canal and on the Mekong International River Commission. Throughout his career he received several honors, most notably the O.B.E. and the Padma Bhushan.

Vincent J. Schaefer (Some Relationships of Experimental Meteorology to Arid Lands Water Resources) – The Munitalp Foundation, Schenectady, New York, USA

Vincent Schaefer left high school at 16 to support his family and joined General Electric as an apprentice. Working at the research laboratory, he became a research assistant to Irving Langmuir, who was awarded the Nobel Prize in 1932 for his work on surface chemistry. Schaefer's focus shifted to precipitation static, aircraft icing, ice nuclei, and cloud physics in the 1940s, and he developed a laboratory method to seed clouds with dry ice. His success resulted in the government-sponsored "Project Cirrus" to study cloud seeding, and he became coordinator of the laboratory portion of the project. In 1952, he joined the Munitalp Foundation to work on its meteorological research program, becoming its director of research two years later. In 1959, he joined the State University of New York, where he helped establish the Atmospheric Sciences Research Center of which he was the first director (1960–1976). He died in 1993.

Knut Schmidt-Nielsen (Animals and Arid Conditions…) – Duke University, Durham, North Carolina, USA

Knut Schmidt-Nielsen is a prominent animal physiologist. Born in Trondheim, Norway, in 1915, he emigrated to the USA in 1946 and became a US citizen in 1952. Having received his advanced college education in zoology at the Universities of Oslo and Copenhagen, Schmidt-Nielsen spent several years at Swarthmore College, Stanford University and the University of Cincinnati before going to Duke University in 1952 as a professor of physiology. He became a James B. Duke professor of physiology in 1963. His work in diverse locations ranging from the Saharan Desert and Australia to the Arctic Circle has focused on the evolutionary adaptations of animals to environmental extremes. Schmidt-Nielsen was recognized for his research on physiological mechanisms of desert animals. This research provided insight into how camels can go without water for weeks, how marine animals can ingest saltwater, and how desert rats manage to survive extreme temperatures without water. He is a member of the National Academy of Sciences, the Royal Society of London, and the French Academy of Sciences, and received the International Prize for Biology in 1992 (Japan). Schmidt-Nielsen retired in the late 1980s.

Homer L. Shantz (History and Problems of Arid Lands Development) – Santa Barbara, California, USA

Homer Shantz was born in Michigan in 1876. He was educated at Colorado College in plant physiology and plant ecology and received his Ph.D. from the University of Nebraska. He began his career teaching botany at the state universities of Missouri and Louisiana and the University of Illinois. He then left teaching to join the Bureau of Plant Industry of the USDA as plant physiologist and botanist, working on drought resistance in plants, dryland crops, plant water requirements, and the relations of soils, climate, plant physiology, transpiration, and wilting. In his time at USDA, Shantz traveled extensively in Africa, studying flora and fauna and observing agricultural practices. Shantz was appointed president of the University of Arizona in 1928 and stayed in that office for eight years. He then became chief of the Division of Wildlife Management of the US Forest Service, where he worked on the development of sound policies and practices of natural resources management. Until his death in 1958, he was engaged in field research, focusing after retirement on vegetation change in the Northern Great Plains.

Terah L. Smiley (Geochronology as an Aid to Study of Arid Lands) – Laboratory of Tree Ring Research, University of Arizona, Arizona, USA

Terah Smiley was born in Kansas in 1914. He attended the Universities of Kansas and Arizona. Smiley moved to Arizona in 1936 and worked at the University of Arizona for nearly four decades until his retirement in 1984. He was director of the University of Arizona's Laboratory of Tree Ring Research from 1958 to 1960 and of the Geochronology Laboratories(later Department of Geosciences) from 1956 to 1969. Smiley was recognized for his contributions to arid lands studies, receiving the Award for Outstanding Contributions in Arid Zones Research of the National Committee on Desert and Arid Zone Research in 1973. He died in 1996.

C. W. Thornthwaite (Climatology in Arid Zone Research) – Director (1955) of the John Hopkins Laboratory of Climatology, Seabrook, New Jersey, USA

C. Warren Thornthwaite was one of the most important climatologists of his time. Born in 1899 in Michigan, he received a Bachelor of Science degree from Central Michigan University in 1922 and a Ph.D. in geography from the University of California, Berkeley in 1930. From 1927 to 1935, he was an instructor of geography at the University of Oklahoma. It was during this time that he came to challenge prevailing classifications of climate and devised his own, based on observed relationships between precipitation and evaporation rather than on temperature. Thornthwaite's approach to climate classification made it possible to more fully describe the physical bases of climate. He went on to refine his concepts with the US Soil Conservation Service and, in 1947, to establish a climate laboratory in rural New Jersey that ultimately led to creation of a consulting firm that still carries his name, C.W. Thornthwaite Associates. He also served as the President of the Commission on Climatology of the World Meteorological Organization. Thornthwaite died in 1963.

Jean Tixeront (Water resources in Arid Regions) – Chief Engineer of Public Works, Tunis

R. O. Whyte (Grazing Resources) – Plant Production Branch, Agriculture Division, FAO, Rome.

Color Plates

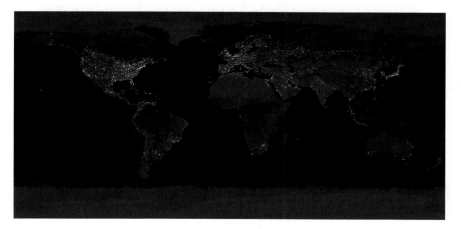

Fig. 2.1 Night lights of the world. Areas with few night lights represent opportunities for development from a global perspective.

Fig. 2.3 Earth rise. This photograph, taken during the Apollo 8 mission in December 1968, became an icon of the environmental movement of the 1970s. (From Apollo Image Gallery, http://www.apolloarchive.com/apollo_gallery.html)

Rainfall variability in the Sahel 1898 - 2002

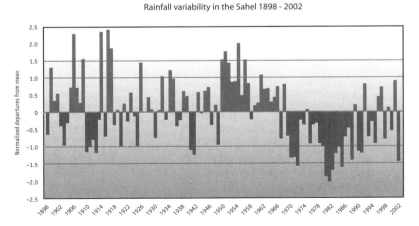

Fig. 2.4 A century of rainfall variability in the Sahel expressed as normalized departures from long-term mean (Nicholson, 2002)

Fig. 3.2 Lake Mead, formed by Hoover Dam on the Arizona–Nevada border, in 2002. The exposed lakeshore signals/indicates a drop in water level resulting from a prolonged drought. (Courtesy of Ken Dewey, High Plains Regional Climate Center)

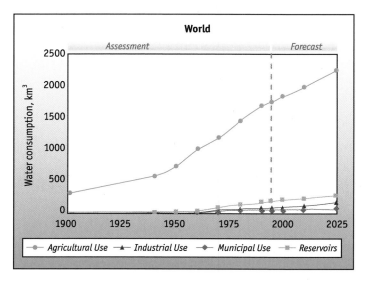

Fig. 3.3 Global water consumption by region. (From UNESCO IHP, http://webworld.unesco.org/water/ihp/db/shiklomanov/summary/html/figure_8.html)

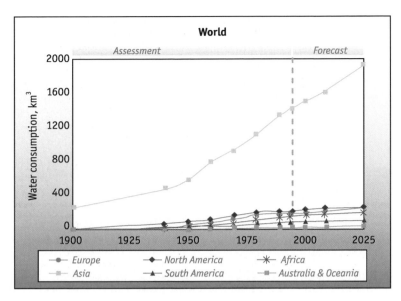

Fig. 3.4 Global water consumption by sector. (From UNESCO IHP, http://webworld.unesco. org/water/ihp/db/shiklomanov/summary/html/figure_9.html)

Fig. 3.5 Drilling for groundwater on the edge of the Kalahari in Botswana (2003). (Courtesy of Frau Dr. Susanne Stadler)

Fig. 3.6 Water retention by stone bunds in the Central Plateau of Burkina Faso. (Courtesy of Melchior Landolt and Terra-Verde e.V [http://www.terra-verde.de])

Fig. 3.7 (**a**) Extent of the Aral Sea in 1973. (From UNEP/GRID-Sioux Falls.)

Fig. 3.7 (**b**) Extent of the Aral Sea in 1986. (From UNEP/GRID-Sioux Falls)

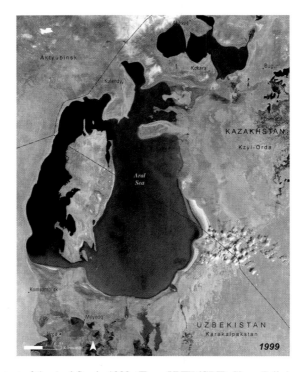

Fig. 3.7 (**c**) Extent of the Aral Sea in 1999. (From UNEP/GRID-Sioux Falls.)

Fig. 3.7 (**d**) Extent of the Aral Sea in 2004. (From UNEP/GRID-Sioux Falls)

Fig. 3.8 Salton Sea Tilapia mass die-off. (Courtesy of Jeff Alu)

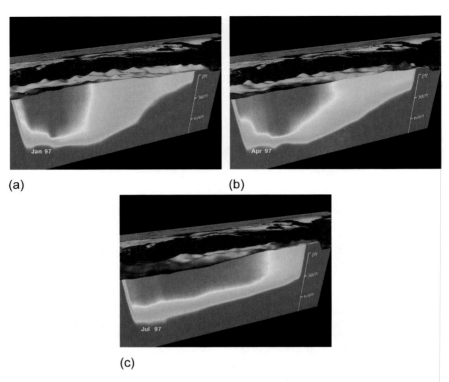

(a)   (b)

(c)

Fig. 4.1 East–west surface water temperature gradient decreases in the Pacific Ocean during the onset of an El Niño (January–July 1997). (**a**) January 1997; (**b**) April 1997; (**c**) July 1997. (From NASA Visible Earth, http://visibleearth.nasa.gov/)

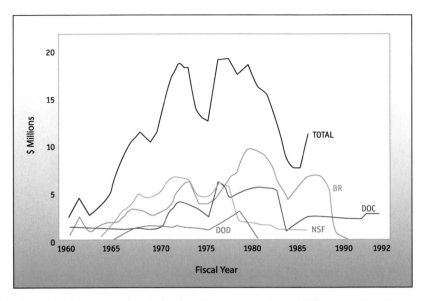

Fig. 4.2 Federal spending levels in the USA for weather modification. [BR (Bureau of Reclamation), DOC (Department of Commerce), DOD (Department of Defense), and NSF (National Science Foundation)]. (Redrawn after Cotton and Pielke 1995)

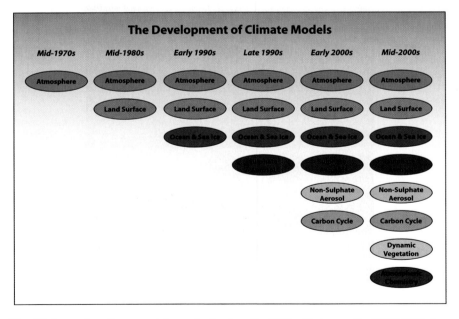

Fig. 4.3 Increasing climate model complexity since the 1970s. (Redrawn after IPCC, 2001c)

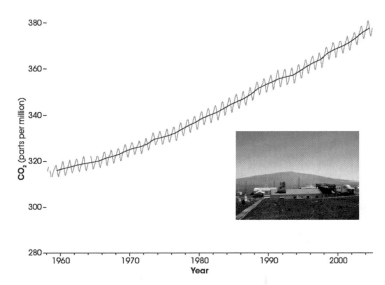

Fig. 4.4 Carbon dioxide measurements charted in the "Keeling curve". (FromNASA Visible Earth, http://visibleearth.nasa.gov)

Fig. 4.5 Saharan dust over the North Sea. This Moderate Resolution Imaging Spectroradiometer (MODIS) image from April 16, 2003, shows African dust blowing over Scotland (left) and across the North Sea to Norway and even southward to Denmark. A few fires have been detected by MODIS and are marked with red dots. (From NASA Visible Earth, http://visibleearth.nasa.gov/)

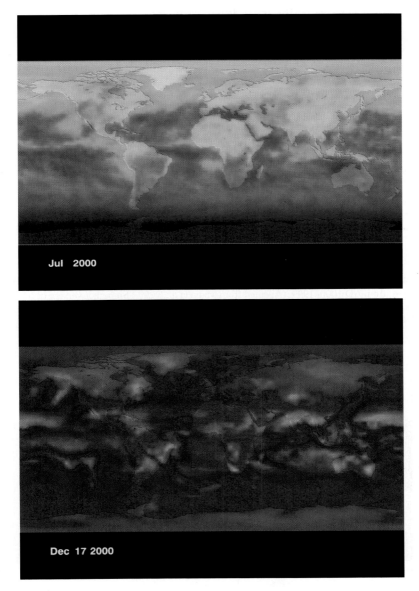

Fig. 4.6 Earth's energy balance. Top: average amount of sunlight reflected from Earth in July 2000 with clouds and high albedo surfaces being highly reflective. Bottom: average amount of heat emitted from the Earth in December 2000, with deserts emitting a lot of heat and cold cloud tops very little. (From NASA Visible Earth, http://visibleearth.nasa.gov/)

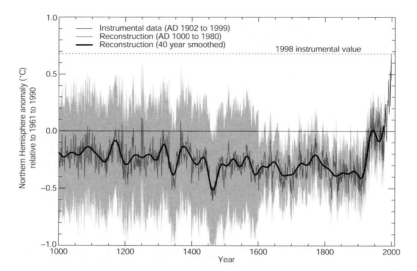

Fig. 4.7 Millennial Northern Hemisphere temperature reconstruction (blue) and instrumental data (red) from AD 1000–1999. (Adapted from Mann et al., 1999.) Smoother version of NH series (black), linear trend from AD 1000–1850 (purple-dashed) and two standard error limits (grey shaded) are shown. (Courtesy of IPCC, 2001c)

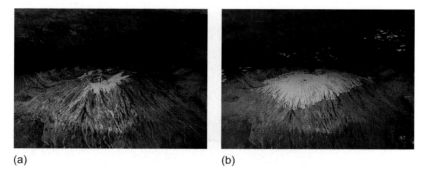

(a)   (b)

Fig. 4.8 Mount Kilimanjaro in February 1993 and 2000. Encroachment of agriculture into the forest zone can be observed in the background. NB: appearance of the summit does not indicate rate of loss of ice. (From NASA Earth Observatory, http://earthobservatory.nasa.gov/)

Fig. 5.1 Cultivated guayule in Arizona. (Courtesy of Bob Roth, Maricopa Agricultural Center)

Fig. 5.4 View of a buffelgrass pasture north of Hermosillo, Mexico, characterized by "chorizos" or rows where native vegetation has been bulldozed into piles to make way for the cultivation of buffelgrass. The photograph was made possible by the kind assistance of Dr. A. Burquez at UNAM and S. Lanham at Environmental Flying Services. (Courtesy of Todd Esque, USGS.)

Fig. 5.5 A rocky southwest-facing talus slope invaded by buffelgrass at Saguaro National Park, near Tucson, Arizona, USA. Should a fire occur on this slope, many of the giant saguaro cactus (>100 years old) would die. (Courtesy of Todd Esque, USGS.)

Fig. 5.6 Burned saguaros and yuccas, 1995 Rio Fire in the Phoenix area. Note: This particular fire was the result of red brome (*Bromus madritensis*), a Mediterranean annual grass. However, a fire resulting from buffelgrass would cause similar or worse damage because of higher fuel loads. (Courtesy of Todd Esque, USGS.)

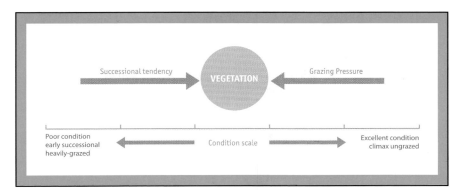

Fig. 6.1 Schematic representation of the succession model: grazing pressure counteracts succesional tendency in moving vegetation along a gradient from poor to excellent condition. (Redrawn from Westoby et al., 1989, p. 267. Copyright Society for Range Management. Reprinted by permission of Alliance Communications Group, a division of Allen Press.)

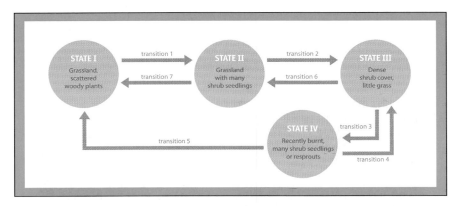

Fig. 6.2 Schematic representation of state-and-transition nonequilibrium model (example of a semiarid grassland/woodland in eastern Australia): A few very good rainfall years produce many shrub seedlings (transition 1). Shrub seedlings grow and establish a seed bank (transition 2). Sufficient rain produces enough vegetation for destructive fires, after which a cover of ephemerals develops (transition 3). Shrub regeneration grows to maturity (transition 4). Fire before transition 4 has reestablished the regeneration capacity of the shrub population (transition 5). Sufficient rain produces a cover of ephemerals, which provide fuel for fire (transition 6). Fire or competition from grasses kills shrub seedlings (transition 7). (Redrawn after Westoby et al., 1989, p. 270. Copyright Society for Range Management. Reprinted by permission of Alliance Communications Group, a division of Allen Press.)

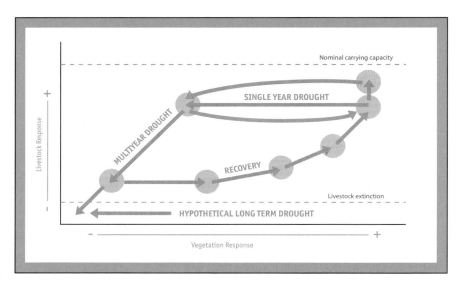

Fig. 6.3 Schematic representation of stochastic nonequilibrium model (example of Turkana, Kenya): Drought perturbations regulate livestock populations independent of livestock density. Single-year droughts affect livestock condition but do not cause livestock mortality. Multiyear droughts result in livestock mortality and reduction of reproductive rates. (Redrawn and simplified after Ellis and Swift, 1988. Copyright 1988 Society for Range Management. Reprinted by permission of Alliance Communications Group, a division of Allen Press.)

Fig. 6.4 Close-up of seedling in biological soil crust (USGS Canyonlands Research Station, http://www.soilcrust.org/gallery.htm/)

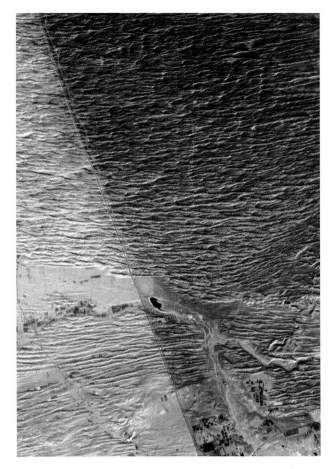

Fig. 6.5 Biological soil crusts in the Negev and their absence on the more heavily grazed Sinai Peninsula make for a sharp contrast in reflectance between the two sides of the Negev–Sinai border as observed from SPOT (Courtesy Arnon Karnieli)

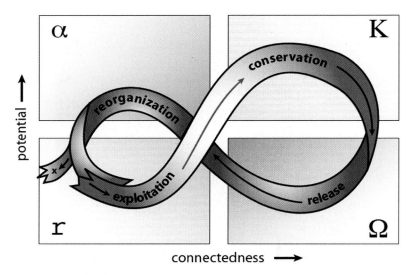

Fig. 6.6 A stylized representation of the four phases of the adaptive cycle. (Gunderson and Holling, 2002)

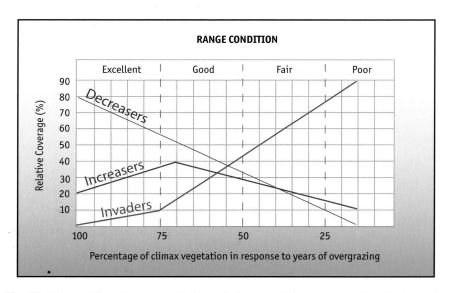

Fig. 6.7 Diagram illustrating a quantitative basis for determining range condition (Dyksterhuis, 1949, p. 109. Copyright Society for Range Management. Reprinted by permission of Alliance Communications Group, a division of Allen Press)

Fig. 6.8 Repeat photography looking looking north into Rothrocks grama range (pasture 6 of SRER) (location marked on Landsat TM false color composite). Increasing abundance of mesquite in the grasslands (McClaran, 2003).

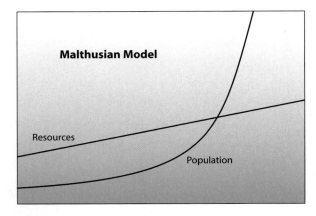

Fig. 7.1 Diagram of Thomas Malthus' prediction that unchecked population growth would eventually surpass agricultural production, leading to dwindling food supply per person. (Malthus, 1798)

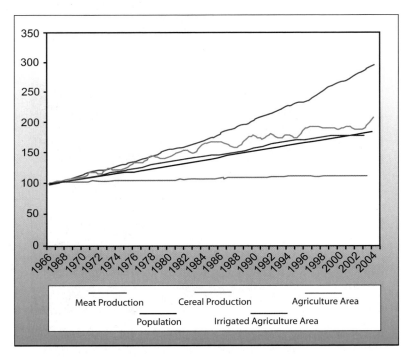

Fig. 7.3 Population, agricultural area and global food production indices (1966 = 100) (FAOSTATS)

Fig. 7.4 Mixed agriculture in Burkina Faso in 2002 (Courtesy Grey Tappan, USGS, EROS Data Center)

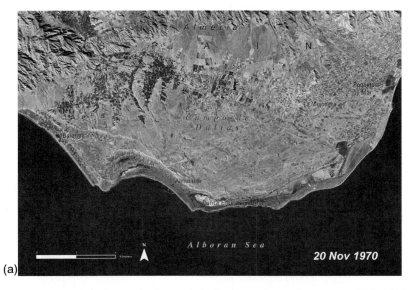

Figs. 7.5a,b, and c Greenhouses in Campo de Dalias, Almeria Province, Spain, 1970–2004. (a) 1970; (b) 1987; (c) 2004 (UNEP/GRID Sioux Falls)

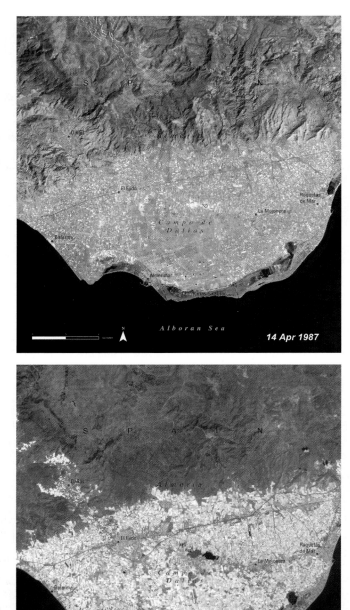

Figs. 7.5b, and 7.5c (continued)

Agricultural Land Use in Campo de Dalias, Almeria

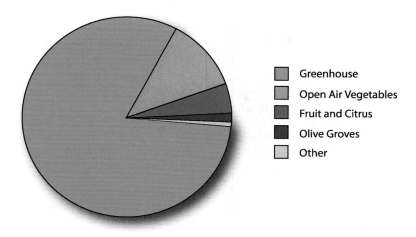

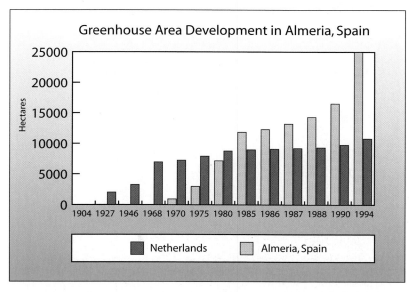

Figs. 7.6a and b Greenhouse area has developed rapidly in Campo de Dalias, Almeria Province, Spain. (a) Currently, greenhouses represent by far the major agricultural land use in the Campo de Dalias area. (b) The land area devoted to greenhouses in Almeria Province overall surpassed the greenhouse area in the Netherlands by the mid-1980s

Figs. 7.7a, 7.7b, and 7.7c Tourism potential in drylands: (a) and (b) scenic views from the Namib and Sonoran deserts

Figs. 7.7c (c) camel trekking with Bedouins in the Sinai peninsula (Courtesy of Stefanie Herrmann)

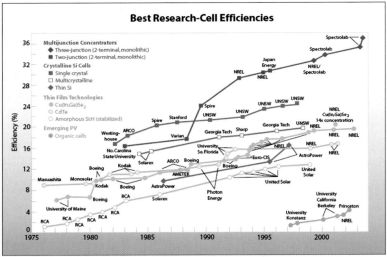

Figs. 7.8a, 7.8b Solar energy potential in drylands (a) Springerville photovoltaic power plant in Arizona (Courtesy Tucson Electric Power Company) (b) Development of photovoltaic cell efficiencies since 1975 (National Renewable Energy Laboratory)

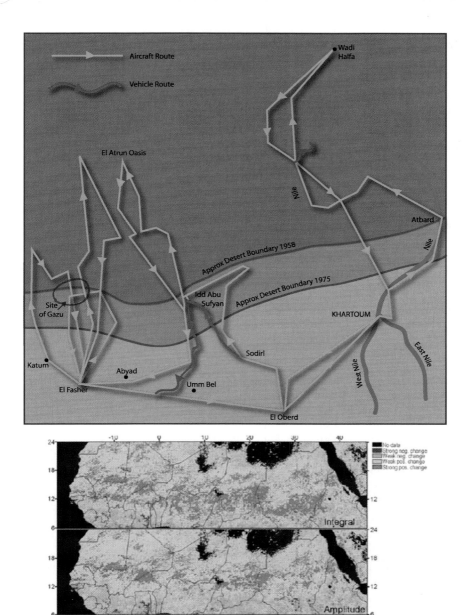

Figs. 7.9a, 7.9b, and 7.9c Early survey of the extent of desertification (Lamprey, 1988) (Fig.7.9a) contrasted with recent examples or remote sensing studies of vegetation greenness as a proxy for bioproductivity in the Sahel (Fig. 7.9b, Fig. 7.9c) (Eklundh and Olsson, 2003; Herrman et al. 2005). Remote sensing has added "observation density" in both the temporal and the spatial dimension and contributed to a change in understanding of vegetation dynamics and desertification. Eklundh and Olsson show positive and negative trends in overall vegetation greenness between 1982 and 1999. Herrmann et al. show trends in vegetation greenness from 1982 to 2003, which are not explained by changes in precipitation during the same time period but are hypothesized to express the outcome of land use and management

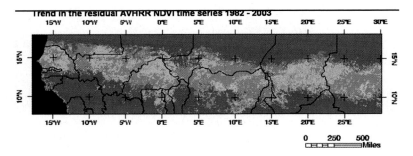

Figs. 7.9c (continued)

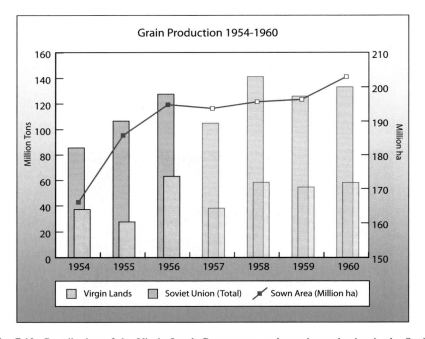

Fig. 7.10 Contribution of the Virgin Lands Programme to the grain production in the Soviet Union. Years after 1956 are set off in color

Fig. 8.1 Conventional food aid: grain supply in a Red Cross storage and distribution center. (Courtesy Stefanie Herrmann)

Fig. 8.2 Villager in Wala Kanta with a new donkey cart, purchased from cash assistance received from the Red Cross. (Courtesy Stefanie Herrmann)

Fig. 8.3 Diversity: Uighur men, the largest ethnic minority in Xinjiang (The Oriental Caravan, http://www.theorientalcaravan.com/)

Fig. 8.4 Development: new silk road under construction (The Oriental Caravan, http://www.theorientalcaravan.com/)

Zai in Burkina Faso (Chris Reij)